جرجی

SMITHSONIAN SCIENTIFIC SERIES

Editor-in-chief
CHARLES GREELEY ABBOT, D.Sc.
Secretary of the
Smithsonian Institution

53

Published by
SMITHSONIAN INSTITUTION SERIES, Inc.
NEW YORK

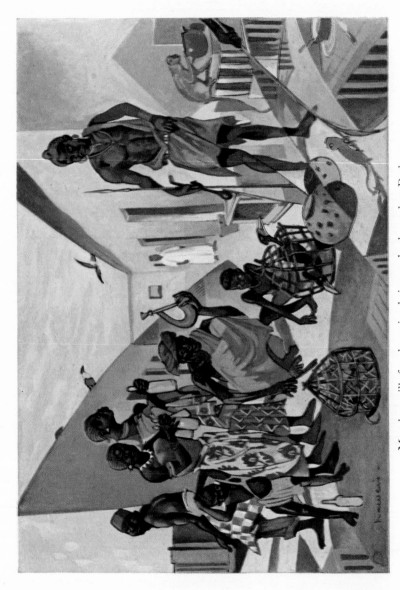

Morning milk for the animals in our back yard at Dodoma
Courtesy of Stephen Haweis

WILD ANIMALS
IN AND OUT OF THE ZOO

By
WILLIAM M. MANN
Director, National Zoological Park

VOLUME SIX
OF THE
SMITHSONIAN SCIENTIFIC SERIES

EDITOR'S FOREWORD TO THE
LATER VOLUMES

THOUGH active in the earlier stages of the planning and preparation of the SMITHSONIAN SCIENTIFIC SERIES, the Editor-in-Chief has come to rely more and more on the associate editors, Mr. John R. Ellingston and Miss Rose A. Palmer. Indeed after Volume IV the editorial work has been practically wholly in their hands. To Mr. Ellingston has fallen the initiation of plans for the volumes, the conferences with authors, the correspondence relating to illustrations and other important details, as well as the improvements in exposition and style which his reading of the text suggested. Miss Palmer has not only attended to the exacting minutiae of scientific editing, but because of her wide knowledge of scientific subjects and her special literary gift has been invaluable in perfecting the text of all the volumes of the SERIES. The Editor-in-Chief offers Mr. Ellingston and Miss Palmer his sincere thanks and congratulations, for the earlier standard of excellence has, he thinks, been more than maintained in their care.

PREFACE

THIS book is about the Zoo—but it is not all about it. The Zoo is a complicated organization, full of personalities and histories, and scarcely an animal or bird is there that has not its own story. I have tried to tell some of these stories and to show in a small way Zoo things that are not ordinarily seen by visitors.

The writer is under obligation to Mr. Thomas Henry who has dug out historical facts and otherwise added to the manuscript. Our Mr. Blackburne has written down some of the tales so well known to his friends, and these are included. Mr. Baker has contributed several accounts drawn from his experience of many years with the Zoo. Mr. Gerrit S. Miller, Jr., Dr. Charles W. Richmond, and Miss Doris Cochran have given freely of their time and expert knowledge to insure the correctness of the scientific nomenclature throughout the book. Mr. John R. Ellingston has read and edited the manuscript and given helpful advice in its preparation. Miss Gladys Visel has typed it, often from fearful copy, and finally, Lucile Quarry Mann has gone over the records of the Zoo and made an annotated list of the residents there during the first forty years of the Park's history.

Many of the illustrations are from snapshots made by the author but the file of photographs in the office has been largely drawn on. Benson Moore has contributed colored sketches of a half dozen rare species as well as the several charming pen-and-ink drawings, and Stephen Haweis has given us the frontispiece.

To all of these the author is deeply grateful.

W. M. M.

CONTENTS

ILLUSTRATIONS

LIST OF PLATES

LIST OF SKETCHES

WILD ANIMALS

IN AND OUT OF THE ZOO

WILD ANIMALS
IN AND OUT OF THE ZOO

CHAPTER I

THE NATIONAL ZOOLOGICAL PARK

THE urge to keep wild animals in captivity seems inherent in man. As far back as we know his history he has pursued his fellow creatures, trapped them and made them his playthings, his servants, and sometimes even his gods, and today we find the practice common to many primitive peoples. While collecting on the Rio Beni in Bolivia we found scarcely an Indian village along the whole river which did not have some pet birds or animals, usually parrots or monkeys, but also penelopes, curassows, and trumpeters, living with the native chickens. At night the chickens retire to a closely built, wild-cat-proof hut and the domesticated wild birds follow them. On the other side of the world the Malays are equally fond of keeping pet animals, and in the Solomon Islands the village cockatoo is one of the common sights.

There is no doubt as to man's universal passion for keeping wild animals in captivity, but why he has this passion is another matter. Perhaps, as in the case of the South American savage, it springs from an admiration for bright colors. Perhaps, again as in South America, when the Indian hunter kills for food a mother animal carrying her young, he brings the young home for the baby to play with, and it grows up in the village.

Large collections of wild animals constitute, of course,

[1]

a luxury possible only to civilized peoples, and it is worthy of comment that wherever nations have attained some stability and economic security, as in ancient Egypt, China, and Rome, they have gathered together rare wild animals. Some fifty years ago zoos began to spring up extensively in the larger American cities.

The National Zoological Park had its origin in a little group of animals brought to Washington and kept in small cages at the rear of the Smithsonian Institution. At that time the Institution was forming a collection of mounted animals representing the fauna of North America and these living specimens were brought to serve as models for the taxidermists. Afterward they were either killed and preserved as part of the mammal collection, or if not needed in that capacity, were forwarded to the zoo at Philadelphia, an institution that had been established in 1872 by public-spirited citizens interested in natural history.

However, the Washington public became increasingly interested in the Smithsonian collection, a fact which led Secretary Langley of the Institution to found a separate department of the National Museum, that of living animals. William T. Hornaday, father of modern taxidermy and well known for his travels and collecting experience in the Far East and elsewhere, was appointed curator, and as a result of his energy the collection had increased to 225 living specimens by the close of the year 1888.

By that time a few interested and intelligent people were commencing to realize that the destruction of game actually destroyed it, and observers noted that where herds of almost countless numbers of game had roamed, there were now only small and widely scattered groups. So to those interested in wild life, it became evident that unless something was done, important native game animals would follow the great auk and the sea cow to extinction.

[2]

PLATE 1

European white swans on Rock Creek

PLATE 2

The wolf pens in winter

THE NATIONAL ZOOLOGICAL PARK

To further legislation for the protection of such animals as remained, public interest was necessary, and Secretary Langley saw that the Smithsonian Institution might do something in this respect. A zoological park would not only be the means of exhibiting animals to people who wanted to see them, but would also increase their interest in them, and the zoo itself might even be of value in breeding and perpetuating some of the nearly gone species.

Mr. Hornaday, under the direction of the Secretary, made a survey of an area of 176 acres in the picturesque valley of Rock Creek, a small tributary of the Potomac— an area of rough land deeply eroded by the periodic floods of the creek, so that there was no less than 200 feet difference in elevation in the tract selected for the park. The real-estate boom had not yet extended to this part of Washington, and the price of the land was not exorbitant. On April 23, 1888, Senator Beck of Kentucky introduced a bill providing for a commission composed of the Secretary of the Interior, the President of the Board of Commissioners of the District of Columbia, and the Secretary of the Smithsonian Institution, which was to have the power to select and obtain land, lay it out as a National Zoological Park, and finally to turn it over to the Regents of the Smithsonian Institution. Senator Morrill gave this bill his earnest support, but it was attached as an amendment to the sundry civil appropriation bill and failed of passage.

At the next session of Congress, Senator Edmunds introduced a similar measure as an amendment to the District of Columbia appropriation bill, and with this was included an appropriation of $200,000 for the purchase of land for the desired site. This became a law on March 2, 1889. On April 30, 1890, Congress passed an act which definitely placed the National Zoological Park under the direction of the Regents of the Smithsonian Institution, and authorized them to transfer to it any living animals in their charge, to exchange specimens, and to administer the Park "for the advancement of science and the instruction and recreation of the people."

A little less than $100,000 was appropriated for roads, walks, bridges, water supply, sewerage, fencing, and buildings, and the National Zoological Park became a physical fact. An experienced landscape architect, Mr. Frederick Law Olmsted, took a deep interest in the Park and gave his advice as to its planning. With the funds at hand it was necessary to limit activities to a small section, namely, in the center of the Park, where previous clearings had already been made, and where there were open fields and grazing land, and areas easily developed into building sites.

Shortly before this Mr. William H. Blackburne, who had spent the preceding twelve years with the Barnum and Bailey Circus, had decided to settle down and had become head keeper of the Park's animals. At this time the Adam Forepaugh Shows presented two elephants to the Government. They marched out from the circus grounds in Washington under charge of Mr. Blackburne, followed by all the small boys in Washington who were not at the circus that day. One of the elephants bore a sheet with the printed announcement that the Adam Forepaugh Shows had presented them to the United States Government. Mr. Blackburne, going ahead, warned the people to look out for their horses. An elderly express driver with an elderly horse, who had a station at Thomas Circle, replied that his horse was too old to run away. He was mistaken. Otherwise, the journey was uneventful. The elephants were chained to a tree, and the Zoo was a fact.

A cheap octagonal frame shed was built for the elephants. Later on the shed was used as a small mammal house, but is again, at the present time, being used to house Kechil, the young elephant from Sumatra. Mr. Blackburne borrowed a wagon from the Humane

Society and brought out all the animals which had been kept at the Smithsonian.

Then a small circus touring West Virginia had two cubs born from its pair of lions. The circus had no other cage than the one in which the cubs made their appearance and needed this for the lion tamer to ride in during the parade, so they gave away the cubs to a blacksmith in the village. One of them died. The blacksmith's wife put the other in a basket with the family cat, and it grew until the neighbors objected. It was brought to the Zoo in a buckboard, the first lion here, and a very fine one.

Then a tiger that had been with a circus for fourteen years got mange so badly that he was not fit for exhibition, so the circus presented him to the United States Government, and he came to the Park. Mr. Blackburne gave him treatments of sulphur and sweet oil and he lived for seventeen years more, finally dying of old age after thirty years of captivity.

The first bird was a sulphur-crested cockatoo which had been given to the old Smithsonian collection by a family in whose possession it had been for five years. It came to the Zoo with the other Smithsonian animals, and after thirty-eight years of waiting for a bird house, was finally moved into a cage especially prepared for it in the fine permanent building erected in 1927.

At first only one building was erected, in which were placed all of the animals requiring artificial heat—carnivorous, nocturnal animals housed with timid, diurnal, herbivorous ones. In all there were 185 animals and birds, large and small, transferred to permanent quarters at the Park.

The first year the public took great interest in the new establishment. Authorization had been made to purchase a few specimens, and the Zoo commenced to grow. But the next year there was elected to the House of Representatives a new flock of members who knew nothing of the Park, and the annual estimates were much reduced. Furthermore, the authority to purchase animals was withdrawn.

A tendency to abolish the Park gained headway. All activities were very much restricted. It was possible to secure specimens only by gifts or by collecting them in Government reservations. The gifts ran chiefly to opossums, racoons, and various small discarded pets; collections were made in the Yellowstone National Park, but this proved to be altogether too costly. In spite of all the collection slowly increased.

Once a kangaroo was offered for sale by a dealer for $75. The Zoo did not have $75, but a well-known Washington dealer in birds and animals bought it and traded it to the Park in exchange for guinea pigs which the Zoo was to raise at fifteen cents per guinea pig. After three years enough had been raised to pay off the debt and the kangaroo belonged to the nation.

One winter the Forepaugh Shows deposited their whole menagerie with the understanding that the Zoo should care for the animals and in return be allowed to exhibit them, and also the Zoo was to keep any animals that might be born during the winter. This arrangement netted two kangaroos and a lion cub to the collection. They greatly increased the popularity of the Institution, and caused a great deal of talk in Congress in regard to the United States Government running a circus.

In *The Smithsonian Institution, 1846–1896, the History of its First Half Century*, published in 1897, Dr. Frank Baker, at that time Director of the National Zoological Park, gives a résumé of the origin of the Zoo and states optimistically that "the future success of the Park can not be doubted. Popular interest everywhere is being awakened upon the subject of the preservation of game and the care of animals in captivity. . . . A feeling of national pride should lead all public-spirited citizens to take an active interest in the increase and suitable

PLATE 3

Sulphur-crested cockatoo, first bird ever to come into the Zoo, and still a young healthy resident after thirty-eight years

PLATE 4

The bird house, first of the modern buildings in the National Zoo

maintenance of the collection. At present it is not as widely known as it should be. When United States officials in all parts of the world become interested in its advancement, it is believed that the scope of the enterprise will be vastly increased."

Since then the Zoo has grown steadily, if slowly. At first only temporary structures could be erected, and these have proved entirely unsatisfactory from the standpoint of administration, their repair being a continual drain on the slender resources of the Zoo; but a small mammal house, now used to shelter the monkey collection, was built out of maintenance funds during a period of four years at a cost of about $44,000. This has been a most satisfactory building. For instance, there has not been a death from tuberculosis in this collection during the past four years.

In 1926 and 1927 Congress appropriated $127,000 to build an exhibition building for birds, and later an additional $30,000 for outside cages. This, now completed, makes the finest exhibit in the Park and will be followed by a reptile house to cost $220,000. It is hoped that these two will be the first of a series of modern buildings needed to house and exhibit the representative collection of animals and birds that should be in the National Zoological Park.

The popularity of the Park has so increased that between 2,500,000 and 3,000,000 visitors come annually. To the residents of the District it is the favorite recreation ground, and visitors come from every State in the Union. One year 114,000 school children came in organized classes. Many naturalists and artists have studied here.

During the past year the Army, Navy, and Marine Corps, the Department of Agriculture, the Bureau of Fisheries, and other Government departments have cooperated in increasing the collection, which at the present time contains about 2,400 specimens.

[7]

CHAPTER II

IN THE FIELD AFTER WILD ANIMALS

Zoos must continually add to their animal population. There is in the first place a certain death rate to balance. In the National Zoological Park it averages about fourteen per cent a year, this, of course, including many naturally short-lived species, though the death rate on the whole is quite low. One method of replenishment is, of course, by birth. Certain species breed well in captivity, and surplus animals raised in this way are often exchanged with other zoos for specimens that are desired. But the main source of new animals continues to be their natural habitat, and there they must be pursued and captured. The collecting of wild animals for sale to zoos and circuses of the world has been developed by several houses of international reputation into an enormous commercial business, and through these dealers is received a steady supply of animals.

Occasionally travelers for scientific expeditions augment this stream, and the National Zoological Park has regularly benefited in this way, and on one noteworthy occasion sent out an expedition for the sole purpose of bringing back live wild animals. On other expeditions the collectors have gathered what they could incidentally and brought them in.

Colonel Roosevelt was responsible for some noteworthy additions to the National Zoological Park collection shortly after he retired from the Presidency. In the spring of 1909 the Smithsonian Institution sent an expedition to British East Africa under his direction to collect natural history material for the United States National Museum. It was also to be on the lookout for animals that could be secured for the Zoo. In July a letter came from the expedition stating that Mr. W. N. McMillan, later Sir Nowlen McMillan, a wealthy American who spent part of his time in East Africa, had on his ranch near Nairobi a small collection of animals which he offered as a gift provided the Park would send for them. There were five lions, a leopard, a cheetah, a wart hog, two gazelles, and a few smaller animals. The Smithsonian accepted the offer by cablegram and dispatched Mr. A. B. Baker, Assistant Superintendent of the National Zoological Park, to bring the animals to America.

A South American expedition that brought into the Zoo many unusual species was the Mulford Biological Exploration of the Amazon Basin in 1921 and 1922, which I accompanied as naturalist. Our party traveled from Arica in Chile to La Paz, Bolivia, and then across and down the eastern slope of the Andes to the junction of the Meguilla and La Paz Rivers, where we camped for three weeks, waiting for Indians down the river to make and bring up rafts for our use.

In the beginning the director of the expedition opposed a collection of live animals, knowing full well the disturbance they generally create about camp. But he was a kindly, elderly man, and when a baby paroquet of delicate green hue and a confiding disposition perched on his finger, his outlook toward live things changed, and from then on we had *carte blanche* to collect anything possible.

The first extended stop was made at Huachi, well down the river, and among low hills. A mealy parrot, obtained here, constituted our initial specimen of importance. Members of a tribe of Indians who lived somewhere in the forest—a twelve days' walk for them, possibly a month's walk for anybody but an Indian—

were in the habit of coming into Huachi every year or so for the purpose of exchanging flat bird skins for salt, apparently their only need. They came while we were there, and had with them this parrot. A handful of salt bought it, and from then on it lived with us on a perch fastened to a barrel hoop, with an empty beef tin at either end for food and water.

The Mosetenas and the Cabinas, Indians with whom we lived later on, were hunters, and depended entirely on the chase for their meat. Monkeys are their favorite game, the rich, almost oily meat appealing much to them. When a big catch was secured they would half roast, half smoke the carcasses over open fires to preserve them. But like other South American Indians, they were fond of bringing in babies of various animals for the children to play with, and in the village were numbers of monkeys, curassows, parrots, a paca or two, and other small fry.

At Huachi, in Bolivia, we secured a very young tapir which we named Billy, and which lived with us in camp for many months, traveling down river on a raft. He was probably the hairy tapir, a mountain form seldom seen in captivity. He was robust and voracious, and had the camp in an uproar half the time. Above all things he loved to chew boot laces, and was continually at ours while we were busy, so that he earned many slaps and thumps. Coming down the Beni on the launch, Billy on deck with the rest of us, the whistle blew. The tapir, which had never heard anything like this before, did the best he could to put his short tail between his legs, and dived overboard. We put out in a canoe, got him, and brought him back. Thereafter, whenever the captain felt that the whistle should be blown, he would notify me and we would lock Billy up in a small room until the noise was over.

The railroad journey from Guajara-Mirim to Porto Velho around the source of the Madeira in Brazil takes two days. Billy, with all the rest of our stock, was put

PLATE 5

Lion brought from East Africa at time of Smithsonian-Roosevelt expedition

in an open cattle car. The engineer considered it his duty to blow the engine whistle almost continuously, and this, with the jiggling of a very bumpy train, reduced the tapir to a state of continual panic. He ate nothing, and when he finally got aboard the large launch which was to take us down the Madeira to the Amazon, he had become very weak. At the end of two or three days he commenced to eat a very little, and I had hopes of getting him safely to the steamer, but one morning when I descended to the lower deck and inquired of Nick, our erstwhile cook, now become a boiler of rice and peeler of bananas for the animals, how the tapir was coming on, he replied, "He'll be all right now. I just gave him a pill."

"What kind of pill?" I asked.

"I don't know what kind, but I got it from that fellow over there," pointing to a sick Barbadian.

Nick, in a blind way, believed in any kind of medicine, and had borrowed some sort of pill from this fellow and popped it down the tapir. The next morning Billy was dead.

This was the severest loss suffered on the expedition. We got what little comfort we could out of an incident which occurred at that time. A Brazilian passenger on our boat had had presented to him a baby tapir the day before he came aboard. The animal, recently taken from its mother, was living on stored-up vitality, and appeared to be very lively. Its owner kept telling me to look at his tapir, and then at mine, and I would see that I really did not know how to take care of tapirs, while he did. But the day that little Billy was thrown overboard, the specimen that he knew how to take care of suffered the same fate, and the two of them floated together down the river.

Our longest stop was made at Rurrenabaque, right at the base of the last ridge of the Andes. On the east side of the river were twelve miles of forest, which terminated suddenly as the pampas commenced, and with this variety of habitats the country was rich in animal life. When travelers are in such a community there is great demand on their medical stores. No day passed without our being visited by numerous people with ailments to be cured. Some of these deserved attention but often all the patient really wanted was a pill. Catering to them took so much of our time that I was finally compelled to make a charge for medical services. Minor services, such as quinine pills for malaria and iodine for cuts, were charged for at the rate of one paroquet, a parrot, or a small monkey; major operations, such as binding up a leg sore, had to be paid for with larger fry. We did quite a thriving medical business, and soon our collection filled the entire courtyard, with three young rheas and the tapir loose among the others. One old Indian kept coming and looking over the animals, and going away again, until finally, after several daily visits, he opened his mouth and pointed to a thoroughly rotted tooth that must have been causing him great agony, and asked me pathetically if there was any animal in the woods that would pay me for pulling this.

Twelve miles below Rurrenabaque was a little launch which makes monthly trips up and down the Rio Beni between Rurrenabaque and Riberalta. Its captain, Castro, a good soul, took an interest in our work and on his journeys notified various rubber *centrales* that when we came down we would buy all the live animals and birds that they could collect, so when we finally left on our way to the Amazon, each village contained something or other for us to buy, and on our arrival at Riberalta the launch was about loaded.

One of the rarer parrots on the river, which is also one of the most brilliant of the South American birds, is the flower-headed caique (*Pionites xanthomeria*). The natives value it so highly as a house pet that we were able to secure only three on the voyage. Once I saw a

PLATE 6

Cock of the rock, from South America. A resident at the
Zoo for eight years

tiny Indian girl with one of these on her shoulder. I stopped to speak to her, and she, with loud shrieks, fled into the house. Her father emerged in a moment and apologized for the rudeness of his small daughter, and explained, "Señor, the reason why she was so frightened was because she saw you looking at her pet parrot, and was afraid that you were going to try and buy it."

Under these conditions we still had only three when we arrived at Riberalta. A Bolivian lady of this town had four of them, and she told us that she would like to sell them to get money for a new dress, but her husband had refused to let her. On our last day she sent word that if we would come quickly, while her husband was away, she would sell them. Captain Castro and I dashed over to the house, bought the parrots, and were carrying them out in a little basket covered with a piece of cloth, when the husband came around the corner. The last thing we heard in Riberalta was these two amiable people telling what they thought of each other in shrill-pitched Spanish. But we now had seven specimens of the flower-headed caique, all of which arrived home safely, and four of which are still thriving. As these have been seen by millions of people, we think we were justified in getting them, even at the cost of a family row.

Often the things you do not succeed in bringing home are the most interesting of all. Besides Billy the tapir, there was a little bush dog. One day at Tumupasa, Pearson and I were hunting close to each other along a trail, when he shouted to me to come quickly, as he had come upon some Indians carrying a wild dog. I ran over to find two Indian men and a girl. The girl carried in a little bag a baby wild dog, one of the rarest of all South American animals. I immediately made the Indians wealthy for life at the American price of a carton of cigarettes, and the dog was mine. He was about ten inches long exclusive of a short tail, and dark brown in color, and very gentle. He lived in camp with us for a week, and then, apparently unable to assimilate any food we could give him, died. When I asked the Indian if there was only one of the dogs, he told me that there had been two in the litter, but that he had given the other to his brother at Ixiamas, so we broke camp the following morning and walked forty miles through the finest forest I had ever seen. When we arrived at the village we found that the other dog had died.

Then there was a monkey, a marmoset type, from the upper Madre de Dios. A friend of Captain Castro had brought it down. It had a black face with a white mark on each side of its neck extending across the cheek, which looked at a distance of a few feet for all the world like a Lord Kitchener moustache. Coming around the falls of the Madeira, on what is without doubt the bumpiest railroad in the world, the catch on the hurriedly improvised cage door was jarred loose, and the monkey got out. From my description of him when back home, it appeared that this was an unknown species, so we know that somewhere on the upper Madre de Dios lives a small and charming monkey that has never come into any collection.

After passing the falls of the Madeira-Mamoré, and getting aboard the river launch, our troubles with transportation were over. These Amazon launches are commodious, big double-deckers, the upper deck for the first-class passengers and the lower deck for the cargo and the apparently dying third-class passengers. It is strange that on the Beni, where everybody has malaria, none seems to suffer very greatly from it, while the type on the Madeira knocks one out. In hammocks on our lower deck a dozen or more were down with it when we came aboard. I gave some quinine to the first one who asked for it, and was promptly met by an appeal from everybody on the lower deck for "*quinina*, señor." With our limited supply of the drug, it was necessary to pick out those who were really in very bad condition

PLATE 7

Upper: Blesbok, a South African antelope
Lower: Coke's hartebeest, obtained from Mr. McMillan in East Africa
through Colonel Roosevelt

PLATE 8

Upper: Congo harnessed antelope and young
Lower: East African nyala, or inyala, thought to be the only specimen
ever imported to America

and divide it among them. One of our passengers died the day we were at Manáos.

The *Tupi*, our boat, was collecting Brazil nuts, so we stopped at every little settlement down the river, and sometimes ran up tributaries to other settlements. The nuts were waiting for us in coarsely made baskets, usually in the shade of a shack on the river's bank. Sometimes the supply was small and the stops were short, but always it was great fun to dash into the village and ask the nearest man, "*Hay macacos?*" (Are there any monkeys in this village?) Usually there was something—a woolly or a capuchin monkey; a curassow; a trumpeter living with the native chickens; a parrot or a paroquet sitting on a perch made by shoving a stick into the walls of the house. A hurried bargain and a dash back to the boat, and our collection would be increased by something interesting.

Years afterward I gave a series of radio talks from the National Zoological Park. A yacht with a friend of mine on board as guest came into the harbor at Washington. He had told the others about his friend at the Zoo, and wondered if I were in town. When they came to anchor in the evening, they tuned in on Washington, and the first words they heard were mine, "Are there any monkeys in this village?"

We reached Manáos early one morning, and found a Booth tramp steamer ready to sail that evening at five. We transferred our cargo at once, securing what we could from the market there. This consisted chiefly of the giant turtle of the Amazon (*Podocnemis expansa*), made classic by Bates, but which, on account of specialized feeding habits which limit its food exclusively to Amazonian water weed, did not do well in captivity.

This voyage was not altogether without interest. Members of our expedition were the only passengers aboard the freighter. We had camped together for nearly a year, and as each of us knew everything that the others

[15]

knew, we had no desire to talk much, and we found my 135 animals wonderful companions for the voyage. We had, in addition to nineteen monkeys, fifty-odd parrots. Some of the latter we kept loose on deck, and they roosted at night on top of the cages and sometimes flew about the ship. One tragedy occurred when one flew out to sea and then caught up again with the boat, only to light on a wet stanchion and fall off into the water, just by the propeller, where she was engulfed at once by the waves. On one occasion three blue-headed parrots got away at the same time and flew quite far out. Unable to see any land, they turned and regained the ship; all of them flew into the safety of my arms, outstretched as perches, and one of them is still living in the Zoo. But even such good companions entail a lot of responsibility. One of the pleasantest meetings that I have experienced was with the agent of the National Zoological Park who was waiting on the dock to take the animals off my hands, unload, and ship them to Washington.

For a long time the National Zoological Park had hoped to be able to make a real zoo expedition, that is, one with the sole object of capturing live animals for the Park. This matter had been brought to the attention of a number of people. In fact I had mentioned it to every one who would listen, and one day we received a telegram: "Chrysler approves African expedition. Go ahead. Make definite plans." Our good genie was Mr. Walter P. Chrysler.

So we took the next steamer to England. There were four of us in the party: Arthur Loveridge, of the Museum of Comparative Zoology of Harvard University, who had spent eight years in Tanganyika, part of the time in the army and the rest as game warden; Fred Carnochan, of New York City, an old classmate of mine; and Stephen Haweis, the artist and traveler, who had been in the field in the West Indies with me years before. He was to be allowed to paint pictures between cleaning bird

PLATE 9

Baby reed buck just after capture in East Africa

cages. The Pathé Review sent Charles Charlton, a camera man, who was to make a pictorial chronicle of the trip and of the work of the expedition.

In London we had a few delightful and hectic days shopping—mainly for tents, camp equipment, guns, and tin chests, and then left Tilbury Dock on the thirty-five day voyage to Dar-es-Salaam. At Zanzibar we transferred to a smaller steamer, which took us into the mainland at Dar. Three days here served to unload our gear and obtain the necessary permits for hunting. Mr. Swinnerton, the chief game warden, secured a governor's license for us, an invaluable document, as it gave us, within reason, *carte blanche* to collect any animals that we could, and then the Colonial Secretary notified various commissioners throughout the colony to help us in securing necessary porters and guides, without whom nothing at all can be done.

We went immediately to Dodoma, about 250 miles inland on the railroad, leaving Dar-es-Salaam at night and waking up in the morning on a high plain, where we saw before breakfast two herds of giraffes. In all we saw forty giraffes that day from the train, which put us in high spirits. Standing near the train on the veldt as they did, young ones among them, they looked to our eyes ridiculously easy to catch.

At Dodoma we rented a large cement house with a big courtyard (see Frontispiece), the property of a Hindu who was living somewhere else, and then notified the natives that we would buy any live things that they would bring in. The natives hereabouts are the Wagogo, an offshoot of the better known Masai, formerly a warlike people who gave Stanley much trouble as he crossed their territory. They are not especially good hunters, but during our stay brought us in numerous small things, chiefly birds, and among them mostly weaver birds. The latter occur in tremendous quantities, so that it is necessary to have a boy stationed in the middle of a

[17]

green field to scare them away. Sometimes he stands on a platform, built for the purpose, at other times avails himself of a high termite nest, and all day long throws stones from a sling at the birds. The birds are trapped in small grass baskets, and many of these were brought in for our collection.

It took several days to organize the Dodoma camp, which was to be our headquarters. Our milk supply for possible young animals had to be arranged. Very soon our arrival and the object of our trip were generally known and each morning a long line of natives would appear, some of them with the daily milk supply in beer bottles, others with freshly cut grass, grain, and the live things they had picked up the previous day.

Having had experience with expeditions before, and wanting to remain friends with my companions, I divided the party up into four, leaving Loveridge in charge at Dodoma; sending Carnochan to Tabora, far to the west, and Haweis down the railroad line to Mahonde, a mission; while I, with a white hunter, left for Umbugwe to go to Lake Meru.

We were disappointed in many ways. Previous experience in South America and other countries had taught me that natives are, after all, the best source of supply for live animals. But the Tanganyika natives, never great hunters, and restrained by game protective laws, had little interest in the larger animals. They brought in from time to time many young antelopes, but the most important things we got from them were small birds and mammals that they had snared.

At Meru, Runton, the white hunter, and I lived a month, capturing a small group of gnu, an account of which appears elsewhere in this book, and numerous other specimens. From time to time we would ship these back to Dodoma.

After this Runton and I moved over into the Ja-Aida country, and had our futile venture for rhinoceroses.

PLATE 10

On the Smithsonian-Chrysler Expedition
Upper: Unloading take-down crates from the railroad
Lower: Animal crate ready to be set up as trap

PLATE 11

First day at sea.   The Smithsonian-Chrysler expedition returning from East Africa

Then I journeyed back to the railway, and south into the Kisaki region, where we secured our giraffes, impallas, and wart hogs.

At the end of four months telegrams were sent to each of the party, and we all gathered on the dock at Dar-es-Salaam, each with the animals he had collected. Again the Government came to our aid, and gave us a large warehouse, open at two ends, where we put the collection. By this time we had 203 crates of birds, animals, and reptiles. We were flooded by visitors—Swahilis, Zanzibar Arabs, Hindus, and Europeans—who came in such crowds to see the animals that we had to appeal for police protection. A guard of Askaris was sent down, and for three days we maintained on the dock at Dar-es-Salaam, East Africa, a branch of the United States National Zoological Park—visiting hours from two to five, and a police force to prevent visitors from annoying the animals.

We were fortunate in having available an almost empty steamer to take us to Ceylon. By going this way we had eleven days of open sea, instead of long waits in the great heat of East Coast harbors, and it proved much better for the animals. Our specimens were placed in lighters, and the firm that did the loading exercised unusual care in handling them. Enormous trays, used normally for handling ivory, carried the cages from the lighter to the deck of the steamer. We got to sea as soon as loaded. Loveridge had stayed behind. Haweis and Carnochan were aboard, and we brought with us, also, two native boys, James and Saidi, the best of our field men, to help care for our animals.

The next morning the boat was rolling a little, and when I came out to look over the crates, I discovered James and Saidi lying on the deck. One of my companions was in bed with a wet towel around his head, the other was holding his hands tightly clasped over his stomach. To feed and care for the animals seemed a

[19]

hopeless task, until good old Malloy, chief engineer, rolled up his sleeves and went to work with me. One of my companions recovered in time to help out, also, and we managed that day at least to feed and water our charges. Malloy did so well that we rewarded him by giving him a line of fifty bird cages to care for during the remainder of the voyage. We landed at Colombo, Ceylon, at five one evening, and transferred to another ship, the *City of Calcutta,* bound for Boston, and sailed the following evening.

Our life aboard ship was more or less routine. We divided the collection up into groups, one of our party taking care of the hoofed animals and monkeys, another the carnivorous animals, another the birds, and James and Saidi assisted everybody. First thing in the morning cages were cleaned. Then food was prepared and served. It meant that we were on the go most of the day, and James and Saidi slept at night among the cages, so as to give the alarm if anything went wrong.

It took thirty days to cross from Calcutta to Boston, where we arrived on a warm and rainy October day. Mr. Blackburne of our Zoo was waiting on the dock with one of the keepers, and the American agent for the firm of Hagenbeck was there too. I had made arrangements to have the animals unloaded. Long lines of stevedores took the crates from the boat directly to large express cars waiting on the dock. The hoofed animals and the swine were taken to a military depot for a two weeks' quarantine. The others left that afternoon and arrived in Washington the following morning.

CHAPTER III

THE MANLIKE APES

THE leading citizens of any zoological community are the anthropoid apes, the gorillas, chimpanzees, orangutans, and gibbons. While other creatures may attain a greater popularity for a time, the visitors always return with renewed interest to the cages of these great apes. Since the topic of human evolution has become material for curbstone debates, heated arguments take place in front of the cages, and some of them would be most amusing to the inmates if they could understand them. "Isn't it human?" "Isn't it disgusting?" are stereotyped remarks often heard, and the last word in humor is to compare the chimpanzee to some friend.

A gorilla is an event in the lifetime of a zoo. This animal is, without doubt, the most spectacular that can be secured, and because of its rarity, the difficulty of transportation, and the great risk of illness and death, the price is generally so high that few zoos can afford to buy one. Since 1847, when Savage described the gorilla, only a limited number have come into collections. The first gorilla we know of in captivity was a young female that formed part of a traveling menagerie in England in 1855. She lived for several months. Fourteen years later, another young specimen came to the London Zoological Gardens, and lived for seven months. The most notable case is that of the female which lived for seven years in the home of the director of the zoo at Breslau, Germany, from 1897 to 1904.

A young male came to Berlin in 1876. When first caught

he was coaxed to drink goat's milk and eat fruits, but he was so small and weak that he would fall asleep over the bottle. For the first few days the infant spent most of his time sleeping, like any other baby of his age. He gained in strength slowly, and was allowed to run at liberty about the camp. He made no attempt to escape, but clung affectionately to the human companions who had nursed him after the death of his mother. He would play in the sand with the negro boys like one of them— an interesting trait, for many apes display an inexplicable dislike for the black race. (This is very noticeable in our big chimpanzee, Soko, perhaps from memories of his capture.) The little gorilla was very clean. He would pick up food fastidiously with the thumb, fore and middle fingers. If he touched a spider's web, he would try to brush it off at once or hold out his hand for some one to perform this service for him. He liked to paddle in water and then roll on the sand in the sun. He loved to beat on hollow objects, anything that would make a noise. Unusual noises, such as thunder, threw him into terror. This gorilla was brought alive to Berlin where he was also given the freedom of the keeper's house. He ate at a table and slept in a bed, generally covering his head with a blanket. As a rule he was well behaved, but would snatch at anything which attracted his attention. He died in a few months of galloping consumption.

One's own gorilla is, of course, the most important of all, and N'Gi at the National Zoological Park is to us nothing less than royalty. N'Gi was captured on January 17, 1928, by Mr. J. L. Buck of Camden, New Jersey, and West Africa. Mr. Buck commutes between his two homes, and has made eight trips, during which time he has captured three gorillas and succeeded in bringing one, N'Gi, to the States. His own account of the capture of N'Gi is as follows:

I have caught three gorillas, but have succeeded in bringing only one, N'Gi, into the States. The gorilla is

[22]

supposed to be a rare animal, but I believe that is because he inhabits only the primitive, almost impenetrable forests, which have a reputation that is at least partly undeserved, for diseases. In some of these places the gorilla is so plentiful that he must be exterminated before cultivation can progress. In a forest extending over a territory of 400 by 600 miles, I have seen at least fifty gorillas.

In the group of which N'Gi was a member, there were six individuals, four adult females, a male, and the baby. We located them by the signs that they left through this swamp, the destruction of certain species of vegetation. I had with me twenty-three Batwa pygmies. When it was evident that the gorillas had passed, the pygmies spread out, fan-shape. Once the animals were located the word passed from one to the other of the pygmies, and the walk began. Had we attacked them at once, they would have scattered and disappeared, or they would have fought us. They travel fairly fast, twenty miles being a good day. We managed to keep the same gait. During the succeeding four days, the male would occasionally try to bluff us off by raising himself to a standing position, and uttering threatening roars. If we had attempted to run, he would have pursued us, and there is no doubt that he would have eventually caught us. Instead, when he tried his intimidating tactics, we sat down and waited for him to go on. Many of his antics were like those of a baboon. He would frequently nonchalantly turn over a stone, pretending he was busy and not noticing us.

During our walk we occasionally collected an antelope for food, but cooked it far in the rear of where we camped. Gorillas have no objection to a wood fire, but they do not take kindly to tobacco.

Each day of the walk the gorillas became a little more accustomed to us, but for ten days the female with the baby was kept quite far in advance of the others. On some occasions she was flogged by the male so that she would go ahead. In about twelve days this enforced speed was not insisted upon, and she was permitted to stay with her companions. The half-breed who was in charge of the pygmies proved his worth by not allowing them to shoot prematurely. On the seventeenth day they shot her with a poisoned arrow. We could have collected other females in the meantime. At first she seemed hardly conscious that she had been shot, but she gradually became weaker, and in about an hour she fell. I then pulled my shirt off and put it into N'Gi's mouth so that he could not bite us, or, more important, call the troop to his defense. The men who stayed with me prepared for a feast of roast gorilla, and after the mother had been eaten by the pygmies we left with the baby.

N'Gi's first meal in captivity was a piece of bread softened with milk, which he ate very gingerly. Within two days he cried for milk. I believe he was nursing, when captured. In four days' time he was quite at home, and within ten days he was permitted to wander about as he wished. On the homeward journey he was a constant source of delight. The captain enjoyed playing with him, and the cooks saved choice bits of food for him to eat. At home we had a platform built for him so that he would be raised above the level of the floor. A staple was driven into the wall, to which he could be chained, when necessary, to keep him out of mischief. On this platform he would play with anything furnished for his amusement. Among his favorite toys were pieces of rope, upon which he could swing, and a double boiler just large enough to fit his head, which he would put on like a hat and then stand on his head. Occasionally he would use the handle as a club and beat himself over the head with it. Another favorite source of amusement was a half-peck measure. He would stand on the edge of this and clap his hands. He likewise played with balloons, newspapers, and balls.

- BENSON B. MOORE -

FIG. 1. Some reasons why N'Gi, the baby gorilla, is the most popular resident of the National Zoo

Sketches by Benson B. Moore

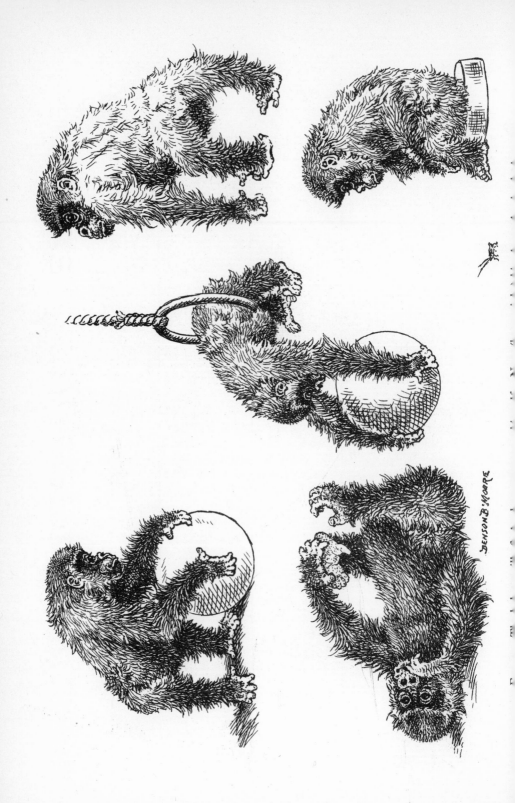

THE MANLIKE APES

N'Gi had been in Mr. Buck's hands for nearly a year before he decided to take him to Cuba, there to sell him to Madame Abreu, who has a notable anthropoid collection. He stopped off between trains in Washington to give us an opportunity to see the gorilla, and we persuaded Mr. Buck to bring N'Gi to the Park so that he could have a few hours of exercise in a large cage. We put him at first in the big cage occupied by Jiggs, the orang-utan, and Bob and Bill, two white-handed gibbons, placing him in the middle of the floor. Most animals would have run directly to the bars and tried to get out. Instead of doing this, N'Gi hurried back to the door and tried to open it. He did not seem to like the looks of his cage mates. He was suspicious of them, and they, in turn, became very excited. Jiggs stared. He moved about more than I have seen him move during the whole past year, and the two gibbons fairly filled the air, hurtling about. Jiggs was fascinated by the stranger, and N'Gi, who had always, according to Mr. Buck, looked down upon other monkeys, showed considerable interest in him. When they had spent four hours in the cage together, Jiggs came to the ground, and N'Gi, after running round and round him a dozen times, in an attempt to come upon him from behind, suddenly burned all his bridges and jumped on top of the orang-utan. Jiggs met him with a fond and tortuous embrace and a shower of kisses, and from then on the two were inseparable, so much so that the following day (yes, we had bought the gorilla in the meantime; no one could have resisted him) N'Gi had to be taken out of the cage. The gorilla is not an arboreal animal; the orang-utan is, and Jiggs is very fond of the upper part of the cage. N'Gi insisted upon following him around, and the gibbons, who had never been particularly fond of Jiggs, suddenly took it upon themselves to defend him from this new and presumptuous visitor. So, while the baby gorilla was laboriously going hand over hand up a pole some fifteen feet in the

air, above a hard floor, Bob would swing down, whack him on the head, chuckle, and then glide, as only a gibbon can, to the other end of the cage. N'Gi clutched at him, lost his balance, and almost fell. The Zoo staff, watching, swallowed hard, and N'Gi was taken out immediately and put in another cage, and alone. He experienced loneliness at once, and cried, angrily, as a three-year-old child would. On the following morning he played, but soberly, standing erect, or lying on his back and clapping his hands, again in a childlike manner. The third day he paid more attention to a soft ball placed in the cage, and made a plaything of his drinking pan.

Since then better quarters have been arranged for him; a ten-by-ten cage with two skylights of ultra-violet glass, which give him a ten per cent proportion of ultra-violet rays. Private sleeping quarters have been provided in the form of a large box near the top. Gymnastic apparatus—climbing perches, a swinging ring, a pair of dumb-bells, and an eight-pound medicine ball—were given to him at the beginning, and he has developed interest in all of them. Two vertical posts were installed in his cage, in which were driven hollow metal crossbars, and the ends stopped with wooden plugs. His first activity in his new home was to pull out one of these plugs with his teeth and investigate the resultant hole with his finger. This done he transferred his attention to the end of each of three other perches and tried to pull the plugs out from them also.

He first manifested interest in the medicine ball by attempting to sit on it, but he rolled off. In a few weeks, however, he learned to balance himself on it fairly well. He uses it also as a drum, but since he has discovered that he can push it around, he has spent hours in having mimic battles with it. Within a week he had learned a new trick, pulling it toward him and running backward, laughing, and biting it when it struck him. Some time later he learned to twirl it, and one of his favorite tricks

is to hang himself through the swinging ring and lift
the ball up with all four feet. It is a little too large for
him to hold, but he will lie on his back and juggle it,
Japanese style, using all four feet.

The dumb-bells he carries from place to place, and when
climbing will place one on his shoulder and hold it there
with his head pressed sideways. His old drinking pan
remains a favorite plaything. He will carry it balanced
on his head, or put it on the floor and stand on his head
in it. Naturally, psychologists were interested in him,
and for the first week, whenever I wanted to look at my
own gorilla it was necessary to elbow aside some distinguished scientist. N'Gi's pat-a-caking with his hands
has been identified as the reaction of a six-month-old
baby, and his manner of waving his arms in answer to
similar waves from friends as the reaction of a child of
eighteen months.

At present he is thoroughly at home in his new quarters,
and will play by himself, but he increases his play energy
when there is an audience, and redoubles it when somebody that he knows is outside. His diet, prescribed for
him by one of Washington's prominent child doctors, is
equivalent to that of a three-year-old infant, and includes
orange juice, apples, eggs and milk, cod-liver oil, cooked
and raw vegetables, and an occasional rice custard.

At 4:30, when the house is closed, a blanket is given
him, which, after mopping up the floor with it and getting
it dirty enough to suit his taste, he carries upstairs into
his sleeping quarters and goes to bed, though not without
a baby's whimper at being left alone. He sleeps on his
back, and does not wrap himself in the blanket, though
he is very fond of playing with a piece of white cloth and
draping it over himself. He has remained very friendly,
though at times he becomes boisterous. His feeding
habits are most genteel. There is no unseemly rush to
his food. He eats with evident enjoyment, and puts
aside what he doesn't want. When course number one

does not please him, he will drop it, and then push it away and reach for course number two. Sometimes, when that does not come up to his expectations, he will return to number one, and after cleaning it sufficiently with his hands, will finish what he had left.

It is doubtful if many live gorillas will be exhibited in the future, as a serious attempt is being made to have them protected throughout their range—a wise move, indeed, and badly needed right now. No animal is more interesting, and the very few thousand that still remain in Africa should be preserved. Probably they never were very abundant. Du Chaillu, during four years in Africa, was able to collect only seventeen. Those interested in the protection of the gorilla have appealed recently to the League of Nations to secure laws that will save him from extinction. There has even been some attempt to give the gorilla the status of native. It is to be fervently hoped that sportsmen will no longer feel that they must shoot a gorilla.

The second day that N'Gi was on exhibition, a lady visitor to the Zoo protested that it was degrading to keep an animal so much like a man in captivity, and demanded to know why it was that it had been taken away from its family. But the ape is not a man. It is not even a close approach to man. Measurements of the skull capacity tell part of the story. The skull cavity of the gorilla, highest of the anthropoids, according to the measurements of Dr. Aleš Hrdlička of the Smithsonian Institution, measures approximately 600 cubic centimeters. The lowest figure for the human race obtained from the thousands of skulls in the National Museum collection is 900 cubic centimeters in the case of some ancient Peruvians who probably were imbecile. The cranial capacity of the normal, adult white man ranges between 1,500 and 2,000 cubic centimeters, so the skull of a gorilla could never be mistaken for that of a human being.

THE MANLIKE APES

Cranial capacity, true enough, is not an absolute criterion of intelligence. The distinction is in the quality of cell material inside the skulls, and this must be determined largely by the evidence of behavior. But in making any assertions regarding the mentality of apes we are always on debatable ground, because there has not been enough opportunity for observation under favorable conditions, while there has been too much opportunity for diverse interpretations from the scanty data which are available. Practically all of the observations of ape behavior have been restricted to those in captivity, where an animal provided with shelter and food, and protected from all enemies, is probably quite a different animal from the same creature struggling for survival in an African jungle. There is little to sharpen what wits the animal has. His humanlike form, coupled with his unusual intelligence, makes it easy to teach the ape to simulate man in many ways. He can smoke a cigar, or eat at a table, but he always remains an ape. In the Zoo we do not dress them up and do not teach them to smoke, because we want apes in the collection, not burlesque men.

Yesterday two small boys stood in front of the cage, and one of them told the other: "That is the gorilla. He is little now, but when he gets big he will be so strong they will have to have a special cage for him, and I'll bet they have started to make that cage already."

The chimpanzee, easiest to exhibit, is by far the best-known of the anthropoids. He appears to be really happy among people, and especially in his youth does he exhibit a friendly attitude toward both spectators and keepers. He does not brood over his troubles, though he is subject to fits of temper, and will go into tantrums like any child. Always a conscious actor, the chimpanzee glories in applause. He acquires readily such complicated behavior as is involved in sitting at a table with a napkin tucked under his chin, and using knives and forks, or in running a lawn mower, or turning a wringer.

Soko, the big chimpanzee in the National Zoological Park, has for more than twelve years been a favorite with the people. Physically he is a very fine animal. At present he weighs about 140 pounds. Mr. Blackburne writes the following account of him:

Soko was purchased from a dealer September 8, 1915. He then weighed thirty-eight pounds and was four or five years old. His estimated weight in 1928, when about seventeen years old, was 130 pounds. When Soko first came to the Zoo a table and a high chair were made fast to the floor of his cage and his meals were served there twice daily. Visitors, both old and young, enjoyed this so much that the building was invariably packed at feeding time—especially Sundays. His manners at the table were very good and his handling of the spoon and fork while eating sliced bananas or rice pudding would compare favorably with those of a carefully taught child. Soko dined at the table in this manner for several years. At each meal he was given a pint of evaporated milk which he poured from a bottle into a half-pint glass, to drink. At his first performance before the public he filled the glass to overflowing, but thereafter he always exercised great care to avoid this. A white bib was placed about his neck and a white tablecloth spread. He was given a menu book which he opened and looked over. He then rang a small dinner bell and the attendant gave him a slip of paper and pencil. He scribbled on the paper what passed for his order—bottle of milk, sliced bananas, or rice pudding. He was very deliberate and patient and quietly watched every movement of the keeper. When through feeding he removed the bib, wiped his mouth, used a toothpick, and brushed himself with a hairbrush. He was then given the key to the padlock of the cage door which he unlocked with ease.

PLATE 12

W. H. Blackburne, in charge of the animals since the National Zoo's
inception, with N'Gi, baby gorilla

PLATE 13

Soko, the chimpanzee, when a tractable youngster

He always put the key in his mouth to wet it before unlocking the padlock.

During warm weather he was taken for walks about the Park and enjoyed visits to the pens or cages of the different animals—bears, elephants, deer, and what he classed as common monkeys. He took great care not to get too close, especially to animals that were more powerful than himself. He was very much afraid of horses, and when one of the larger animals resented his presence he would get behind me and peep at them or pull on the leash to move away.

He disliked negroes, and they, of course, always followed him during his outings. Frequently he chased a good-sized boy, grabbed him by the foot with his hand and jerked the leg upwards, tossing the boy head foremost to the ground. On one occasion he led the keeper into Rock Creek Park. He had become somewhat unruly and refused to obey. The keeper tied him to a tree and telephoned for help, so I hurried off to the rescue in an automobile. When Soko saw me he welcomed me with loud calls and put his arms around my neck. He enjoyed the ride back home but was very uneasy while fording the Creek, taking a strong grip on my legs and peeping out cautiously at the water. He soon became too powerful to take out for exercise as he could lead one where he wished and his animosity to colored people made him dangerous. He grew tired finally of displaying his civilized manners at the table and he tore both table and chair loose from their fastenings and gave a regular roughhouse exhibition of how to demolish and break up furniture.

During his younger life he was very amiable and gentle. He loved attention and was apt at learning. He enjoyed riding a bicycle, raking up leaves, and pushing baby carriages. He would bear down on the handle occasionally to get a peep at the baby and look longingly at the nursing bottle ; then in a questioning manner point to it. He understood the meaning of "No."

At first, after arrival here, he grabbed at my eyeglasses and watch charm. I caught his hands, slapped them, then pointing to my glasses and charm, cautioned him never to do so again, and he never did. He would carefully wind my watch and liked to hear it tick.

But Soko has now lost most of his playfulness. The practice of feeding him at a table was discontinued, for one reason, as Mr. Blackburne said, because he eventually smashed all his furniture, and also because pickpockets availed themselves of the large crowds that gathered in front of the cage. In his old age he has no friends beyond two or three keepers and a policeman who spends considerable time in his house. He will call the policeman by a buzzing noise when he is thirsty, and point to the faucet. When he takes a dislike to visitors watching him he will fly into fits of fearful rage, running up and down the cage, standing erect and knocking the bars with his knuckles and wrists. This is repeated for several moments, after which he will sit down and seize the door of his cage with all four feet, and rattle it for several more minutes, and then repeat his running. These tantrums are terminated always in one of two ways. Either he will jump to the top of his cage and hit the ceiling a hard punch, or he will suddenly catch a handful of sawdust from the floor, and throw it at the person who has attracted his disfavor. Then he sits down, apparently having forgotten what excited him. A visitor in the building after hours may set him off on one of these rampages, and the building, hitherto quiet for the night, becomes a bedlam. The lions in a nearby cage roar, the hippo grunts, and sometimes even the alligators join in the discord.

Soko, during his long residence at the Zoo, has shown remarkable intelligence in many instances. On one occasion he was troubled with a bad tooth, and Mr. Blackburne pulled it. Some months later he called to

PLATE 14

Orang-utan from Sumatra.   Prefers tree-dwelling

PLATE 15

White-handed gibbon from southeastern Asia. Smallest and most agile of the anthropoids

Mr. Blackburne with a loud buzzing noise that he uses to attract his attention, and opening his mouth pointed to another tooth, loose and evidently aching, and waited patiently for it to be pulled out. The morning on which this is being written, while we were standing in front of his cage, he extended his hind foot and spread his toes, indicating to his keeper that it was about time to trim the nails.

The largest chimpanzee of which we have record was one sent to the Melbourne Zoo some years ago by Ellis Joseph, a noted naturalist, collector, and dealer. Now Joseph himself is a superman physically, and he can wrestle fairly well with a chimpanzee. Whenever he visited Melbourne, he always called on the chimpanzee. Once, after being away for about six months, he entered the cage, as he had been accustomed to do, but the chimpanzee became excited, threw his arms about him, and instead of biting gently, made his teeth meet through Joseph's chin. The attacked man was strong enough to stun the chimpanzee by a blow of his fist. He then went out of the cage and walked to the hospital.

There is no doubt that the chimpanzee is a great deal stronger than a man, but we have recently heard of a specimen with a circus on the Pacific coast that was so intractable that the circus owner employed a pugilist to handle him. The boxer met the frontal attack of the chimpanzee by a knock-out blow, and afterward the chimpanzee not only respected him, but they became great friends.

Next to the chimpanzee the most available of the great apes for a zoological collection is the red-haired, long-armed, funny-faced anthropoid from Borneo and Sumatra —the orang-utan, "man of the woods." Though he has got rid entirely of any vestiges of a tail, his general make-up is less human than that of either the chimpanzee or the gorilla. His broad, flattened face, due to a lateral expansion of the cheeks caused by a kind of warty growth, gives him a peculiarly goblinlike appearance.

The orang shows little inclination towards a stage career. There is no joy in his performances, no delight in applause. One of the most agile of creatures in the jungle tree tops, he is slow and deliberate in captivity. Most of the time he seems plunged in deep thought or day dreams. He accepts his fate philosophically. He is not particularly interested in the crowds that flock in front of his cage. Like the other anthropoids, the orang tends to become ill-tempered with age.

Recently orang-utans have come upon the market in great numbers. An English dealer imported into the States more than twenty of them in one shipment. There were in the lot several groups of father, mother, and young, all kept in small shipping crates because, had they been taken out and put in larger quarters, it would have been impossible to put them back into smaller boxes for shipping. The story is that these animals were obtained by building fires beneath the trees in which they had their nests, and rendering them unconscious by a sleep-inducing smoke.

Jiggs, the orang-utan at the National Zoological Park, came from a New York animal dealer. For a long time he lived with Joe Mendi, the chimpanzee, but Joe was altogether too rough for him. There was nothing malicious in his playing, but every time Jiggs would attempt to walk, Joe would hurl himself upon him, so that for the last several months that they lived together Jiggs was afraid to stand up, and slid about the floor. It was thought that he would get along much better away from his mate, so he was put into a large cage with a duo of gibbons, and from then on he blossomed out into a real personality. He was able to walk and climb about unnoticed, except for an occasional tap on the head from one of the gibbons. He is especially fond of playing with a burlap bag, part of his sleeping paraphernalia. He

FIG. 3. Soko on a rampage, beating his bars. By Benson B. Moore

will double it over a pole and then hang by the two ends. Sometimes he will fall, but only when he is playing near the ground. He has so far never taken any chances by letting go one end of the bag while at any altitude. At night he takes the burlap bag with him and climbs into a manger, formerly a food box for a giraffe, and sleeps there. He was so excited during the short visit of the gorilla in his cage that he changed his sleeping place, or rather sat up all night, with his arm around a pole.

This ape has a long memory. Several years ago an American physician, then in Calcutta, was called to treat one of them for some minor malady. Later the animal was sold to the London Zoo. Three years afterwards the doctor stopped in front of one of the ape cages and the inmate, catching sight of him, rushed to the bars and screamed to attract his attention. Inquiry revealed that it was the same orang he had befriended at Calcutta.

Like the chimpanzee or the gorilla, the orang is most engaging in infancy. The celebrated English naturalist, Alfred Russel Wallace, relates the history of one which he received in Borneo when the baby was only a foot high. When first carried home this tiny creature took such a firm grasp on his new owner's beard that he could hardly be pulled away. At first there were no signs of teeth, but in a few days two of the lower incisors were cut. Mr. Wallace could obtain no milk for the little ape but he overcame this difficulty by feeding him on rice water, which he sucked from a bottle by means of a quill through a cork. Later sugar and coconut milk were added to this mixture. When caressed this ape was contented and happy but soon began to scream when laid down. He was kept in a box with a thick mat at the bottom. The little fellow seemed to appreciate frequent baths and when he wanted one would announce the fact by loud screams. The process of drying and rubbing after each bath seemed to be the source of much enjoyment. He loved to have his hair combed. At first he clutched vigorously with all four limbs at any object within reach and his owner constantly had to guard his beard. When he could find nothing better to do he would suck his own toes.

After a few weeks a young macaque monkey was introduced to the orang and the two soon became fast friends. Mr. Wallace noted the helplessness of the ape compared with the macaque, a characteristic which distinguishes the young of all the anthropoids. Even when the orang had been more than a month in captivity he was quite unsteady on his hands and feet and frequently would topple over, like an infant learning to walk. When he required attention he would cry loudly for a time, but if this met with no reply he would remain still until he heard footsteps approaching, when the cries would be renewed. He died of fever when about two months old.

The last and lowest of the anthropoid apes—the smallest, the most docile, and the least intelligent—is the gibbon. Although these apes abound in southeastern Asia and are not difficult to capture, there is little historical reference to them in the records of zoological collections. It is likely that they have not been exhibited to any great extent except in the last half century. In the Zoological Gardens at Calcutta they do well. In the United States and Europe they constantly are threatened with consumption, even when the greatest care is bestowed upon them. They are gentle and confiding animals. When captured young they can be tamed so as to make excellent pets. They have some tendency, in common with all the other apes, to become morose after they have passed the stage of adolescence.

The agility of the wou-wou, or agile gibbon (*Hylobates agilis*) was demonstrated in 1840 at the Jardin des Plantes in Paris when a live bird was released in its cage. After watching the flight for a moment the ape swung suddenly to a distant bar to which it clung with one hand while it grabbed the bird with the other. The hoolock (*Hylobates hoolock*), the gibbon seen most frequently in captivity, is very fond of small birds, although it subsists mainly on fruit and leaves, feeding occasionally on insects, spiders, and eggs.

We have always found small gibbons a "bad buy." They appear to be happy, healthy, and playful, and nearly always are friendly, but it seems to be a matter of only a short time before they die. The most noted gibbon of all is one at Philadelphia that has lived for more than a quarter of a century. This is a white-handed species (*Hylobates lar*), which seems to be the best of all for life in a cage. The two in the National Zoological Park are both white-handed. One is black and one yellowish brown, there being a great deal of variation in color in the species.

There is no more graceful animal in the world than a gibbon, and these two, when in action, make their thirty-foot cage look as though it were full of gibbons.

Sunshine and fresh air are essential to keeping any of the apes successfully in captivity. Perhaps it would be better if they could be allowed complete liberty about the zoological parks in fair weather. This, of course, is not practical in the modern zoo with its great crowds eager to feed and touch the animals. They must be kept as far from contact with human beings as possible, not only for the protection of the men and women but for the well-being of the apes. All these animals are extremely liable to infections from humans and when they are indoors it is preferable to keep them in glass cages where the germs of respiratory diseases spread by coughing and spitting can not reach them. An infection that would cause only a slight cold in a human being might cause fatal pneumonia or tuberculosis in an ape. The present tendency is to pay less attention to chills and drafts and more to infections. A reasonably warm shelter to which the animal can retire when it begins to feel uncomfortable probably is a sufficient protection, even in northern countries. There probably is more danger in keeping them too warm than in subjecting them to undue cold. According to Mr. Carl Hagenbeck, the celebrated German animal dealer, whose park outside of Hamburg is a model for zoological gardens, the animal is the best judge of the kind of weather that is good for it. When a tropical animal, after a few months of acclimatization wants to roll in the snow, it may safely do so. Nature will tell it when it is going too far.

CHAPTER IV

THE MONKEY TRIBE

THE National Zoological Park maintains a collection of from forty to fifty species of monkeys, exclusive of the larger anthropoids. The monkey house, originally built as a small mammal house, contains a collection of moods and dispositions, as well as of animals. It is a house of personalities. When one gets behind the bars in front of the baby koodoo, an African antelope, and the koodoo comes over to be petted, one knows that it would come to be petted by anyone else as well. This is true of many animals. But the monkey, in addition to having personality himself, recognizes it in others.

Many people like to attract the attention of animals to themselves. That is why they make friendly gestures and sounds in front of the cage, and that is how one of our baby leopards has drawn blood three times this year on visitors. Instead of letting him sleep, as he wants to, the visitor likes to reach over the guard rail and snap his fingers at him, just a little too close. Officially, we are always very sorry when something like this happens. Many animals, and especially the big cats, are most superb snobs, who look past or through a would-be friend, utterly ignoring him. But the monkey takes an interest in the crowds. He loves their applause, as well as their peanuts. A few are exceptions, of course.

One long-armed Chacma baboon from Rhodesia we once had was the world's prize humorist, who understood the visitors better than they did him, and dearly loved his little joke. He would lie next to the bars of his

cage, his eyes half closed, and one arm hanging out the
cage. Often he would rotate a straw carelessly between
his thumb and finger, his whole attention apparently
concentrated on that. The visitor would make various
attempts to attract his notice, often by poking an umbrella toward him. Then the arm would dart out twice
as far as seemed possible, and the umbrella would be
taken in the cage. He had learned, himself, how to open
one, and as soon as he had it open, would depart for his
outside cage. As the door through which he had to pass
was less than two feet square, the umbrella came out of
the ordeal fit only for a monkey plaything. He could
skillfully break a cane, and during his career at the Zoo
the keepers counted sixty-eight umbrellas and canes
captured by him. Once a gold watch, dangled on the
end of a gold chain to attract him, gave him one of the
happiest half hours of his life. A marabou boa furnished
joy for an afternoon. He was defeated only once. He
took an old-time policeman's helmet from a policeman
who was waving it, but he could not get it through the
bars because of the metal reinforcing in the hat. He did,
however, get the band and part of the brim. The rest
he struggled with unsuccessfully for hours, and was
never quite the same monkey afterward.

One of the duties of a zoological park director is to tell
mothers and fathers not to get pet monkeys for the
children. Around Christmas time we receive many letters
and telephone calls in regard to this. Nearly all monkeys
are affectionate, docile creatures in youth, but only a
few of them do not become surly as they grow old, and
although from time immemorial they have been kept as
pets, they can not be recommended for this purpose.
They seldom like children, although a few of the smaller
South American kinds do make charming house companions for a time. A lady writes and asks if we will
accept Mike, a capuchin monkey, who has become too
mischievous around the house. We accept it. A week

PLATE 16

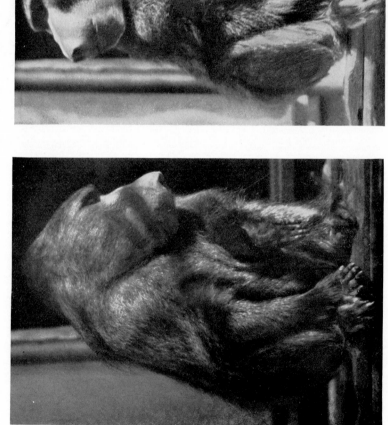

The Chacma baboon from Africa, who has lived out of doors here for eighteen years, often shutting himself in his own house at night

boys around trees containing troops of them. The monkeys became demoralized and dropped down to run through the grass to another tree, whereupon we would grab one, pop it into a bag, and after rubbing some iodine where it had bitten, go after another. The procedure was always the same. One vervet we kept upon a string about camp, and he became very tame. On the ship he was adopted by the crew. The second day at sea he became violently seasick, but didn't let that interfere with his dinner. He would swallow a mouthful of banana, then become seasick, and then swallow another mouthful of banana.

The guenons are really the finest type of monkey for zoos. In addition to diversity in form and in color, they are characterized by extreme agility and activity. They have a full bag of tricks, can amuse themselves, and in addition are hardy and good natured.

The sooty mangabey from West Africa is perhaps the most gentle in disposition of all the monkeys in the collection. This monkey receives a great deal of sympathy from the visitors. He has no hair on his face, and the bald cheeks are sunken in badly, giving him the face of a thinker, with deep-set eyes under a predominant brow. Visitors usually conclude that he is in the last stage of tuberculosis, a disease which, by the way, is actually very rare in our monkey house. Pneumonia and enteric troubles are the great sources of loss.

A white-collared mangabey and a Hagenbeck's mangabey lived together for years. The former was a young one when he came, and the Hagenbeck mangabey bullied him considerably. The white-collared specimen waited for some years. As he attained maturity, the Hagenbeck grew old, and one day the cage became the scene of a royal fight. From this time on conditions were reversed; the white-collar has been boss. He no longer bullies the Hagenbeck, but it is an understood thing that when dainty morsels are thrown into the cage he is to have first choice.

from the Bronx to the Pennsylvania depot in New York City, where it was to take train for St. Louis. This animal had developed a violent fear of its owner, an animal trader of tremendous bulk, and took up with anyone of smaller size. It lived only a few months.

The guenons, whose name in French means "one who grimaces," are represented by about twenty species of monkeys, and all come from Africa. Small, pretty and intelligent, they are ideal monkeys for a zoo. The mona guenon of West Africa is one of the commoner forms. A pair at the National Zoological Park have produced eight young, all of which were raised to maturity.

Perhaps the most beautiful of all this family is the West African Diana, rarely seen in zoos, which derived its name from the fancied resemblance of the white crescent on its forehead to the silver bow of the goddess. Black of face, it has a long white beard and white throat and shoulders, with the upper part of the body and the forelegs iron gray, speckled with a pepper-and-salt arrangement of dots. In the center of the back is a deep chestnut patch and the lower parts are a brilliant yellow. This is an extremely friendly creature, and takes a great deal of care of its beautiful fur. One that was kept in confinement is said to have always drawn its beard aside with the hand when drinking to prevent wetting. The last Diana that we had at the National Zoo lived for five years, and was the pride of the monkey house. A visitor came in one day carrying a little bunch of laurel (the carrying of flowers in the Park was not prohibited then) and when the monkey reached out his hand for the leaves the visitor let him have them. A few minutes later the monkey died in convulsions, and we have never been able to obtain another of its kind since.

The vervets, as common in parts of East Africa as gray squirrels are around Washington, live well in collections. On the recent African trip we brought home about thirty. We had captured these by throwing a circle of native

stay, available for purchases, all the animal stores in town kept open until midnight. Dark little holes they were, all of them, lighted only by candles or by our matches, which made shopping difficult. The night's catch consisted of a number of green fruit pigeons, quantities of spice finches, a mynah bird, a large gunny sack full of turtles, and eleven specimens of this purple-faced monkey. Aboard ship the captain told us that he had plied for years between Ceylon and London, and had never seen one of these animals, out of many taken aboard, arrive alive in England. Ours were placed under every condition that we could think of—tied to strings on deck; several in a large cage, kept gloomy; several in another large cage, kept in the bright light; and others in solitary confinement— and we fed them almost everything we could think of. They all ate well, and except for being very timid, seemed to be thriving. However, we landed with only five, and but one of these lived for more than six months.

Once, last year, in a New York animal dealer's store, we saw the stuffed skin of a proboscis monkey from Borneo. This animal had died when a few days out from New York City, and his death must have been a sad blow to the dealer, for one has never been seen alive in any American collection. A little one once reached Amsterdam, but lived only a few weeks. Several have been kept in Calcutta, and Sányál says, "Whatever may be the habits of the proboscis monkey in a wild state, it is silent, slow and phlegmatic in captivity, and sits for hours together in one place, scarcely noticing the visitors standing outside the cage. The only time that it has ever been seen to become lively is at the hour of feeding." The langur has very much the same habits.

The Colobus, especially the East African variety called *guereza*, makes a notable exhibit when it can be obtained. Several have come to the United States, and the Chicago Zoo obtained one nearly two years ago which is still alive. I once had the pleasure of holding a Colobus in a taxi

later the lady writes that Johnny will not console himself for the loss of the monkey, and asks if we will please send it back. We send it back, and the lady finds that Mike, in his week at the Zoo, has become an entirely different animal from the one she sent us, so in two days more he returns and becomes a permanent resident.

The langurs, long-tailed monkeys of southeastern Asia, are usually considered the highest in the monkey scale of intelligence, below the anthropoid apes. The best known of these is the hanuman (*Pygathrix entellus*), the sacred monkey of India, dedicated to the god Hanuman. Its whitish color, except for a black face and the overhanging brows of long, stiff black hair, and its long tail give it a striking appearance. In India it is considered a sacrilege to kill one of these, and the townspeople allow them to plunder food shops at will. In consequence they have become tame and utterly fearless in the presence of man, yet it is almost impossible to keep them alive in captivity for any length of time. Most probably this is due to their food habits, as they live naturally on leaves, young shoots, and buds of various sorts, and even in the zoological garden at Calcutta their life is usually very short.

In general, monkeys that live in nature on buds and leaves are most difficult to keep in captivity. In addition to the langurs, the interesting howling monkey of South America, the proboscis monkey (*Nasalis larvatus*) of Borneo, and the species of Colobus confined to Africa are all leaf eaters, and notoriously difficult to keep alive for any length of time, though recently specimens of Colobus have lived upwards of three years in American zoos, and one howling monkey for three years.

On its way back from East Africa, the Smithsonian-Chrysler Expedition secured several purple-faced monkeys (*Pygathrix cephalopterus*) of Ceylon, a relative of the langur. We had cabled ahead that we were in the market for animals, and during the one evening of our

PLATE 17

De Brazza's guenon, an African species. An ideal monkey for a
zoo, but rare

THE MONKEY TRIBE

Mr. Blackburne tells the story of a well-known circus proprietor whom he heard one afternoon in the show's menagerie tent, bewailing the public's lack of discretion. "That $12,000 rhino over there—six people in front of the cage. Everybody else in the show hanging around a $45 collection of monkeys." These were the rhesus, the animals that spell *monkey* to the average person. They are imported into the United States in lots of hundreds, or even thousands, and retailed at small prices as pets, show animals, or for use in medical laboratories. They breed readily in captivity, and the colony that we have had for fifteen years came to us from a Government medical laboratory and has maintained itself ever since, living in a large cage out-of-doors without artificial heat, though a stout shelter has been given to them for the winter.

Sányál of Calcutta has probably had more rhesus under his care than has any other zoological park official, and he says of them in his *Hand-Book of the Management of Animals in Captivity in Lower Bengal:*

They pass most of their time in alternate fighting and playing; after a violent quarrel they change to the other extreme, and behave as if they were the mildest of creatures. . . . They fight most during feeding time, if not checked by the keeper; but it is not easy, even with close observation, to ascribe a cause for each particular skirmish. The sudden violence of their fury is extraordinary. Animals at one moment living in perfect amity and concord become in an instant deadly foes, ready to tear each other to pieces. The weak or the sickly and the new-comers fare badly. Monkeys of this species are proverbially mischievous: they constantly snatch away a stick or umbrella, or even an eye-glass, and when attempts are made to recover the articles their behavior shows how they enjoy their mischief. Sometimes they appear to rob visitors from simple curiosity and inquisitiveness, and not in a wicked or mischievous spirit. They also are addicted to playing with their drinking water and splashing it about. However quarrelsome and mischievous they may be, these monkeys generally are submissive to their keeper, having by experience learnt to dread his power; but should a new keeper happen to enter their cage, he is likely to be attacked by the whole troop, led generally by an aggressive old male. Keepers often have been wounded in such outbreaks; but if they are firm and exhibit no nervousness, the monkeys soon recognize their master and resume a peaceful attitude.

Both the rhesus and the macaque monkeys are fond of water and swim and dive well. A number of young monkeys (*M. rhesus* and *M. cynomolgus*) were at one time allowed to run loose in the garden; they greatly enjoyed their freedom, and were often seen on a sultry afternoon perched on one of the trees near the Serpentine lake, and jumping one after another into the water and indulging in a swim. On one occasion they appeared to be engaged in a regular diving match; they were divided into two parties, sitting on opposite banks of a narrow arm of the lake. . . . On one occasion, one of them having noticed an official of the adjacent Meteorological Observatory in the act of taking some observation with the aid of certain instruments, proceeded stealthily to the observatory and was seen deliberately to upset one of the instruments. On another occasion one of them intruded into the drawing-room of a lady, then living in the house next to the garden, upset an inkstand and spoiled, it was said, some valuable documents. He did this, it was conjectured, in his uncouth attempt to imitate the lady whom he had observed writing.

A monkey's capacity for showing affection was exhibited in the behavior of one of a pair of rhesus monkeys from the Simla Hills, whose companion had been severely wounded and was therefore kept confined in a small cage for treatment. While the patient was in this condition the one who was still at large and well was much concerned and would sit almost the whole day by the side of the cage and affectionately caress the invalid in various ways through the bars.

These monkeys are almost omnivorous. Boiled rice, soaked gram, biscuits, pumpkin, cucumber, brinjal, and other vegetables constitute their ordinary food. Eggs are occasionally added to their diet as substitutes for the insects and spiders which, in their wild state, they eat besides fruits and vegetables. . . . Minced meat is sometimes, but rarely, given them. . . .

Female monkeys nurse their young with great tenderness, and are competent to protect them from harm; the older animals do not molest the young, so that the latter have been reared in the midst of a number, but it is always better, as elsewhere remarked, to segregate the female when a birth is expected. . . .

In about a month the young one begins to pick up gram and other food, and then the struggle for life soon begins, and the mother and the young one commence to fight over their food, although their natural instincts bind them to each other at other times.

The Philippine macaque, another species, is a smaller and handsomer monkey than the Indian, and it is es-

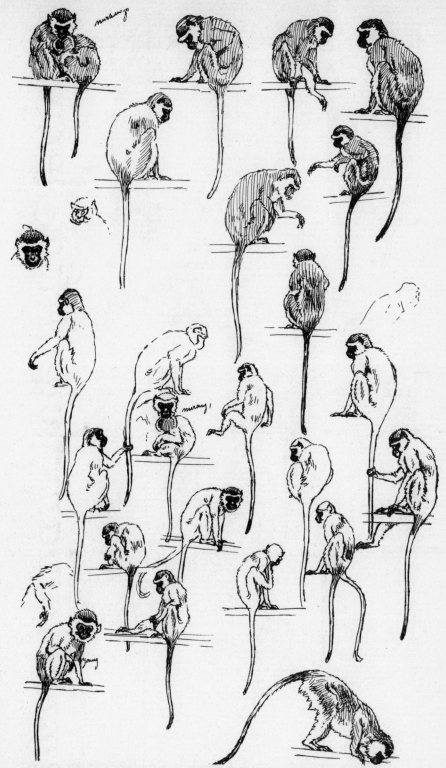

FIG. 4. Sketches from an artist's note book. By Benson B. Moore

Fig. 5. Sketches from an artist's note book. By Benson B. Moore

pecially interesting because at the present time it is the only warm-blooded Philippine animal living in the United States. It was officially barred from entry because of certain blood diseases which might be communicated through it to live stock in the States. Probably all three specimens in our collection have been smuggled in. We do not know how this was accomplished, but we have heard of the case of a mascot belonging to an army band. When one day out from San Francisco they heard that the monkey would not be allowed to land, so they brought him ashore in the bass drum, which was beaten as the band played on the march from the boat to the barracks. One would like to know the condition of the macaque's nerves at the end of the parade.

The least likable monkey is the Java macaque, yet it is the best breeder of all. Our little troop rarely fails to produce at least one young each year.

The Japanese red-faced monkey, which is likewise a macaque, comes from farthest north of all the monkey family, with the exception of a variety from northern China. Our pair have produced three young, one of which died after dropping from the bars of the cage and injuring its spine. The other two are thriving. Last summer the keeper entered the cage with the four of them, as had been his habit every day, having with him only a broom. A broom, by the way, is one of the most serviceable implements in an animal cage, not only serving to sweep, but in case of need as a defense against the animals, and also to corner an animal one is trying to catch. One of the babies shrieked, apparently for no reason, but in a second the other three in the cage were on top of the keeper. Before he could get out he was so severely lacerated that he had to spend two weeks in a hospital.

George, the Park's formidable male magot, or Barbary ape, and his mate are said to have been caught on the Rock of Gibraltar itself, and to have come to a steamship captain as pets, though this is highly improbable. Of large size, powerful build, and wicked disposition, they belong in the category of the most dangerous animals in the Park. The two are kept out-of-doors all the year long and have never shown any discomfort during the cold weather. George has developed a bad temper and is also intelligent. He can hurl a stone with great force and considerable accuracy, and has several times cut boys in the face. If he would hit only the boy who has thrown the stone into the cage there would be no serious objection, but he does not distinguish between visitors, so we have had to put wire mesh on the outside of his cage. He was very skillful with a tin basin of water, also. By making weird grimaces he would concentrate the attention of the public on his face, at which time he would quietly and quickly seize the water basin and hurl its contents, again with accuracy, into the face of some particular bystander. So we gave him a large cement drinking pan that he could not throw, but he learned in a short time to cup his hand, and in that way splash visitors.

The Barbary ape supplied man with a knowledge of anatomy in very early times. This species is probably the *pithecus* described by Aristotle, and an account of its anatomy by Galen has come down to our times. The European foothold of these monkeys is Gibraltar, where the Government carefully protects them despite their destructiveness. At times they have faced extinction, and at other times they have been so abundant that the local government has seriously considered reducing their numbers.

The Barbary ape has long been kept as a pet in Europe. Young ones are playful and great mimics. The French priest, Caubasson, relates a laughable anecdote of one of the animals which he brought up and which became so attached to him as to want to accompany him wherever he went. One day the animal escaped and, without the priest's knowledge, followed him to church. He climbed

PLATE 18

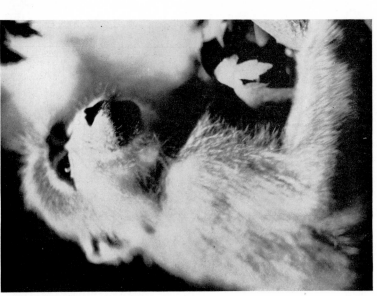

Sarah, young olive baboon from East Africa

silently to the top of the sounding board above the pulpit, where he lay perfectly still until the sermon began. He then crept to the edge and imitated the preacher's gestures in so grotesque a manner that the worshipers were convulsed with laughter. Caubasson did not know what was causing the merriment. He reproved the congregation for its ill-timed levity. The women giggled and the men roared. The priest lost his temper. The angrier he became the more maliciously the monkey imitated his movements and the more the congregation laughed. Finally a friend stepped up to the altar and told the clergyman what was the trouble. The animal was removed and peace restored in the church.

In spite of its large size, great strength, and resistance to cold, the Barbary ape does not generally do well in captivity in America.

The pig-tailed macaque, a common species, has a representative in our collection in the person of Pops, who has been here now eight years, and still preserves a fairly good disposition. This is the monkey which natives of some districts of Sumatra train to climb coconut palms to pick and throw down the ripe fruit—the only monkey that has ever been trained as an agricultural animal. He has another claim to uniqueness among such servants of the human race in that his value depends largely upon his only expression of intelligence, namely, his ability to select the ripe fruits. Why did not primitive man, while studying and domesticating the horse, pig, sheep, and cow, also breed a more tractable family of apes? Soko, our chimpanzee, could run a lawn mower. Why could not a gorilla, domesticated through a thousand generations, work a plow, or an orang-utan hoe potatoes? Anyway, Pops is intelligent, and often, as we gaze at his expression, we think he would make a nice addition to our police force.

Next to macaques, baboons occur most commonly in collections, several species being usual to most zoos. In

Africa, where they run in large troops and do great damage to cultivated crops, they are considered a nuisance, and often a bounty is offered for their destruction. The director of agriculture of the Gold Coast tells us that when the big, malignant Anubis baboons raid the plantations the natives are afraid to attempt to drive them off. A spear or an arrow wounding one would cause the entire troop to charge. Nothing could be more fearful than these large, powerful, vicious, and intelligent opponents. In Tanganyika they are sometimes destroyed in quantities by the use of nets. During the day the animals troop around on the ground, but at night go into a tree to sleep. The natives locate these sleeping places and during the night arrange a high net around the base of the tree. The baboons, when attempting to get through or over, are clubbed from the outside. The bounty in Tanganyika was sixpence per animal, and this was paid on presentation of the tail. We saw a young one kept as a pet by a white lady. The native who captured it had cut off the tail, obtained the sixpence bounty for it, and then sold the rest of the animal for another sixpence.

Very seldom do we see an adult baboon live long in captivity. It is surprising that with so many young coming into the market, so few attain maturity. This is partly due, of course, to cage paralysis, which seems to attack the majority of young monkeys in captivity. It is evidently a form of rickets. The hind legs become paralyzed, and eventually the animal dies.

In East Africa we succeeded in obtaining all we wanted of young olive baboons without difficulty. Natives would bring them into the camp and sell them for a few cents. One that we had was named Emma, as eccentric an old maid as ever lived in a monkey community. She was crabbed, complaining, and combative, as well as sulky, and the other baboons let her alone. One day Sarah, a most scrawny little baboon of the same species, was brought in and spent the first day screeching at everything, including Emma. The second day found them both fast friends, and Emma would actually stand aside while little Sarah had her pick of the food, an occurrence very rare among monkeys.

Bringing home a shipment of monkeys constitutes an experience that one would rather look back upon than go through. In our forty-day trip returning from East Africa, we had seventy-odd monkeys in the collection— vervets, baboons of various types, purple-faced monkeys, and Moor macaques that we picked up in a bird store at Port Said. The first day at sea these were scattered helter-skelter on the ship's deck, but later on we got them all caged, and the cages placed three tiers deep in a neat row. Many of the animals were recently caught specimens, and it required some time before they took kindly to their new quarters. Monkeys are often com- pared to children, without any sound basis for doing so, but there is one point in which a monkey does strikingly resemble a willful child. When he wants something he will screech for it. My lot of monkeys came to know me, and as soon as I hove in sight with a basket of food, raucous yells would come out of every cage. They got on my nerves so that I would prepare the food out of sight and then dash into the monkey quarters and get it into the cages as fast as possible. A plate of food in a cage would hush that one, and by the time I had reached the end of the line, the last screech was over. An hour later, when I would be working with other animals in the same vicinity, the commotion would start again. Seventy monkeys howling their loudest at close range are difficult to bear, and so I was glad to discover that a handful of Kafir corn thrown into each cage would keep the occu- pants busy hunting for it, and consequently quiet.

Of New World monkeys, the most intelligent is the spider monkey, varieties of which occur from southern Mexico throughout the warm, wooded parts of South America. Besides being the most intelligent, he is the most smelly; two or three of them suffice to change the atmosphere of an otherwise clean monkey house.

Certain South American monkeys are notoriously delicate and difficult to rear. When the natives were asked for some of these species, the reply was almost invariably the same: "It is only the *infieles* who understand how to rear these." The *infieles* are the unbaptized savages on the upper reaches of the tributaries. In one of their villages we found three baby howling monkeys.

We once shot a large female black spider monkey on the shores of the Little Rio Negro, in Bolivia. Shooting monkeys may be sport where they are in the tops of high trees and running, so one can't see their expression when hit. But once I brought one down at close range, and I never again shall fire at one. However, this female was shot partly for food for my Indian companions, and partly to get a young one, which I saw clinging to her. She dropped dead. I took the little one away and tied him with a string on the deck of the launch alongside my cot, where he shrieked himself to sleep. In the morning when I awoke, he was sitting there looking at me. I lifted him to my knee and gave him a piece of banana, and he sat there calmly eating it, having evidently made up his mind that if he had to be a pet monkey, he was going to start right there. On this trip we had many small animals in cages, some of them very rare and delicate monkeys, so that I kept them in the room of the native house in which I happened to be staying. On account of the unusual fragrance of the spider monkey, I preferred having him outside, but he would sit at the door and howl until I let him in with the other animals, when he was contented.

José Mañana was a black spider monkey given to me in Honduras. José had been taken from his mother when very small, a year before, and the limit of the world to him was a string stretched between the rear veranda and the cook shed of a fruit plantation house. At first he

PLATE 19

Ring-tailed lemur. Playful, gentle, and a good zoo subject

didn't like travel, which is not to be wondered at, for he had his maiden trip on a little automobile car on the railroad track, a means of transportation which always makes a windy voyage. But when he finally got aboard ship where the sailors played with him, he was obviously delighted with the world and its variety. In New York I had to leave him checked at the railroad station for a half day. When I called for him in the evening he protested in unmistakable language that it had been a very boring experience. But he displayed his greatest emotion when brought to Washington and placed in the monkey house. For a year he had not seen another monkey. He had no fear of them, and his thrill at seeing so many, and his energy in trying to express himself about them, were "almost human."[1]

The spider monkey is to the gibbon what beer is to champagne. It is the poor zoo's gibbon, and one of the most graceful in motion of all animals, providing it has a sufficiently roomy cage. It is very active and intelligent and one of the few monkeys which harbor lice in quantities.

The woolly monkeys, near cousins to the spiders, have the gentlest disposition of all the families. In a few days one becomes tame, and even individuals captured when adult are never very fierce. They get their name from their fine coat of hair. Their prehensile tails are developed, if anything, even more than the spider monkey's.

I once brought to the Park an adult brown woolly monkey from the Amazon, whom I called Jack. He lived in the Park for about two years. In the summer time he had a habit of eating leaves from the trees, the branches of which drooped above his cage. He would soon eat all of those that he could reach with his long forearms, and then he would back up to the cage and with the tip of his long tail pull off and bring into the cage those leaves that were farther away. We were in the habit of taking

[1] A statement which every writer on animals should avoid.

advantage of this facility to offer Jack a peanut out of reach of his long forearms, whereupon he would encompass the nut with the fingerlike tip of his tail as he did the distant leaves. This was long before I had become officially connected with the Zoo. I liked to show off this accomplishment of Jack's, and wished to do so one evening just as the keepers were leaving, for the benefit of some young ladies. Visitors are not supposed to go behind the guard rail without special permission, so I asked the departing keeper if I could go behind and give Jack a peanut. With permission granted I stepped inside, and Jack was performing beautifully for our audience, when a rich Irish voice invited me to "come out of it, and what are you doing in there?" It was a new policeman who did not know me, but who knew that people should not go behind the rails. I explained that I had just received permission. He demanded to see the permission. I couldn't show it to him, and didn't know where the keeper was gone, so it looked bad for a time until the head keeper, who had stayed over for a picnic supper with his wife, rescued me. He afterwards gave me a card with permission to go behind the guard rails, but the joke of my being arrested for giving my own monkey a peanut got abroad, and served to cheer my revered chief in the Department of Agriculture through an otherwise dull summer.

The woolly monkey is really the only one that makes a good pet. Its single drawback lies in its extreme delicacy. Very rarely does one live any appreciable length of time. One species, Humboldt's woolly monkey, inhabits the upper Amazon, and in going down the Rio Madeira we found that the price among the natives for these animals about doubled with each day's journey down the river. In the section where the bird and animal venders hold forth in the great municipal market at Pará we found two woollies. One of them, nearly adult, was a magnificent specimen, and I returned from day to day to bargain for him. His owner refused to sell because, as he said, the monkey was as one of his family, but he finally gave him to me in return for a token of high esteem in the form of a large gold coin. Barrigudo (his native name, given to him on account of a protruding abdomen) became the leading man of our animal actors on the poop deck of the steamer. One day he escaped from his leash, and when I found him he was sitting on the deck happily engaged in bouncing up and down a wicker cage which up to the time he had seized it had contained fourteen living, very beautiful small birds. As I approached he bounced it even harder, and beamed at me with the air of one accomplishing a good as well as a clever deed, and then leaped into my arms. I found it hard in a case like this to punish the murderer, even though, before he had accomplished these things, he had accumulated an inch of grease from an exposed part of the steering gear, which he deposited on my shirt front.

A companion of mine on an expedition became very indignant at the moving-picture man, and told him that it was lucky he was born in this generation instead of the previous one, adding that a few years ago the only way a man could make a living turning a crank was by having a monkey help him. The capuchin is the common monkey assistant to the organ grinder man, even today. There are a dozen kinds. They all come from tropical America. In general, like all other American monkeys, they do not breed well in captivity, even while in the semi-wild state in which they are kept in the villages in South America.

Mathias was the capuchin that I knew best. A Government launch came to our village on the Rio Beni, and the natives from the nearby territory were called in so that conscripts could be selected for the army. Those who were going away were lined up, and their friends stood in a mass opposite them. One Indian girl was weeping because her boy was going away to be a soldier. Mathias, then a very small capuchin, sat on her shoulder. I took him off and thrust a bill into the girl's hand. She stopped crying long enough to say, "Thank you," and to hand the money to her soldier. Mathias was one of the friendliest monkeys I have ever known, but he was so badly afflicted with worms that I was afraid to let him live among the other monkeys, and finally one day in desperation I popped a santonin pill down him, telling him apologetically that if it didn't kill him it would make him better; and Mathias lived more than two years longer than all of the other youngsters of his tribe that we brought home to Washington. Cage paralysis eventually overcame him, but even when he could no longer crawl, he would roll over to the bars to be petted. On the voyage home he lived in an empty coal bunker with the other animals, and he would play busily all the time that I was feeding and caring for the stock. As soon as I would climb the ladder to the deck, he would curl around the base of a cluster of electric lights and snooze until I returned. Apparently he cared to play only while somebody was watching him.

Of all the American monkeys, the capuchins are the hardiest in captivity, comparatively short-lived though they are. They are great beggars, whether hungry or not, and when food is given to them that they do not want they play with it for a few moments and then return to begging. They are the commonest American monkeys in zoos.

A baby white-throated capuchin, recently captured, that I had in Honduras could give at first five distinct calls. He was brought to me by a hunter at Choloma and for the first half hour of captivity sat tied to a window sill and gave a plaintive, shrill cry, evidently the call to his mother. He seemed to forget this almost immediately, and never afterward repeated it. Like all baby monkeys, he was very fond of hanging on to anybody, and by reason of this made himself a great nuisance. He was violently afraid of flies, and would shriek and strike

PLATE 20

The household pet, Zanzi. Garnett's galago from Zanzibar, a member
of the lemur family

out whenever one approached him. This may have been due to experience with wasps in the tree tops.

The monkey with the worst penchant for clinging to one is the titi, or squirrel monkey (*Saimiri sciureus*), another South American animal. Except for this habit he is a gentle, playful, and pleasant pet. But once he develops a taste for being held, he will shriek without stopping until picked up. The resemblance of the physiognomy of this monkey to that of a child was long ago noted by Humboldt. He wears a similar expression of innocence, a similar playful smile, and makes a similar sudden change from joy to sorrow. His movements are light and graceful. The natives sell these monkeys in boxes like pigeon crates in the markets at Pará, at ridiculously low prices. Their reputation for living in captivity is not good. I had the idea that this was due to lonesomeness, and determined to bring home a lot of them to put in one cage. One had lived with me for six months on the river, and was doing well, so I acquired a dozen more. Just before we went aboard the ship I secured a cage of eighteen in the market, and transferred them to a roomier box. Next morning twelve out of the lot of eighteen were dead, I have no idea why. A dozen reached Washington in good health, where they lasted scarcely eighteen months.

The upper Amazon is tenanted by dozens of species of weird monkeys which seldom or never come into captivity. The bearded saki (*Pithecia chiropotes*) is one of these— slow moving, pathetic in expression, and with a long black beard. I saw one once in the zoo at Amsterdam that had lived there for eighteen months, but that was a rare record. Another saki (*Pithecia monachus*) is grayish in color. A Brazilian lady at Porto Velho had two of these that lived as members of the family, even sleeping at night in miniature hammocks in true Brazilian style. When I tried to buy them she said, "Perhaps, señor, one of my other children, but certainly neither of these two." We have had one red ouakari (*Cacajao rubicundus*) from Colombia in the Park. Its long red hair and slow movements suggest a miniature orang-utan.

The smallest of all the monkeys are the marmosets—gentle, delicate little creatures, with a call hardly to be distinguished from the chirp of a bird. The brightness of their small eyes makes them appear very intelligent, which they are not, though they take to captivity very readily. A young one that I had on the upper Amazon shrieked lustily until I gave him a woollen sock into which he dived, curling up in the toe for the night. Ever after at bedtime he would shriek for this same sock. He was a very rare species, and I kept him in a cage close to my bed, where he would wake me up every morning with a discordant chirping. The sight of a cockroach or a spider would cause him to chirp like a whole flock of birds, and he would accept a cockroach offered to him with forceps and eat it voraciously.

The douroucouli, owl monkey, or night monkey, of which we have had three species, is the only one of the family that is nocturnal. He is a great favorite in Brazil as a pet, and is seen frequently on the shoulders of women. Like many other delicate monkeys, this species thrives much better when kept as a pet, with reasonably intelligent care, than it does in a cage, although we have had specimens for more than six years. It is largely wasted in a zoo, because it spends the day curled up in sleep. One that we had in camp became more or less diurnal. He was given the run of a large native house, and spent a great deal of time exploring. He was fond of going into paper bags, and sometimes out of sheer exuberance would jump straight up a foot or so in the air, and sing "Whoo! Whoo!" with each jump.

A rare Cebus monkey is the pale capuchin. One belonged to an Indian who had him tied by a short chain to a peg, and who put a basket over him at night. His one possession was a pair of trousers that had become too dilapidated for the Indian to wear, which is dilapidation to the nth degree. When we caged the animal we had to remove this garment, and he mourned for it a good hour. This fellow and his mate were very nervous and timid, and it took weeks to get their confidence, but eventually I could put my hand in the cage and we would have a nice rough-house, with the monkeys pretending to bite my fingers. One day the male got my thumb between his canines, and bit harder than either of us had intended. My face was against the bars, and I said, "Ouch!" very loudly. The sound of my voice in the box so terrified them that months passed before they became tame again.

The cages in which we were bringing home our collection had been improvised from anything available in camp, and some of them were as weird and wonderful as the animals themselves. We eventually got our collection to Manáos, and loaded it aboard the steamer ready for the sixteen days' trip to New York. The captain in command did not like animals. On the previous voyage some of the sailors had bought pets to take to New York. Monkeys had got loose, and in addition to the commotion about the ship, newspaper men got hold of the story and wrote things that the captain did not like, so he had called the crew together on the voyage down and had promised to knock the head off any man who brought anything alive aboard the ship. The agent at Manáos had given me permission to bring home the collection before the captain knew of it. I installed the animals on the poop deck behind an unused galley structure, in which I could store food. As the captain came aboard in the evening just before sailing, he waved gaily to me, but when he got beyond the galley and saw the animals, some caged, some tied with string, and others just sitting around, his face fell.

"Is that all?" he asked, with what seemed to me a

bit of sarcasm in the tone, and I had to reply, "Oh, no, sir, there are more coming," and point alongside to a boat rowed by four men and bearing two crates of deer, four giant Amazonian turtles, a wild-cat, half a dozen trumpeters, and a few other things that I had been able to pick up in the local market. The captain's heart was about broken, but he bore up quite well, and at the end of four days would come out and have his morning exercise helping me cut up pumpkins for the animals. Later on, when the weather commenced to get cold, he informed me that while he never did care much for "crows," especially on his ship, he didn't like to see them die, after the work that had been spent gathering them, so he emptied a coal bunker and we lived there the last six days of the voyage. It was weeks before some of the animals could be accurately identified afterward, on account of the coal dust that had seeped on and in them during this last week.

During the entire voyage the pale Cebus were thorns in the sides of all of us. They would open the door of any sort of cage that I could put them in, and they escaped at least a dozen times. Once, while I was sitting in the dining room, one of them came in and ran across fifteen feet of fresh cloth on the table and hopped through a porthole to the forward deck. Stopping only to bribe the steward to change the tablecloth before the captain could see the footmarks on it, I dashed out after the monkey in time to see him go into the forecastle. Sailors were sleeping on both sides. One of them, half awake, asked me what I wanted. I told him the monkey was loose again.

"So that is what just stepped on my face!" he said.

After an hour of monkey-chasing up and down the deck of the rolling ship, I sat down exhausted for a moment's rest before starting the chase anew. Just then the captain came up, his face redder than usual, and all benevolence gone out of it. With the air of one having

PLATE 21

Potto, from Liberia.   A small member of the lemur family
Photographed by Edward A. Baker

authority he said, "I hear that that —— red monkey of yours is out again. Now I want you to catch him and lock him up right away."

We eventually got him and locked him up, and nailed the door of the cage, so whenever I gave him his pan of water, it was necessary to take a hammer, pull the nail, and after the monkey had drunk, nail the door up again.

One of the most frequent questions asked at the Zoo concerns the care of monkeys. They must be kept out of drafts, and dry. We feed ours twice a day and arrange a continual variation in the diet. Carrots, potatoes, sugar beets, onions, kale, lettuce, cabbage, and occasionally bananas and apples make up their vegetable fare, and they are given bread. Of course all monkeys get water twice a day.

The lemurs, aptly termed by Cornish "ghosts of the tropical forest," since they are mostly nocturnal creatures, make excellent subjects for the zoo. The ring-tailed and ruffed lemurs are mainly diurnal, and the mongoose lemur, the black lemur, and the red-fronted lemur take to diurnal habits very easily. They are playful and gentle as well as handsome animals though not especially blessed, or cursed, with intelligence. Some of them live a surprising length of time in captivity, and recently Sol Stephan, Nestor of animal men, showed me a specimen in the Cincinnati Zoo that had lived there for twenty-eight years, now blind, but otherwise in excellent condition.

True lemurs are all natives of Madagascar, where it is said there is scarcely a woody copse, no matter how small, that does not contain one or more families of them. Some thirty species have been kept in captivity, the five mentioned above being the commonest, but occasionally even such a rare thing as the tarsier (*Tarsius spectrum*) comes into collections. I saw one in the excellent zoological garden at Amsterdam, where it had lived for several months.

The commonest type of lemur in Africa is the galago,

a number of species of which occur, ranging in size from a little larger than a rat to as large as a domestic cat. They are strictly nocturnal, and their raucous call is a characteristic sound in the African bush. The very small ones are known in the colonies as "bush babies," and are beautiful but rather stupid pets.

A medium-sized species, *Galago garnetti*, occurs in Zanzibar. We have had one of these as a house pet for more than two years. During our short stop in Zanzibar on the way to the mainland, we strolled to the museum, a fascinating museum by the way, with a splendid collection of relics from Stanley, Livingstone, and Tippoo Tib. On the way back a boy offered us a galago scarcely larger than a gray squirrel—the price asked for both galago and the piece of string with which he was tied being thirty cents. We did not want any animals at the time, and yet could not resist this one. We christened him Zanzi. He lived half at liberty about camp until our collection grew so that it was necessary to cage him. He was the first of all our animals ashore when we arrived at Boston. I handed him to a small girl friend on the dock, and the first thing he did was to draw blood in three places on her hand.

For a time in Washington he lived in a cage in the Park, but we took him out in order to get him tame enough to appear at a function at the Smithsonian. Each branch of the Institution was represented by a small exhibit. The guests at the function were to include Presidents, Cabinet members, Regents, and Congressmen. We assumed that these are, after all, human beings, and human beings always like to handle animals, so Zanzi was taken for that purpose.

A week's experience with him in the house caused my wife to make up our mind that he should stay there afterward, and so he has remained ever since, with headquarters in a small cage in a small hall. Being a member of the family has suited him, for of a dozen galagos of various types brought back at the same time, he is the only one still alive.

Zanzi is the ideal "business man's" pet. After a short frolic in the morning, when he is liberated from his cage, he rolls himself up into a neat package in a newspaper on the floor, and sleeps there until five in the evening, when he wakes, slowly emerges, stretches and yawns, and then cleans himself up thoroughly. The rest of the evening, up to midnight, he is in continual action, never tiring of exploring door jambs, chairs, or of chewing on a zebra skin when he can get to it. He will literally spend hours chewing on this skin. When playing by himself he will stand erect and hop like a kangaroo on a smooth floor, but if any stranger approaches, he becomes thoroughly terrified, and makes for the nearest climbable object. When he is climbing nothing frightens him. He makes a chewing acquaintance with everything he meets. That is the only way he can express his affection for his owner, as he has sharp teeth and chews incessantly and painfully, though he does not puncture the skin.

For a year the question as to whether or not he had brains furnished an important point of dissension in our household. I had always maintained that he had no brains, and behaved more like a bat (which he resembles very much in facial expression and in the ability to fold up his ears) than a monkey. However, a noted animal psychologist visited us one evening, and after psycho-analyzing Zanzi for two hours he stated, "There is some doubt; he really does have a little intelligence." Like many nocturnal animals, the large protruding eyes give an appearance of intelligence which is not merited.

He has a half dozen different calls, the usual one a chattering not unlike that of a gray squirrel, which he gives when one plays with him. Alone, he usually remains silent, but at times has spells of making a loud, clucking noise, monotonously repeated. The first time we heard this we dashed to him, thinking there was something wrong. But there was nothing wrong, and to make him stop we gave him some food. To our great surprise he kept on clucking while he ate, and we noticed he made the sound with his throat, and without opening his mouth. Once he was lying on a chair while I talked to the proprietor of a lecture bureau. I told my caller that I had just thought of a new joke for my lecture, when Zanzi interrupted with a distinct "Ho! Ho!" He hadn't heard the joke, and he has never repeated this call since. The commonest call is a raucous, hoarse bark. He will often answer a cough at night by this bark, and this is the call that one hears night after night in the bush in Africa.

On one occasion in Africa, Charley Goss, a noted elephant hunter, and I had built a platform over a water hole, and were lying there in the hope of securing a young rhinoceros, whose tracks we had seen about the hole. We got on the platform early in the evening, and maintained silence until after dark. When night fell a galago occupying a hollow branch about eight feet above our heads emerged for his evening prowl. Noticing us, he gave up everything else and devoted a solid hour to vituperation. The incessant, discordant bark at such close quarters got on my nerves, and I wondered what Charley was thinking of it. Eventually he rolled over and, putting his mouth to my ear, whispered tensely, "I do wish that bloody thing would stop."

Zanzi is fed once a day, usually late at night, and he eats almost anything edible. He is especially fond of juicy fruits and vegetables, but curiously he tires of a food very quickly. For a week he will seize his lettuce first. The following week he will have nothing to do with lettuce. Apples were a favorite for three days, after which he took a week's rest from them. By having a variety of foods he will always eat heartily. His great fondness is for anything fermented. Sauerkraut he will fight for, and a half teaspoonful of wine is taken *"mit Verstand."*

PLATE 22

Hamadryas or Arabian baboon, whose ruff stands out when angered

THE MONKEY TRIBE

All in all, Zanzi makes the most delightful pet we have had in the house. Nothing could be cleaner or daintier, or look at you with bulging eyes and fold up its ears so feelingly, and at the same time be such a quiet, inoffensive pet. He reverts to the primitive only occasionally, when we give him a saucer of live meal worms to eat. Then he becomes pure savage, and incidentally forgets all his table manners, as he hurriedly chews and gulps what is to him the daintiest of dainties.

We have had only one potto in the National collection, (*Perodicticus potto*), a gift from Harvey Firestone, Jr. It had been captured on a plantation in Liberia. It is like a miniature bear, five inches long, with monkey paws except for a curious spinelike claw on the hind foot, bright eyes, and a mean disposition greatly out of proportion to its small size. We kept it for a time in our house for observation. It spent an entire evening exploring one chair; each step was made slowly and cautiously, and the only really swift movement of which it seemed capable was striking to bite. It suggested a slow picture of an ordinary lemur. J. L. Buck, who has spent years collecting animals in West Africa, and who is a keen observer, tells me that he has seen only one sociable potto of the many kept as pets there. At the same time, it is a beautiful little golden-brown creature and completely inoffensive. On account of its weird structure the potto attracted attention when discovered, and a description of it published in 1704 by Bosman, its discoverer, is far stranger than the animal itself:

Some writers affirm, that when this creature has climbed upon a Tree, he doth not leave it until he hath eaten up not only the Fruit, but the leaves entirely; and then descends fat and in very good case in order to get up into another Tree; but before his slow pace can compass this he becomes as poor and lean as 'tis possible to imagine; and if the tree be high, or the way anything distant, and he meets nothing on his journey, he invariably dies of

Hunger betwixt one tree and the other. Thus 'tis represented by others, but I will not undertake for the truth of it, though the *Negroes* are apt to believe something like it.

This is such a horrible ugly Creature that I don't believe anything besides so very disagreeable is to be found on the whole Earth; the Print is a very lively description of it. Its fore feet are very like Hands, the Head, strangely disproportionately large; that from which this Print was taken was of a pale Mouse color, but it was then very young, and his skin yet smooth, but when old, as I saw one at Elmina in the year 1699, 'tis red and covered with a sort of Hair as thick set as Flocks of Wool. I know nothing more of this animal than that 'tis impossible to look on him without Horrour, and that he hath nothing very particular but his odious Ugliness.

We could not better close this long section on the monkey family than by two choice tales of the tribe culled from the long experience of Mr. Blackburne:

Some years ago a large male bonnet monkey (*Macacus sinicus*), adorned by earrings worn in pierced ears, was presented to the Park. The monkey was a mischievous animal and delighted in tormenting a spotted hyena that occupied an adjoining cage. One of his chief sources of amusement was to push stiff pieces of straw through the keyhole in the door between the two cages, which never failed to irritate the hyena. The latter invariably reacted in the same manner; in a rage he would bite the offending straws and pull them through the keyhole. When the monkey tired of this method of tantalizing his neighbor, he would try another prank. Reaching through the bars of his own cage and between those of the adjoining one, he would tap the hyena on the nose and skillfully draw his arm away just in time to avoid being bitten. This was a real feat because the monkey could not see the hyena, as the partition between the two cages was of solid boards. It is the most daring thing I have ever seen a monkey do, and constitutes a rare example of judgment. The monkey evidently thoroughly enjoyed it, because he made it a daily practice.

A Philippine macaque once forced a Brazil nut, small end first, into his cheek pouch, where it remained for several days. When I became aware of it I tried to remove the nut, but found I could not do so without making an incision. We finally performed the operation, stitched up the incision, and the monkey began to recover. One day he removed all of the stitches, and amused himself and his cage mates by passing blades of hay and peanuts through the pouch and cheek. Thurston's magic never caused more astonishment than did this monkey magician's among his audience. When the macaque was removed to quiet quarters, the incision restitched, and the patient given a soft diet, the wound soon healed.

CHAPTER V

THE BIG CATS

DURING the forty years of the National Zoological Park's existence there have been fifty-one lions in the collection, some on short loans, others as permanent deposits. Thirteen years for one and fifteen and a half years for another constitute the records for longevity. The lion attains maturity at about five years of age. At eight he is in the prime of life, and after that steadily declines. It is interesting to note that at the zoo in Dublin, famous for its success in raising lions, the record for longevity in a female is eleven years.

Nineteen baby lions have been born in the National Zoological Park. Unfortunately, a number of these sprang from very poor stock. Caste exists among lions as in other animals, and for a number of years ours were distinctly "low brow." However, the mayor and citizens of Johannesberg in South Africa presented to President Coolidge a pair of cubs, and these are growing up into magnificent lions.

One of Mr. Blackburne's fondest memories of animals centers about the first lion that ever came to the National Zoo. He tells the story of that magnificent animal here:

Our first lion, a male, was purchased from Mrs. Susan E. Bebout of Alderson, West Virginia, September 12, 1891. He was then about one year old and a very fine and tame specimen. He had had the liberty of the lower floor of his owner's house. Windows were protected by iron bars, as the neighbors had protested against his presence and were quite uneasy regarding their safety.

THE BIG CATS

He also had the run of the back yard where the fencing was made a safe height. His playmate was a common female cat which he frequently picked up in his mouth and carried about the house. This was done with the greatest of care, the cat offering no resistance whatever. The cat's head, hind legs, and tail were about all that could be seen while in the lion's mouth. At times he would lift the cat up on an old-fashioned bed and there they would play. The mattress, the quilt, and the bed posts were badly clawed. This was the lion's bed.

This lion had been given to Mrs. Bebout the day it was born, by the proprietor of a small traveling show then exhibiting in Alderson. The showman wanted to dispose of the cub because otherwise he would have had to take the lioness out of the act to care for her youngster, and so stop the performance of the lions.

Mrs. Bebout fed the cub, which had not as yet nursed, from a bottle containing condensed milk. She also put the lion in a box with the cat who was nursing some newly-born kittens. The cat objected at first but finally consented to try caring for it. The cat licked and cleaned it and kept it warm, but could not feed it as her teats were much too small for the lion cub to nurse, although he tried so hard he clawed her belly. Then the cat would leave the box to escape this rough treatment, so the bottle was offered and its contents taken freely. The lion was very fond of the cat and very gentle with her when they played together. It worried him greatly when she climbed over the back-yard fence and disappeared. The lion would then pace the yard looking up at the top of the fence or stand upright against it, moaning constantly. This he would keep up until the cat returned. Sometimes when the cat would be gone for some hours, the lion worried so that it got on his owner's nerves and she would go and look the cat up in order to restore peace and quiet. When his playmate finally returned the lion showed his affection by licking it and moaning and following it about the yard or house. On one occasion the lion was placed on exhibition at a country fair grounds. He mourned and refused his rations, so it was thought best to take him home. However, Mrs. Bebout thought of the cat and hurried home to get it. As soon as his companion arrived, the lion cheered up. He ate and was perfectly satisfied to continue to fill out the contract, earning ten dollars a day for his mistress.

A sign nailed to the fence in front of the Bebout house read, "10¢ to see the lion." I do not think enough money was taken to supply the milk and beef the lion consumed; hence his sale.

On his arrival at the Park, he took up quarters in a cage where he was greatly admired by the public. He was so gentle and affectionate that he allowed any one to pat and fondle him and he remained tame when he became adult and throughout his life in the Park. This lion would leave his meat and come to the bars of his cage when I called him, put his paws out and draw my arm to the bars without exposing his claws. He was the only lion I ever knew to do such a thing.

While lions are being shot continually in Africa, I think it very reasonable to say that they will probably exist in captivity long after they have been exterminated in their native wilds, considering the number being bred in zoos throughout the world. I have a friend who journeyed from the Cape to Cairo without hearing a lion roar during his entire trip. Another friend spent some six months in South and East Africa, and the only lions he saw or heard were in the Pretoria Zoo.

However, the lion does maintain himself, and most abundantly, in certain places, and even during our short sojourn in Tanganyika we made contact with them five times. When we were crossing a low mountain pass between Kondoa Irangi and Umbugwe we came to a village with a mission house. Coming up the hill we met a

Catholic missionary followed by eight perspiring natives carrying an organ for his services that afternoon. He was from Ufiumi, and we asked about game in his section, intending, perhaps, to go over and try to make a catch there. But he told us that the game had been driven out of the immediate neighborhood by lions, and that a pair of these had become man eaters.

We did not see our first lion. We were in camp near Magi-motu and our boys had gathered into little groups in the vicinity of camp. They were having their evening porridge, when suddenly a lion gave a grunting cough very close to camp. The impressive thing about it was the speed, and yet the dignity, with which the boys walked up to our camp and huddled in larger groups, near the tents and the guns.

Several days later George and I came over the crest of a hill and looked into a little clearing where a herd of impalla antelopes were gathered. We stopped to watch them, and observed that they moved forward together quickly for about forty feet at a time. Then they would stop, and then all take another spurt forward, apparently watching us all the time. One of the boys whispered, "*Simba!*" and pointed to a spot some fifty feet away from them, where a lion, evidently a youngster, though with a good mane, was trying to creep up on the herd. As he would approach a few feet, they would all move away. The one thing that stands out in memory about the lion is his tail, which was switching from side to side, and though he was more than a hundred yards from me, I fancied I could hear it hit his sides. Then the impallas, sizing up our party again, disappeared into the bush, leaving the lion alone. He looked in our direction, and George whispered, "Here's your chance for a lion." Everybody who comes to Africa wants to shoot a lion, though I don't see why. So I fired—and missed him. He ran away from us a hundred yards, and then stopped, and I fired again and missed. Then, at the edge of a clump of brush, he stopped once more and I made my last miss, after which he disappeared. At the time I was shooting I suffered two conflicting emotions, equally strong. I wanted to see a lion charge, and I did hope this one wouldn't charge. Anyway, I was able to add "lion" to the list of big game I have missed.

At another time, walking in savannalike country in the early morning, we came across a party of five, evidently returning from a night's hunting. George threw up his gun and the cartridge missed fire, for which we were very glad, because it is said that a female lion will always charge when wounded, while not more than fifty per cent of the males do. And this party contained three sizable females. We were on the open ground close to them, with little possibility of stopping a charge before one of our party had been clawed. They all trotted off, the largest female behind the others, and looking at us as she disappeared.

Our last encounter with a lion had a touch of humor to it. We were in Tula, and had been catching wart hogs in nets. Four of them seemed enough, so we asked about bush pigs, and the natives told us that there were plenty in a certain canebrake close to camp. In the morning we went to the brake, put up our long line of native nets, and then sent from either end of it an encircling party. Charley Goss and I took up our position behind the nets with lariats in hand, waiting for what the natives would drive into it. The cane was higher than the boys' heads, though we could see their spears projecting above. One by one they dropped off the line at intervals of five or ten feet. The rest went on, until eventually they had a circle inclosing the high cane. Then the line moved forward, closing in with the usual driving cry, "Hia! Hia!" We waited patiently to see what would emerge from the cane, when suddenly a lion grunted, apparently right in the center of the circle. We could not see the boys, but noticed that the spear tips that had been in an orderly line resolved themselves into two

PLATE 23

The Siberian or long-haired tiger after ten years of captivity

PLATE 24

East African leopard

masses, one to the right and one to the left, and the
yelling became more concerted and impressively louder.
Presently two black gobs of boys emerged. The lion,
of course, ran away. Then we heard some shrieking, and
two natives came out assisting a third, who appeared
badly scratched about his face. His mind must have
been on something else than the drive, for he had not heard
the lion, and not noticing that the other boys had hurriedly massed together, continued to advance by himself
waving his spear, and yelling "Hia!" He did not see
the lion, but a female buffalo, probably a young one,
sleeping in the cane, was awakened and frightened by
the noise. Escaping, she hit him in passing, as it were,
and went on. He fell to the ground in the cane, and the
scratches were simply due to the fall. He came to me
and asked permission to go back to the camp to die.
On his right breast was a little round wound to the center
of a rib. Above or below the rib it might have been
serious, but it was trivial, especially considering how
close the man had been to actual death from encountering
two wild animals. We disinfected the wound and sent
the boy back to camp, and that evening after dinner was
over he came to me with his chief as interpreter and
wanted to know if I did not think that such a wound
received in my service was worthy of a bit of baksheesh.
Three shillings made him happy, and I suppose the chief
let him keep part of it for himself.

One day, while at Dodoma, we received a telegram
from a storekeeper up the railroad line, who had just
bought from a native two tiny nursling lions. The
chances of keeping these alive in the field were slight,
considering all the other young animals we had to care
for, but I telegraphed, asking the price. He replied,
"Am offered sixty. Will accept eighty pounds." As
these same baby lions would be worth about $50 each at
New York City, we did not reply, and heard afterwards
that both had died within the next few days.

WILD ANIMALS

We came across no young lions at all on our trip. Yet the lion is very abundant, and even on the coast, at Dar-es-Salaam, where the Government maintains an experimental stock farm, pens for cattle have been made lion-proof, ever since a lion jumped over a fence one night and killed eight cows.

Once at Arusha a Boer came into the hotel and informed me that he had a six-months'-old lion at his farm. We bargained for it over a stein of beer. The animal was to be in good condition, and I was to pay so much; so he sent the boys to the farm to bring back the animal. After they had gone he was suddenly reminded that the animal "is hurt a little in one leg, but will soon get well." Some hours later the boys brought it in, a pitiful specimen, its foreleg shot through the elbow, swollen out of all proportion and gangrenous. The owner tried to persuade me that it was only a slight wound, and in two or three days would be all right. I could not see it that way, so we parted bad friends all around.

Mr. Blackburne, as is noted elsewhere in this book, first gained intimate acquaintance with animals in the circus. He was the lion tamer for Barnum and Bailey and in this rôle adventures befell him such as few men have had. One such adventure is reported here in his own words:

During the summer of 1889, while the Barnum and Bailey Circus was traveling through the United States, preparations were going on to transport the show to London for the winter season of 1889–1890. The steamship *Fernesia* was chartered and all the circus paraphernalia was landed at a Brooklyn dock, where the task of loading the ship began. The running gear of all cages was removed, and the cages, containing the animals, were hoisted by derricks and lowered into the hold. Then the horses, both ring and draft animals, were lifted in crates and they, too, were lowered into the hold. There a separate narrow stall was provided for each horse, with six inches of tanbark underfoot. They were haltered up tight to prevent them from lying down during the voyage, and for the first three days they suffered considerably.

The elephants were the last to be loaded. The large ones walked up a gangplank and each was chained separately into a heavily built stall built on the aft mid-deck. Some twelve smaller elephants, however, were lifted in slings to a height of about thirty feet, and lowered into the hold. This proved the most exciting task in the loading of the steamer. As the derrick jerked up each elephant, he struggled to free himself, and screamed at the top of his voice, while all those waiting their turn joined in. I am sure no lot of wild elephants ever screamed louder, nor were any so humiliated, roughly handled, or frightened. At last the ship sailed, with the greatest cargo of large-sized wild animals that had ever crossed the Atlantic.

We sailed by the southern route to avoid rough weather, and after ten days tied up at the Prince Albert docks in London. The horses came off first, and were led into the freight sheds, where they found a good bed of straw already prepared for them. The voyage had made them so stiff they could hardly walk or stand, and in the sheds they lay down and rolled, moaned, and grunted. That night they had their first real sleep for two weeks. They got two days of rest while the ship was unloading, after which they hauled the rolling stock to the Olympia Building, where the circus was to exhibit.

After a few weeks for the preparation of the building and rehearsals, the show opened, and for three months gave two performances daily to crowded houses. About ten days before Christmas, Mr. Bailey said he wanted the animals in the dens to be trained by the holidays to perform while the dens were drawn around the hippodrome track. Some of the large cats had never been trained, so this seemed very short notice. However, Mr. Bailey's word was law, and we went to work twice daily to teach the animals some easy tricks.

I had a den with four adult lions, two of which were trained. The other two had been purchased just before sailing, and no one had ever been in the cage with them. As a preliminary, we had to cut their claws, so we put a stout collar on each of the untrained animals and tied them to opposite corners of the cage by a chain, which was short enough to prevent the animals from reaching me as I sat on a stool midway between them. After their claws were cut, training began. My weapons consisted of a broom, a hickory stick two feet long, and a rawhide whip. I also had with me my pipe and some tobacco. As I sat on the stool watching the lions trying to slip their collars or break the chains I would allow smoke coils to settle around them. This seemed to intimidate them, and at length they settled down to look me over carefully and watch the smoke. In the meantime I would talk to them kindly, assuring them that no harm would be done them as long as they behaved. The next step was to attempt to brush them with the broom, which they naturally resented. When they attempted to strike with their paws, I gave them a few taps on the knuckles with the stick. Then they tried to bite the broom, and were given a few taps on the tongue with the rawhide. The nose, tongue and knuckles are the weak points of the great cats, and they soon learn that their trainer knows it. After a few days these two lions stood up at a word of command, resting their forefeet on the crossbar at the front of the cage, allowing me to brush them with the broom. They did not enjoy this, as their expressions revealed, but they submitted nevertheless.

That was as far as the lessons could go while the animals were chained. The next step was to teach them to jump over a hurdle or gate of three slats. This they soon accomplished, and the two trained lions jumped back and forth with them. Rehearsals continued twice

Fig. 6. Sketches from an artist's note book. By Benson B. Moore

Fig. 1.—Sketches from an artist's note-book.   By Benson B. Moore

daily for a week, and considering the short time allowed them, they performed very well.

During rehearsals there was nothing to excite the animals, so I wondered how they would react to the music and the motion of the cage as it was being hauled around the hippodrome track. At the first performance my attendant pushed the gate into the cage, which frightened the lions. When I commanded them to jump, one of the new animals ran into the hurdle gate, breaking the center slat. His head went through, and as he attempted to draw back, the ends of the broken board became lodged back of his jaw bones, preventing him from freeing himself. I was sitting astride the gate, which the animal carried with him as he plunged to the end of the cage. There he could not turn, so he backed to the other end, with the gate still fast about his neck. This was repeated several times, when he at last succeeded in freeing himself. In the middle of the roof of the cage there was a ventilator about eighteen inches square, covered with iron bars, and it was this that saved me. As the lion rushed from end to end of the cage with the gate about his neck, I grasped the bars in the ventilator and swung myself upward. During the commotion the other lions were greatly frightened, and huddled in their corner, occasionally leaving it to jump over the hurdle as it moved up and down the cage. My own position was not an enviable one, and I had no time to consider the audience, which must have been somewhat puzzled, no doubt believing that this acrobatic performance was part of the show.

At one performance the den stopped in front of the royal box while the lions were doing their tricks. I glanced up, and as the cage passed on I bowed to the occupants of the box, among whom was the Prince of Wales, afterward Edward VII.

The first tiger to come to the National Zoological Park had belonged to a circus. It had become so mangy as to be unfit for exhibition, so the circus presented it to the United States Government. Mr. Blackburne gives the following account of it:

One day while Dr. Frank Baker was Superintendent of the National Zoological Park a representative of the Adam Forepaugh Circus called to offer an adult Bengal tiger on temporary deposit. The Park's animal collection was very meager, and the offer of a tiger, even on deposit, was an event. We arranged a spacious cage, and on June 11, 1893, the tiger arrived. To our great disappointment the fine, sleek animal that we had pictured when we accepted him turned out to be the thinnest, poorest specimen I had ever seen, but worst of all, he was a victim of sarcoptic mange. He was not fit for exhibition, yet the only place we had for him was the specially prepared exhibition cage. My first impulse was to shoot him, to prevent a spread of the mange to the other animals, but I decided to try to effect a cure. Accordingly, half a bucketful of sulphur and oil was prepared, and climbing to the top of his cage I succeeded, with a tin cup, in pouring the mixture over him as he lay on the floor. He got a complete bath, since the liquid which did not fall directly upon him was absorbed from the floor. I administered this treatment twice weekly for three weeks, when three additional treatments were given at intervals of a week. The cure was complete. As his appetite had not suffered (he ate twelve pounds of beef daily) he soon gained in weight, and at the end of three months he was a splendid exhibition animal.

With advancing years our tiger's teeth suffered, and this resulted in frequent attacks of indigestion. On one occasion he became bloated, groaned with agony, and was unable to stand up. Castor-oil treatment was indicated, but feeding castor oil to a tiger is a problem. Again we resorted to the top of the cage. Through the bars I annoyed the animal by dragging the lash of a carriage whip over his mouth and head. This he naturally resented, and bit viciously at the whip. To his great surprise he suddenly found his mouth full of castor oil, with the remainder of a quart over his head and fore paws, which he proceeded to lick in an effort to become clean once more. Two hours later he was entirely well. Some time after this he was operated upon for a bursa on the elbow.

On January 20, 1906, the tiger was chloroformed. He was then about thirty years old, and had lost the use of his hind legs. An autopsy discovered a 45-caliber bullet in his shoulder. We do not know whether he was shot in the wild state, or in captivity before coming to the Park. We estimated, though, that his residence in the Park had prolonged his life by at least twelve years.

Since that time we have had ten other Bengal tigers, including four born at the National Zoological Park. Old Ben, the single specimen of this species that we have at present, has been here for fourteen years.

In 1918 we received two specimens of the long-haired variety, the Siberian or Manchurian tiger, the first we had had. They proved a magnificent pair, and have produced twenty-three young since their arrival, only six of which were brought to maturity. The mother, after nine years in captivity, had to be shot. She neglected her first litter but later on she took good care of the young, so we were able to send specimens from this family to the zoos in New York, Philadelphia, and Baltimore. The father is still in fine condition, after more than ten years of captivity.

The tiger is one of the finest animals that lives. In the cage he is the most snobbish of all aristocrats, his contempt for those who jostle in front of his bars being nothing less than magnificent. He is dignity itself. He condescends to no boyish antics to attract attention as does the chimpanzee, to no begging for sweets as do the bear and the elephant, and to no pacific, philosophic acceptance of fate such as the hippopotamus displays. When he does get into action he means business. You can not set him roaring by making faces or shaking your fist at him, and you can not win his favor by a stick of candy. He is above rage or gratitude, and he looks right past you. However, Ben loves one of his keepers and hates another, and is unmistakably very fond of Mr. Blackburne, speaking to him with a grunt when he comes in sight. I tried for two years to make friends with him, and at the end of that time I was rewarded one morning by a grunt of recognition. This is occasionally given now, but never with the regularity with which he greets those who attend him daily, and often I am unable to attract his attention at all.

The tiger is especially hardy in temperate climates. He lives and breeds well in captivity, and can stand outdoor weather unless winters are very severe. Quite different from the lion, he loves to swim, and when we had the space to give one a cage with a large tank in it, he would disport in the water. Fed ten to sixteen pounds of beef a day, according to his size, with liver on Mondays and Thursdays, and water twice a day, he is one of the easier animals to keep.

Sometimes adult tigers are captured in traps and sold into captivity. These find their way to circuses, and have been trained. One of the American circuses possesses a cage of ten. Their keeper, a very superior trainer, makes them perform as another man would spaniels. They jump over him, through hoops, walk a pole in lieu of a tight rope. In the arena they make a ferocious looking group of beasts; in the menagerie tent, confined in their small cages like so many kittens, the keeper can put his hand into their mouths and rub their teeth. After his act one day, when he came out to sit with me in the audience during the show, he complained bitterly about their tranquillity. I told him truthfully that his was the best tiger act I had ever seen. He shrugged his

PLATE 25

East African leopard and kittens

PLATE 26

African cheetah that lived for fifteen years in the Zoo. Swiftest of animals for short distance

shoulders and asked, "What can a man do? I tell the owner every day that I can not make a show with ten tame tigers. I must have five more mean ones to add to the act."

Accounts of catching adult tigers in the East Indies are plentiful. The lair of the animal is located in some dense tangle of cane and creeper thicket where he spends most of his time in alert slumber. Near a watering place, where footprints show that he comes to drink, a bottle-shaped pit is excavated, ten feet deep, ten feet in diameter at the base, but only seven feet across at the top. This is covered with a network of cane and bamboo, and a kid tied in the center of the frail cover to advertise its presence by bleating. Then the trapper waits patiently, it may be for days, until the tiger comes upon the goat. He stops close to it, and then with one powerful leap from the concealing brush lands on the little goat. The platform gives way, and tiger and goat go headlong into the bottom of the pit, from which there is no escape because of the overhanging walls which allow no foothold. Sometimes a contraption like a gigantic mousetrap is placed at the bottom of the pit, the door of which snaps shut after the tiger has fallen through. Then the trap, tiger and all, is pulled up with ropes and taken to the nearest settlement. Another method of getting the tiger out of the pit is preferred by East Indians. A net of rattan ropes, ten feet square, is thrown into the pit. The frenzied tiger attacks it, biting and tearing. One after the other, he pokes his paws through the meshes. He becomes more and more tangled in the net until he has succeeded in binding himself head and paws. Then the trapper can descend into the pit and pass ropes around the tired body. The animal is hauled up, placed in a cage on wheels, and driven away. Box traps, also, are used, but the pit method is the most frequent one. It seems better adapted to the habits of the tiger. Sometimes the newly captured beast is actually led to market. A stout rattan collar is put around the neck and then twenty-foot ropes are attached to each side. Each rope is manned by a group of hunters who pull against each other in a sort of tug of war.

The tiger has been trapped in much the same manner since the beginning of civilization. He had a prominent place in the menageries of Indian and Chinese monarchs before the Christian era and first appeared in Europe about the time of the eastern conquests of Alexander, when the city of Athens received a tiger as a gift from the king of Syria. The animal was well-known to the Romans. It was most dreaded of all the beasts that appeared in the arena.

A question often asked the office of the Zoo is, "If an adult lion and tiger were to fight, which would win?" As we try to keep our adult lions and tigers in the Zoo from fighting, we did not know until in the records of the Roman arena we found that the tiger was usually victorious in such a combat.

The thought of a tiger escaping is one that gives pause to the man who has them in charge, though, curiously, in the number of instances of escapes recorded, no great harm has been done. A story is told of an English animal dealer, who found one of his tigers that had cost him considerable money and out of which he expected to make a gratifying profit, loose in the alley in front of his warehouse. In his excitement he straddled it and rode it back into the barn.

Sányál records one instance where two tigers escaped, through the carelessness of some native workmen who had left a gate open. He describes the incident as follows:

The keepers, who were on the roof of the house engaged in raising the gratings to let the animals into their inner dens, first noticed the escape. The officers rushed to the opposite end of the building to verify the fact, and having ascertained its truth beat a rapid retreat towards the nearest bird house, and thence towards the entrance gate, discussing the steps to be taken for keeping the animals within the garden enclosure during the night and securing them, if possible, in the morning. It was decided to keep the roadside lamps of the garden burning and to maintain perfect silence inside the garden, so as not to disturb or terrify the beasts. The news of the escape soon spread in the neighbourhood; the shops were closed and the bazars presented an unusually deserted appearance early that night. Meanwhile at the request of the Commissioner of Police, to whom a report had been conveyed, a company of sepoys of the regiment stationed in the immediate neighbourhood was turned out to form a cordon round the garden, with orders to continue shouting and yelling the whole night. This plan succeeded admirably. The tigers remained inside the garden and abstained, while at large, from killing or molesting a single animal, although they had ample opportunity of doing so. This unexpected moderation on their part may be ascribed to their freedom from hunger, as they had been fed immediately before the escape, or more probably to their astonishment and alarm at the novelty of their situation. In their rambles one of the tigers twice passed quite close to the Superintendent of the garden, who was seated in the small ticket office made of *durmah* mats only—there was no entrance lodge then—to keep himself informed of the movements of the beasts, with the help of the two keepers watching them from the top of the Burdwan House. . . . About midnight both the tigers retired inside the walled enclosure. . . . Hopes were then entertained of securing them in the morning, and, everything considered, the position of the house at one corner of the enclosure with sliding doors, the height of the wall (7 feet as it was then) and the nature of the beasts, there would have been a good chance of capturing them. The Commissioner of Police, however, decided in the interests of the public safety to run no further risks, marshalled his forces on the roof of the Burdwan House at 5 a. m., and at the third volley the beasts fell.

We have had twenty-one leopards in the Park, mostly from Africa, and the longest life record is fifteen years. An account of the first specimen we had is given by Mr. Blackburne:

The first leopard in the collection was a female, presented by J. Dorsy Mohun, United States Consul at Booma, Congo Free State, Africa, November 16, 1894. This was a gentle animal and a very beautiful one, except for a deformed tail, which curled against the right hind leg in the form of a complete hoop, and which could not be straightened, even forcibly. Because of this deformity walking was somewhat difficult and quite frequently while lying down the leopard's hind leg would become entangled in the curve of the tail. She found it hard to disentangle because of the tenacity with which the tail clung to her belly.

On March 4, 1897, we received a male leopard from the Barnum and Bailey Circus, in exchange for another animal. The pair got along amicably together and bred. In August, when the kittens were due, we met with disappointment. The female was unable to deliver her young and she died of peritonitis on August 7, 1897.

The male leopard was a large, ferocious specimen, whose disposition the circus found too uncertain to permit of training. He never missed an opportunity to strike at us through the bars as we passed in front of his cage.

One day while in my office in the lion house I heard shrieks. There were no watchmen in the building, so I dashed down stairs and found that two elderly ladies and a child, who had apparently failed to notice an eight-foot door for visitors, had entered a narrow service door back of the guard rail, and were in front of the leopard cage, completely paralyzed with fright, with the leopard trying his best to reach them. I hastily put the child through the guard rail and escorted one of the women to safety, cautioning the one who remained to stand perfectly still until I could return for her. As I started back for the second woman, the first one, apparently hysterical, followed me in again, and the leopard got his claws in her cape and pulled her close to the bars. As she fell I snatched her out of the cape and put her over the guard rail. After a great deal of hysteria the three visitors went away, to return an hour or so later, considerably more composed, demanding that the Government replace the cape which the leopard had completely ruined.

"Madam," I replied, "I am sorry this happened, but you are extremely lucky to escape with the loss of your cape."

On our recent expedition to Tanganyika we caught five full-grown East African leopards in the kopjes near Dodoma. Leopards are still abundant throughout the continent, but are very seldom seen. George, our white hunter, had been in the field in Tanganyika for three years and had not once seen any but trapped leopards. Because of their depredations on the native stock, and also for the value of their hides, they are continually trapped and killed. A little compound with a long, narrow entrance is built, and a goat tied on the inside. The leopard creeps into the narrow passageway to get at him, presses against a string, which discharges a gun, pointing directly downward and usually heavily loaded with shot. Many are killed in this way.

We had taken with us a number of unassembled crates for the shipment of animals, and used these like glorified rabbit traps, but baited with goats instead of cabbage. We would build a heavy *boma*, or corral, of thorn strongly roofed over, also with thorn, and tether a goat on the inside. Then we placed the box traps against the corral so that the goat was visible through iron bars at one end. The entrance end had a sliding door pulled up. Our ingenious Freddy fastened a string to this and extended the string over the branch of a tree and down inside the cage to a simple wooden treadle. The leopard would hear the goat bleat. From its tracks in the morning we could tell that he had gone round and round, seeking some way to get at it, and then he would come into the cage and touch the treadle. In the morning the boys would bring into camp what I shall always believe to be the angriest leopards I have known, for in addition to suddenly finding themselves trapped, each one had the tip of his tail pinched by the door dropping on it. The doors were bolted, and the traps served as cages in which the animals lived until they arrived in Washington. One died shortly after of pneumonia. The other two pairs are still in most excellent condition, and both mated and bred the first year in captivity, each producing a litter of two young.

In a kopje near Dodoma there lives a family of leopards which is partly albino. The district commissioner showed me a skin of one of these spotted with large patches of pure white. This is a most unusual variation in the leopard, and I have never seen one alive. Black leopards are very rare in Africa, but not at all uncommon in eastern Asia. We have had two in the collection. The one living here at present was formerly a performer in a circus. I found it in the hands of an animal dealer in New York. In ancient bachelor days, when my fiancée accompanied me on shopping excursions for animals among the dealers, it was a beautiful, sleek leopard, and so gentle that I was able to open its mouth with my hands and examine its teeth before buying. The fiancée prepared a poetic name for it, and we shipped it on to Washington, but the day after, when I arrived, I found that the keepers had already christened it "Nig," which name it still bears. Nig was very tame for a time, and still appears to be, but is tricky. At first whenever I came to the cage she would rub against the bars to have her sides scratched. It is often safe to pet cats, but usually best to do so from the side. I learned this from Nig, one day, when I started to pet her as she faced me. She reached out with one foot, caught a scarf around my neck and tore it from me.

Because of their lightning quickness of movement leopards are more dangerous than the other big cats. Several times in the Park visitors who reached over too far have been scratched. One female leopard here some years ago was especially adept at seizing hats and umbrellas waved by visitors in order to attract her attention. Once she succeeded in demolishing a beautiful fur boa.

The Park has been fortunate in having two specimens of the rare snow leopard which comes from the Himalayas. One of these lived six and a half years, and became a great favorite with the visiting public. This had been shipped to a dealer in New York, from India, and then forwarded to Washington. It seems that there had been too many animals in the cargo for the keeper to keep careful watch on them. The snow leopard was transferred from her traveling crate to a larger crate to get exercise for a day or two. Then the traveling crate was cleaned out and in it were two baby snow leopards that had been born there and died unnoticed by the attendant. The mother animal was shipped on, but developed such a very bad cold that the dealer actually remitted $200 of the price. She eventually got well, however. She was playful and quite tame, though very quick and tricky, and ready to strike. She would come and put her head against the wire mesh of the cage to have it stroked. After she died we secured another, a young one, but pneumonia carried it off in a few months. The softest in color and the most graceful in form of all the leopards, and with a long bushy tail, it is one of the most attractive of the cats.

Several varieties of the leopard's small American cousin, the ocelot, have been represented in our collection by thirty-one specimens, six years being the longest that any of them lived. Three attained this age, one of which, by the way, was a present from His Excellency, Dr. J. Paes de Carbalho, Governor of the State of Pará, Brazil, through Mr. Kennedy, the United States Consul there. Doctor Carbalho seemed to pick animals that would live, for another specimen he sent, an anaconda, lived in the Park for over twenty-nine years.

As a kitten, the ocelot is playful and tames easily, but there always comes a day when it scratches, and then the zoo falls heir to it. This is true of most feline pets. I once tried to buy a small kitten belonging to a merchant on the west coast of Mexico. The owner would not sell it because "the baby loves it so." By good fortune I was able to remain in the town for some days, waiting. One evening I was told that the kitten had scratched the baby so I strolled past the house. The merchant called me in and the deal was consummated right there. This I consider good applied psychology.

Two of the ocelots at present in our collection have been pets, and one of them, though an adult, is still fairly tame. Another, an adult trapped in Texas, is by far the fiercest cat we have in the collection.

Of the myriads of small cats that come into the market from time to time, and are exhibited in zoos, the yaguarundi (*Felis yagouaroundi*) is one of the most desired because of its grace. Somewhat larger than a house cat, long and slender, continually in motion, it is very popular with the visitors, while naturalists like to argue as to whether the specimen before them is a yaguarundi or an eyra cat (*Felis eyra*). Probably both belong to the same species, which varies in color from black to red. It is known in Central America by the not very good name of "dog of the mountain."

As in other commodities, there are sometimes bargain sales in cats, and on one occasion we secured for $65 one specimen each of three rare species: a flat-headed cat from Siam (*Ailurin planiceps*), a marbled cat (*Felis marmorata*),

PLATE 27

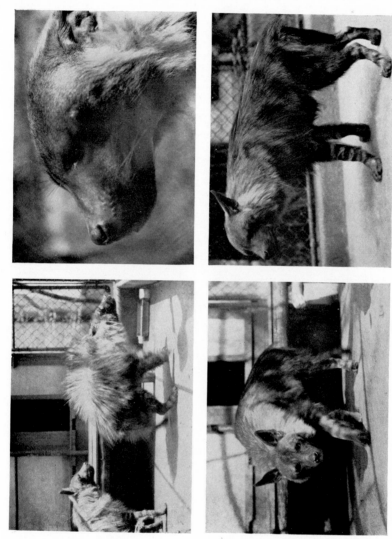

Brown or maned hyena from South Africa, rarest of its group.   The only pair now in America

PLATE 28

Pair of Mexican pumas or mountain lions

and a beautiful clouded leopard (*Felis nebulosa*). Two of them died shortly, but the clouded leopard remains with us still, after six years. It is much darker in color than other specimens we have seen, and probably after its death will be found to be a species distinct from the splendid specimen now living at the Philadelphia Zoo.

The jaguar, which takes the place of the leopard in this hemisphere, is quite similar to it, but heavier in body and with much larger head and feet. One specimen lived in the Park as long as thirteen years; another lived nine years, when it had to be put out of the way on account of infirmities due to old age. Ten have been in the Park during its history.

Though the jaguar abounds in parts of South America, it does not come into the market nearly as often as do leopards, because animal catching and marketing have not been systematized in South America as they have in Africa and Asia.

Of the three cheetahs that we have had in our Zoo, one pair is most notable. Mr. Blackburne tells about them as follows:

While in the zoological gardens at Giza, Egypt, in 1913, my curiosity prompted me to peep through a crack in the board fence that surrounded the property yard. There, somewhat to my surprise, I saw two beautiful young cheetahs closely confined in a small cage. Although the park had two adult specimens on exhibition, it seemed odd that these two fine young animals were not also shown. When I asked Captain Flower, the Director, if he wished to dispose of them he stated that they did not belong to the zoo, but were the property of an Arab merchant in Cairo. He undertook to consult the owner, who finally agreed to sell them for £20 each. Accompanied by an Arab keeper, I carefully examined the animals to determine their soundness. The keeper said they were quite tame. As he lifted them out of their cage and placed them on the ground, the animals made

[89]

off like a flash at a speed of twenty or more miles per hour after a lot of chickens confined in a wire-mesh inclosure within the property yard. Their chase was short-lived, for they came into unexpected contact with the wire fence and both cheetahs dropped apparently lifeless for a time. When they began to recover we returned them to their cage. For several days I studied them closely, and was finally convinced that they were uninjured. I bought the animals, and they arrived safely at the National Zoological Park August 8, 1913. They were the only specimens of their kind in the United States for a number of years, and were greatly admired by visitors to the Park, especially by directors of other zoos, animal dealers, photographers, and artists. They thrived, and gave the Park a record for longevity which has probably never been equaled; the female lived thirteen years and seven months and the male almost as long. During the growing period their morning meal consisted of milk and eggs and in the evening they were given chickens or pigeons. When they became adult about four pounds of beef or horse flesh were fed them each day, to which a pound of liver once or twice a week was added.

Cheetahs are still fairly abundant, usually in open country in East Africa, but the young are in such demand that they are difficult to get. One was offered me at Mombasa by an Arab dealer. He wanted a hundred pounds for it. When I stated that the price was quite high he told me what was really the truth, that he could send it to India and get more.

For generations African cheetahs have been sent to India to be used in hunting, especially in the northern states. In fact, while there is a distinct race of Indian cheetah native to the country, it is very difficult to get a pure specimen on account of the great preponderance of African animals that have been sent over. These animals are used for running down antelopes, chiefly the black buck. The cheetah is taken blindfolded to the vicinity of a herd, and released. For a short distance he is the swiftest animal that runs; he overtakes and runs down one of the bucks, after which the natives run up, bleed the buck, and give the cheetah a bowl of the blood. Then they blindfold him again.

When our pair died we were naturally anxious to secure another, and recently did get one from a traveling theatrical troupe of midgets. These midgets had as part of their performance some trained animals including Mitzi, the cheetah which had been brought from Berlin to pose with them. However, she frightened the elephants so that the troupe had to get rid of her. Thus she came to the Zoo. The day before the midgets left town they came out to say good-bye to their old pet, and caused us some nervousness by shoving their little arms through the bars and patting her, despite the fact that she made frequent snaps at them.

The average life of a cheetah in a zoo is about three years, but we have been spoiled by the record of the two that Mr. Blackburne brought home, and expect Mitzi to be with us for many years.

We have in the office a sketch of a sitting serval posed front on, and while it is a faithful reproduction of the animal, visitors frequently laugh at it, thinking it to be a caricature of a domestic cat. It is a long, drawn-out, spotted cat, usually gentler in disposition than the leopard, and quite amenable to captivity. Two that we brought from East Africa had been nest mates, and we kept them in a small shipping box during forty days at sea, where they lived together without any undue ferocity toward each other. As soon as we got them to Washington we placed them together in a large cage where almost the first thing they did was to fight so hard that we had to separate them.

The serval often lives near villages, and is fond of robbing chicken roosts, so that the natives hate him.

While we were at Dodoma the natives discovered one in a chicken house. They pounded him with clubs, until one remembered that the white men who had rented Barum Singh's house were buying all sorts of live animals, so they trussed it on a pole and brought it in for sale. Of course we put it out of its misery immediately, but unfortunately one of our men took a snapshot of it. This was selected by a picture editor to go into a page plate of illustrations of the expedition, and afterwards I had to devote considerable time to writing explanatory letters to humane societies. One young lady, more indignant and less reasonable than the others, when I stated the conditions wrote a return letter, demanding that the natives who had done this be punished. Unfortunately they were ten thousand miles away at the time, and I could do nothing about it. Besides, while I am much more fond of servals, except for eating purposes, than of chickens, I believe even natives have some right to defend their own property.

The Kafir or Egyptian cat, which has long been known from mummies in Egyptian tombs and was certainly one of the ancestors of our domestic cat, was very abundant in Tanganyika. There they bred with domestic cats kept by the natives, and several unmistakable hybrids were brought to us with wild caught animals. They were just as fierce as the pure-bloods. Practically all of them died of intestinal worms shortly after their arrival in Washington.

Again we draw upon Mr. Blackburne's unlimited experience for a few tales of common cats with wild animals:

A very shy half-grown cat took up its quarters with a group of six llamas, one of which was a large buff-colored male with a very heavy pelt. This one seemed to be the cat's choice for companionship. At feeding time the cat, back and tail up, would rub against all four of the llama's legs. Finally he learned to eat some of the other's rations, which consisted of oats. Frequently, when the llama was lying down the cat would be found curled up on its back, asleep. On several occasions, while the llama walked about the inclosure, grazing, the cat calmly nestled on its back. When nearly grown the cat disappeared.

An adult female cat took up quarters with a pair of blue foxes, and hid in a burrow with them under a shelter box. Several times the cat was removed, but the next morning was invariably found with the foxes again. Eventually the foxes had a litter of pups, but the cat remained and occupied the same burrow. One day she left as suddenly as she had come.

A litter of kittens was born in the cellar of the lion house. When they grew strong enough to climb the stairs the mother sometimes brought them out for an airing, through a door near the open outside cages. The first of these was occupied by a male leopard, who exhibited much interest in the kittens. Perhaps his instinct told him that at some time one would be foolish enough to crawl through the bars. If such was the case, his hopes were realized. One of the kittens did crawl into the outside cage. Out of the door the leopard pounced, after the kitten. The mother cat was sitting not far away. She leaped into the cage, onto the leopard's back, and clawed his head several times, after which she made a hasty exit, following the kitten, which had run out meanwhile. Cat and kittens, all very much excited, retreated hurriedly to the cellar, and were not seen about the cage for several days. They had learned to keep away from the leopard and never again ventured too close to the cage.

CHAPTER VI

FIFTEEN KINDS OF BEARS

At the present time we have some forty-five bears in the Park, representing fifteen varieties. The fat, apparently clumsy and muddle-headed bruin is one of the clowns of the Zoo, and a great favorite with visitors.

Mr. A. B. Baker, assistant superintendent of the Park since its foundation, contributes the following account of the early and most noteworthy of our bears:

The first of our long line of bears was a grizzly, purchased for twenty-five dollars in Billings, Montana, in 1888, two years before the Park was organized. This was followed not very long afterwards by another grizzly and a cinnamon, both of whom were adult and came directly from the wilds of the Yellowstone National Park. The cinnamon settled down to a long and contented life, while the grizzly escaped by scaling a cliff, and was killed resisting capture.

Shortly after this came the biggest grizzly ever in the collection. From its beginning, in 1890, the Zoo has had the advantage of the cordial cooperation of the Yellowstone National Park authorities in securing animals for its collection. Successive superintendents in charge there have interested themselves in procuring such animals and birds as were available. Early in 1894 Captain George S. Anderson, then in charge, wrote that a grizzly bear, which he described as being "as big as a cow," was making trouble in the Yellowstone, and stated that he would be glad to send him on to Washington, if the Zoo would furnish a trap to catch him in. This seemed too good an opportunity to be missed, so all the mechanical genius that the Zoo had was enlisted to devise a trap which could both catch the animal and serve as a shipping crate in which to transport him. A box made all of steel was prepared in a few weeks and shipped out to Captain Anderson. In due time there came a telegram saying, "Your bear is on the road." The grizzly had fallen a victim to his love for pork, having carried off a pig from the butcher's pen, eaten half of it, and left the remainder to serve as bait for catching him.

The bear reached Washington safely and was transferred to a commodious cage in the Park. He proved to be of a size that fully justified Captain Anderson's comparison with a cow, as he weighed 730 pounds. His appetite had apparently not been impaired by the change in climate, for he promptly took sixteen loaves of bread at one meal. He had a surprisingly quiet disposition for an animal caught wild when fully adult, and very soon settled down contentedly to his new life. He reached Washington on July 30, 1894, and he lived until May 9, 1913. During each of the last three winters he became very weak, though remaining in good flesh, and each spring it required very careful feeding to bring him up again to vigor. At the close of the last winter, however, though still retaining good weight, he was so weak that in spite of diligent nursing he continued to fail until it became necessary to end his existence. His age was probably thirty years, as he must have been at least ten years old when captured.

The record of the bear in captivity is almost as ancient and diversified as that of the lion. It was common in the menageries of Rome, brought there after the legions began to penetrate the forests beyond the Alps. The bear was introduced into the arena, where trained animal fighters were able to break his weak skull with a single powerful blow delivered before he realized his situation. The populace does not give the bear the credit due him, because he seems so utterly lacking in dignity, and invites laughter from his behavior. Probably bear day in the Roman arena was "burlesque day."

During the centuries when commerce between Europe and Africa and the East dropped to a low ebb, the bear became practically the only powerful and savage animal which could be obtained in the northern countries. In consequence he took the place of the lion and the tiger in the collections of the wealthy princes of France, England, and Germany, and the practice of bear-baiting grew up as a popular amusement. It endured as a common Sunday and holiday sport in England from the time of the Norman conquest well into the eighteenth century. The bear ordinarily was tied to a stake by the neck or one of the hind legs, and then worried by dogs. Thirteen bears were employed in a spectacle of this kind staged for the benefit of Queen Elizabeth and the event was described by a writer of the period as a very pleasant sport. The bear tore after the dogs, and when bitten by them would bite and claw and roar, and nimbly tumble himself free from them. When he was loose he would shake himself "with blood and slaver hanging about his physiognomy." It is to be hoped that the royal lady was pleased and edified on this afternoon. It seems strange to think that after seeing this show, she might have attended a *première* of one of Shakespeare's plays the same evening.

Bear baiting was a horror to the Puritans. They tried to prohibit it, according to Macauley, not because it gave pain to the bear but because it gave pleasure to the spectators. However, immediately after the Restoration the sport was revived, though it was never universally approved, even among the Cavaliers, as is shown by the following passage from Evelyn's *Diary:*

I went with some friends to the Bear Garden, where was cock-fighting, dog-fighting, bear and bull-baiting, it being a famous day for all these butcherly sports, or rather barbarous cruelties. The bulls

PLATE 29

Alaska and European brown bears waiting for the man with the wheelbarrow and the bread

did exceeding well, but the Irish wolf-dog exceeded, which was a tall greyhound, a stately creature indeed, who beat a cruel mastiff. One of the bulls tossed a dog full into a lady's lap as she sate in one of the boxes at a considerable height from the arena. Two poor dogs were killed, and so all ended with the ape on horseback, and I most heartily weary of the rude and dirty pastime, which I had not seen, I think, in twenty years before.

Bears have always been popular subjects for training, partly because they are very hardy in captivity and comparatively easy to obtain and transport. Well into the last century itinerant showmen exhibited trained bears from village to village throughout Europe. Some peasants made a business of capturing cubs for which there was always a good market, and there arose even "academies of bears" where the bears were taught tricks. One of the most notable of these was in the village of Smorgoni in Poland.

Usually two showmen accompanied each bear. One played a violin or tambourine while his companion and the animal went through their antics. They generally dressed the bear in a burlesque costume, with balls and spangles, in which he danced and went through pantomime performances. These shows enjoyed great popularity, but the training of the bears was conducted with such cruelty that it caused vigorous complaints, and finally in 1867 the Russian Government prohibited bear shows.

According to Loisel, a village of bear tamers existed in France early in the present century. Even today the trained bear is not an uncommon sight in America and Europe. Only a few months ago such an animal fell into the hands of the police in the District of Columbia. It was a large black bear in the possession of two men who were traveling in a battered automobile from city to city, giving street-corner performances and begging. A kindly lady gave the animal a coin and was bitten in return for her charity, so bruin spent a night and a day in a cell at one of the station houses. Probably he found it one of the pleasantest days and nights of his existence, for the policemen catered generously to his taste for sweets. They had, however, no permanent place for such a mascot, so they released the animal to his owners, with a warning to keep out of the National Capital in the future.

A small Pyrenean bear, tame but restrained by a strong steel muzzle, was exhibited during 1891 and 1892 in the streets of London, and attracted so much attention that he ultimately had an audience with Queen Victoria at Windsor Castle. He got to be a familiar acquaintance of most of London's police magistrates, because wherever exhibited he became the center of the crowd, which increased until the constable on duty considered himself bound to take the bear into custody for obstructing traffic. Almost invariably at the dock next morning there was a "dismissal with a caution." As a malefactor he won the hearts of the officers, one of whom, a constable who had arrested him, took up a collection for his benefit the moment the case was dismissed. The beast was owned by a genial Frenchman, who shared his bed with him, and told the queen that he was a "*brave bête, doux comme un enfant.*"

Bears are never safe pets except when very tiny, and then they are great favorites—all of which is well for zoos, because they eventually come into the collections. One of our black bears arrived suddenly as a present from a troupe of gypsies. It had become too large and powerful. Another, long a pet and mascot at a station of Coast Guard cadets, also drifted at last into the Zoo.

A great many zoo animals become beggars, some much more than others, and the bear vies with the monkey in its attempts to amuse the public in return for expected tidbits. Individuals pick up special begging tricks. One of our gigantic Alaskan Kodiaks will sit down, stretch out his hind legs, and hold his hind feet with the front

PLATE 30

Upper: Marian is captured in the Polar seas
Lower: She arrives at the Zoo

PLATE 31

Marian casts a reflection

ones, looking very much like a fat old lady extending her apron to have things thrown into it. Peter, the unique glacier or blue bear, comes to the front of his cage and stands up, lifts one foot very slowly to the lower crossbar of the cage, and then puts his foot back on the floor, and puts the other one up. After he has gone through this performance he waits for the reward.

Molly, our specimen of the common brown bear of Europe, is the best mother the Zoo has ever had. Every other year since 1911 she has produced a litter of from one to four cubs. In December she disappears into her retiring cage and stays there several weeks without food. In January the keepers hear a humming noise, a sound made by baby bears nursing. It is always more than a month afterward before she comes out to eat, after a long fast, bringing the babies with her. From then on these babies, comical little balls of fur and fat, are the principal attraction at the Zoo, biting and playing noisily with each other and with their mother without pause. The first litter was a single female cub born January 19, 1911, the father being another species, the Kidder's bear. The baby weighed sixteen ounces. On January 10, 1913, three stillborn cubs arrived, two males and a female. This time the father was an Alaskan brown bear. After this she was mated with a bear of her own kind. On January 15, 1915, there were three cubs; January 13, 1917, three cubs; January 12, 1919, four cubs; January 7, 1921, three cubs; January 7, 1923, four cubs; January 8, 1925, three cubs; January 7, 1927, three cubs. The newly-born baby bear is curiously small, no larger than a rat, and for some time is absolutely helpless.

A lady who is a great friend of the Zoo, and also very fond of personal pets, dropped in for a visit one afternoon on her way home from Canada to Florida, and told us that she had secured in Canada a very wonderful baby black bear for a pet for herself. We thanked her kindly for it—in advance—but were emphatically assured that it was such a nice pet we never would get it. So the lady took the bear on to Florida, and we received it as soon as the express company could bring it back again.

A black bear once got loose in our park. The head keeper saw it walking across the lawn, shouted to some of the men for assistance, grabbed a pitchfork, and started after the bear. The latter went up a tree and was held there by threatening him with the pitchfork until mechanics from the shop had hurriedly made a cage at the base of the tree, which the bear was driven into. Other mechanics had, in the meantime, patched up the break in his cage. He was immediately put back, and the incident closed. In general an attempt would be made to capture without hurting almost any wild animal that escaped at the Zoo, but we have guns always ready in case any other animal gets out.

During the heat of the summer the bears receive a great deal of sympathy from Zoo Park visitors, because of their fancied suffering. Yet they disport in their water tanks and apparently are little less comfortable than during cooler weather, despite their heavy coats, while, incongruously, we see the lions, tigers, and leopards panting from the heat. Even our polar bears have never given any evidence of being at all affected. One of them has lived here twenty-seven summers and another twenty-three, which of itself shows that the heat can not be very bad for them.

Our newest polar bear, Marian, was captured by the U. S. Coast Guard ship *Marion*, which lassoed her and pulled her aboard the ship when she was a youngster. The crew improvised a cage of stout poles interlaced with wire, except for the roof, which was of planks. As fast as Marian would eat a plank out they would nail another on. When she arrived she had developed a bad disposition, and as soon as liberated in the large cage she dashed at the bears next door. One assumes that everything she had dashed at previously had retreated. Here her neighbors failed to do so, but came close to the bars to examine the new arrival, which nonplussed Marian very much. It took only a day, however, to accustom her to the others, and since then she has appeared perfectly at home. Recently we put in the den with her a Kodiak bear, and she tried the same tactics, rushing at him; but the Kodiak bear, a bit confused at the large size of the bears in the adjoining dens, paid no attention to Marian, who thereupon stopped rushing and they are gradually becoming friends.

There are many species of bears. The family is on the whole a homogeneous one, but several stand out conspicuously from the rest. Among these are the polar bear, which is put in a genus by itself and inhabits only the Arctic regions, and the sloth bear (*Melursus ursinus*), also a distinct animal. Our specimen of the latter was collected by Roy Chapman Andrews in northern India and has been with us for more than ten years, living in an outside cage next to a pair of cinnamon bears from Alaska. As far as we can judge from appearances he is mild mannered, but not at all to be trusted, and like many of his bear relatives has a habit of sucking his paws, making a loud humming sound as he does it.

Another unusual bear, and one of the rarest in collections, is the South American spectacled bear (*Tremarctos ornatus*), characterized by tawny rings around its eyes, which give it a bespectacled appearance. The National Zoological Park has never been able to obtain a specimen. The Bronx Zoo in New York had one for some time, and I saw three beautiful specimens living in the zoological gardens at Lima. I was told that they were not especially rare on the slopes of the mountains.

At Espía, Bolivia, which though it has a name, is nothing else than the most miserable sand bar in the world hemmed in on one side by a steep hill and on the other by the La Paz River, which is here joined by the Meguilla to form the Bopi, we camped for three weeks, enough time to spoil the morale of any expedition, waiting for Mosetena Indians to make and drag up the river some balsa rafts on which we expected to float down into the Promised Land below. The first lot of these Indians came in one morning dragging four rafts with them. Towing these rafts, by the way, is a somewhat laborious process. It takes fifteen days going up river to traverse a distance which can be covered in one day going down, and even the down voyage is not altogether a smooth one. The Indians had with them the results of their hunting on the way upstream. There were large baskets of half roasted, half smoked spider monkeys, with long tails coiled like watch springs; there were baskets of land tortoises, a live spider monkey, and a baby douroucouli to be sent into the highlands for sale. After waiting as we had been doing without opportunity to collect, this plethora of animals made the same impression upon us as that produced among the Israelites when the two spies returned from the Holy Land, carrying between them on a pole that enormous bunch of grapes, so well illustrated in our Sunday schools. Most exciting of all was the skin of a black bear that had been shot ten miles below the junction of the river. It lacked the eye markings of the typical spectacled bear. We bought the skin and the skull from the Indians, and hurriedly preparing it, packed it into a case of botanical specimens which were afterwards dispatched to our Museum. In some unaccountable way the skin was lost. This may have been simply an aberrant spectacled bear, or it may be that there is waiting, still undiscovered, another kind of South American bear.

There can be no doubt that of all the bears, the Malay sun bear makes as a baby the most fascinating pet. More slender in form than the usual run of bears, with a handsome white chevron on its throat, and the most playful disposition imaginable, it is a favorite with residents and travelers in the East Indies, and is one of the commonest bears to be brought into the United States. As soon as the babies develop a little strength, they get more and more mischievous, so that they are always turned over to some one else, and often to zoos. A dealer visiting us once had one on his hands, and asked me if I knew of any small zoo to which he could give the animal. He had got it from Singapore, and on the way home it had killed in play animals of ten times its market value. He was unable to sell it because all the zoos had specimens which had been given to them by disgusted owners.

Peggy, who represents this species in our Park, is an incessant mischief maker. Her cage is floored with sheet metal which must be replaced at least once a year. A shelf on which she sleeps is two inches thick, of hard wood, and we have had to reinforce this, top and bottom, with metal, to keep her from chewing through once a month. She never seems to take a rest or lose an opportunity to destroy something in the cage. At present we have limited her to a stump in the center of the cage, and this has to be renewed with great regularity.

Mr. Baker has prepared the following account of the blue bear:

Probably the most eagerly sought of all American bears is the glacier or "blue" bear (*Euarctos emmonsii*), which is found only within a very limited area in Alaska. A few skins brought out from that region by hunters supplied the data on which naturalists established the scientific name. The popular name "blue" bear was given to the animal by the hunters because of its color. So far as we know the first and only one of these bears to be taken alive was caught by an Indian, Stick Lee Hansen, in May, 1916, near the head of Yakutat Bay. Through E. M. Axelson of Yakutat, word of this capture and the offer of the animal for sale reached the National Zoological Park, one of whose friends presented the bear to the Park.

Arrangements were made with Mr. Axelson for boxing and shipping the bear and the express companies were asked to give it special care on transshipment at Seattle.

The bear reached Washington, July 25, 1917, in perfect condition. It was very tame and at once settled down contentedly here. It has now been in the Park for twelve years, but shows no decrease in vigor nor other sign of old age.

Mr. Baker and Mr. Blackburne have collaborated to tell the story of the biggest bear:

From the earliest historic days of Alaska, rumors came down of bears of fabulous size. Finally, skins and skulls came into the hands of naturalists, the measurements of which showed these bears to be actually bigger than any other carnivorous land animal.

An animal of such preeminence, that had been seen by so very few people, was of course greatly desired for the collection of the new National Zoo, but efforts made to secure one resulted for some time only in disappointment. At last the Alaska Commercial Company reported that a cub had been captured on the Peninsula near Kadiak Island. The youngster was taken May 24, 1921, when probably about four months old. His mother had to be killed in order to effect the capture. Her skin measured eleven feet eight inches from tip to tip, so the youngster evidently came from large stock. He was kept in Alaska until near the end of the year, and then brought on to Washington, arriving here January 9, 1902.

As a cub he was a very promising animal, and he more than justified expectations. He weighed eighteen pounds at the time of capture, 180 eleven months later, and when put on the scales at the age of ten years he tipped the beam at 1,160 pounds, a greater weight than that reached by any other bear ever in the collection. He was fifty-one inches high at the shoulder, and when standing nearly erect on his hind feet he took an apple in his mouth from the end of a stick nine feet three inches from the ground. His size and weight soon began to attract attention, and visitors frequently exclaimed, "Isn't he a buster?" As he

PLATE 32

Buster, the Alaska Peninsula bear who reached a record weight of
1,160 pounds

PLATE 33

Alaska Peninsula bear, Billy

had not yet been christened, this name was officially confirmed, and thereafter he was known as "Buster." He was of pleasant disposition, playful, and always responded promptly to efforts made to amuse him.

At one time Buster became so helpless from corns on both forefeet that he could not walk. Doctor Turner and a veterinarian from the Bureau of Animal Industry were called into consultation. The bear was lying on a deep bed of straw well soaked with disinfectant. Cotton soaked with two pounds of ether and placed in a funnel was held to his nose. We waited for him to doze off under the anaesthetic, but at the end of an hour he was still conscious. I decided to rope him and tie him up for the operation. A stout rope was placed around his shoulders, with one foreleg through the loop. He was then drawn to the bars and a rope looped around each foot. This feat proved a most difficult task, owing to Buster's size and his struggles to keep free of the ropes, but once accomplished, the operation could be performed with safety. Two large corns on each forefoot practically covered the soles. They were removed, the wounds well dressed, and the ropes taken off, but his feet were in such bad condition that recovery of their use seemed impossible. When the operation was over the ether became effective, and Buster slept for nearly two days. While recovering he was kept closely confined on a thick bed of straw, and in a few weeks his feet had completely healed. He never had corns again.

One day when he was trying to make love to the female polar next door through the small apertures in the partition an accident befell him. She took off the tip of his tongue. On September 30, 1914, he attempted to take part in a bear fight which was going on in an adjoining cage, and, due to the excitement, died instantly of rupture of the aorta, without having shown the slightest indication that he was failing in any degree, or had a weakness of any kind.

In the proportions of this bear, and in the lines of his head and shoulders, there was a symmetry and statuesque quality that no other bear here of any species ever equaled.

CHAPTER VII

THE WILD DOGS

WOLVES, foxes, coyotes, jackals, and other wild dogs are usually represented in the collection by a dozen species or more. They are generally distributed throughout the world. Most of them do well in captivity, fifteen years being not an unusual age for them. Our source of supply is in the main the branch of the United States Biological Survey that deals with the control of predatory animals. The Survey field men frequently find the lairs of these animals and send in cubs to our Zoo.

Mr. Blackburne's experiences with wolves in the Park surpass many adventure fiction tales in interest:

In February, 1891, when I was first placed in charge of the animals in the National Zoological Park, the few in the collection, all temporarily housed in small wooden sheds at the rear of the Smithsonian Building, included wolves and coyotes, leading a very quiet, indoor life. I prepared two outdoor cages for these groups to reduce the odor in the buildings and to give the animals some fresh air. The transfer to these cages seemed to delight the animals, and they frisked about in the sunshine.

This transfer gave occasion for the "call of the wild" to be sounded for the first time in the National Zoo, for at noon of that day the blowing of steam whistles from nearby factories served as a signal for the wolves to break forth into a howling chorus. They had found their voices and they used them to the utmost. This was an occurrence so new and startling to the community that employees of the Smithsonian Institution and the National

Museum, joined by many people of the neighborhood, rushed out to discover the cause of the commotion.

Several years later the Park was presented with a fine pair of gray wolves from the West. They bred, and the female reared four fine pups. They were all tame and became very fond of their keeper. On one occasion they managed to break through the wire-mesh inclosure of their pens, and the four pups, then nearly as large as the adults, accompanied by their parents, gained their freedom and came directly to the rear door of the lion house, where they waited for the keeper to come with their rations. When discovered they were waiting very patiently, and no one knew just how long they had been there. I realized that an attempt to catch them would be futile, and would probably result in the animals scattering over the Park. Following my instructions, the keeper picked up the bucket containing their food and walked toward the waiting animals. Their actions suggested six collie dogs as they followed the keeper back into their inclosure.

On another occasion the Park received as a gift two half-grown, pseudo-tame wolves. They were very timid and much afraid of their keepers, even though the latter worked as quietly as possible to avoid startling their charges. The animals' terror was so pitiful that I determined to show them that we intended them no harm. While the keepers were cleaning their quarters I entered the cage and sat down. At first they were so frightened that they rushed for the wire mesh which surrounded the inclosure and tried to break through. When they found that escape was impossible they settled down and looked me over carefully, though somewhat doubtfully. I talked to them steadily and deliberately, and at length they approached cautiously, and with their noses examined my hands and legs. Before I left the cage one of the wolves jumped up on me and licked my face.

Several months later this pair of wolves escaped. The

PLATE 34

The bush dog, from Brazil.   Unique in captivity

keepers started after them, but without success. This had been going on for some time when a visitor who met me in the upper part of the Park informed me of the escape and the pursuit. I hurried off in the general direction of the chase, and on reaching the flagpole I found some twenty of the Park's employees gazing longingly toward the Creek, where sat the two wolves. I cautioned the men to remain very still, while I advanced toward the animals. I talked to them as I had done when trying to become acquainted with them, and instead of running from me, they wagged their tails and showed plainly that they were glad to see me. Finally they came toward me, and as I bent down they came up to me, jumping about and licking my hand. When they were in the position I had waited for, I grabbed each wolf by the ear farthest from me, and in this way was able to keep their jaws from closing on my hands. The men rushed down the hillside and carried the wolves back to their inclosure. It was some time before I again gained their confidence.

Our collection at the present time has living in it all of the three existing species of hyenas: the striped (*Hyaena striata*), the spotted (*Crocuta crocuta*), the East African spotted (*Crocuta crocuta germinans*), and the seldom-seen brown (*Hyaena brunnea*). The last comes from South West Africa, where it is said to be not uncommon, but for some reason is seldom caught and brought into captivity. The public is surprised to find in it a hyena which is really attractive. The beautiful light-colored ruff around the neck and the tremendous mane extending along the back, which can be elevated nearly a foot high, and which has given it the name of the "maned" hyena, are the most characteristic features of this animal. Our two specimens are quite gentle.

When we got our pair we naturally were excited and enthusiastic, because of their rarity in captivity, and we spent a great deal of time around the cage taking snapshots and getting acquainted with them. It happens that in the cage adjoining lives Chac, our giant Chacma baboon, who has been there, winter and summer, without artificial heat, since 1911. Chac is a union monkey. At 4:30 his day's work is over, and he goes into his house and closes the door. He was always very friendly with me and would come out at my approach and smack his lips, which is Chacma for polite conversation. Only once had he misbehaved, and that was when Mr. Baker was inspecting the cage next door, then in process of construction. He stooped over when within reach of Chac, and then had to telephone for his wife to bring his other pair of trousers to the Park. After many long visits with the brown hyenas I passed Chac's cage and spoke to him. Instead of responding in a friendly way as usual, he dashed across and made a jump that would have landed him at my throat had there not been a heavy screen mesh in the way. It was evident that he had become insanely jealous at the attention bestowed upon the animals in the adjoining cage. He has never regained completely his former friendliness.

One of our spotted hyenas that lived in the Zoo for years was especially gentle and very fond of having his neck rubbed, especially by our sergeant of police. This animal had a curious fear of the outdoors, and during his many years of captivity would never go through an open door that led to his outside yard. This door would be kept open more than half the year, day and night, and many attempts were made to get him to come out. Food was kept from him until he was very hungry and then placed in the outside yard, but some awful fear of the open door made him prefer starvation to passing through it. Once he was roped and dragged outside, and when released, gave a sudden bound into the house. One wonders if some experience had given him this fear of open spaces.

I believe the hyena is in general a much maligned

PLATE 35

Plains wolf from North Dakota

PLATE 36

Eskimo dog puppies, descendants of the Peary North Pole dogs

animal. He is of course very timid, but there are few wild animals that are not. Perhaps his large size and apparently powerful build lead one to expect more belligerence from him, but at the same time the lion and the leopard will run from man, and they certainly do not know him as well as does the hyena, who lives in the vicinity of villages and during the night prowls around the streets doing very efficient sanitary work for the natives. At Dodoma we could see the hyenas any night in the streets, and they annoyed us considerably by prowling around our quarters, trying to get in where we had many small animals confined. Heavy thorn scrub piled outside made a perfectly good hyena-proof fence, however, and they did no damage to us. We trapped some in the same sort of box that we used for the leopards, and they were much easier to catch than the leopards. Once we rigged an antelope crate as a trap just outside the house, hoping to catch some jackals; instead a large hyena was caught in it and during the night he ate his way out through an inch of pine board and escaped.

In Africa the call of the hyena that one hears so often is a loud *wa-hoo* with the accent on the *hoo*, a mournful note. It gives the laughing call when in the presence of food. The first time I ever heard this we were camping among the ruins of Petra in South Palestine, on a little flat into which opened a couple of high-walled, narrow canyons. With temples cut in solid rock, and with pillars eroded into fantastic shapes by a thousand years of blowing sand, with strange legend and stranger history, it is an indescribably weird and wonderful place. The first evening my companion, Phillips, had gone out for a stroll, and I was sitting alone in the tent writing notes, when suddenly the flap was drawn aside, and a ragged Arab entered. A Mohammedan policeman was guarding the door, so I assumed the man had had permission to enter, and greeted him in my best Arabic. His reply was a gurgle. A second look at him showed that he was even more ragged than the average, his hair more fuzzy, and there was an unpleasant amount of white in his eyes. He advanced toward me, gurgling. When he was within a few feet of my chair I placed my hand on a revolver lying on the table, whereupon he fell to his knees, bumped his head in the dirt several times, then beat his hands on his breast and extended both arms to me in supplication. I shouted for the interpreter, Solomon Demetrius. He stepped in, and without a word bundled my visitor out of the tent, and then explained that this was simply the local insane man. Especially blessed is one who has had his soul taken away from him by Allah, for He keeps it for him in Paradise, and when its owner eventually dies and arrives there, he is given it back, pure and untainted. So no good Mohammedan will touch a madman, and my guard at the door had simply stepped aside and let him in. He wanted a piece of bread. The whole affair left me in an unpleasant frame of mind, and that night I heard my first hyena yowl. We had set traps during the early evening and this hyena, coming across one with some animal caught in it, took a moment to tell the world about it. A thousand insane giants rolled into one might have laughed as he did, the sound reverberating through the canyon. Feeling my back hair slowly rise, I again called to Solomon for an explanation, and he told me that it was nothing but a hyena.

We came to hate this hyena personally very much during the week that we camped and trapped at Petra, for he got a good percentage of our larger mammals, and incidentally several traps which he carried off, bait or specimen and all.

We could always make our spotted hyena in the Park laugh by holding his meat an extra moment or two on the outside of the bars, when he would laugh and gurgle and froth at the mouth enough to convince any visitor who did not believe in the laughing hyena.

Mr. Blackburne tells a story of old circus days in which

FIG. 8.   Sketches from an artist's note book.   By Benson B. Moore

he gave a "Hip, hip, hoorah!" act. Twelve horses drew a large cage containing twelve hyenas, six striped and six spotted, with Mr. Blackburne, who had them jump through hoops as the wagon went round the hippodrome. One day a sick horse was replaced by one unaccustomed to the job, and he, frightened by the band, ran away, forcing the team in a mad race three times around the hippodrome, with Mr. Blackburne hanging onto the top of the cage trying to keep his legs out of the way of twelve very much excited and bumped-about hyenas. Finally the team broke through into the menagerie tent and was stopped by knocking over a platform containing the Congo Cannibals, terminating one of the most thrilling animal acts ever put on by the Barnum and Bailey Circus.

The hyena usually lives many years, and in moderately warm climates does not require artificial heat. Curiously, four hyenas in the National Zoological Park have died from goiter.

Closely related to the hyena, is the aard-wolf (*Proteles cristatus*), which in structure is really a delicately formed hyena, but strikingly different in certain characters. It has longer ears and a more pointed muzzle and, like the brown hyena, a mane which can be erected at will. It differs, also, from the hyena in having five toes on the front feet, whereas the hyena has only four, but especially in the rudimentary nature of its teeth. The teeth of the hyena are very strong and with remarkably developed sharp cutting blades, as well as others fitted for crushing. No other carnivorous animal has such powerful teeth or jaws as the hyena. In the aard-wolf, on the other hand, the teeth are almost rudimentary, especially those in the cheek series, which are not continuous but separated from each other.

Its food in the wild state consists chiefly of termites, though it is said also to eat carrion. It is really a small hyena turned ant-eater and modified for its different habits. Our specimen, which has lived now for over six years, establishing a record for longevity in captivity, has subsisted on boiled meat, finely ground, with an occasional egg, raw or cooked, added to it.

Like the hyena, the aard-wolf is nocturnal, but the former becomes accustomed to the cage and moves about during the day, whereas our aard-wolf generally sleeps until toward five in the evening. In nature it is a burrowing animal.

We ran across them on Lake Meru on several occasions, and twice succeeded in surrounding one by a line of boys thrown around the edge of the lake, but in each case he glided through the line.

CHAPTER VIII

INHABITANTS OF TANK AND POOL

OTTERS stand in the front ranks of animals suitable for exhibition; playful, ingenious, intelligent, constantly on the move and graceful in action, they also develop quaint individual habits. One example in the National Zoological Park liked to balance a rock on his nose while he swam. When he tired of the amusement he put the rock away in a certain niche and always went back for the same rock the next time.

If captured young the otter can be domesticated, and has been made a pet in many of the countries where it is found. In the National Zoo we have had success with both the northern and the southern forms. A Florida otter was born January 5, 1915, and died November 27, 1928. The first otter to come to the collection, from the Adirondacks, also lived a little more than thirteen years. Out of the twenty-six specimens that have been exhibited in the National Zoological Park, four were born here.

The most striking characteristic of this animal is that it seems to enjoy itself thoroughly, whatever the circumstances of its confinement. It invents means to play, and few other animals seem to get such unadulterated zestful pleasure. We keep our family in a large pen with a stream of water running through it. There is a little wooden house for shelter, and there are some nice banks to slide down from the house to the water. In the little pool is a ledge of rock, half in, half out of the water, about which one of the otters will repeat the same movement hour after hour. He jumps from the top of this rock into the water, swims rapidly to the opposite side, emerges, turns a back somersault off a stone, then swims toward the first rock, gliding under it and then up and over as if pulled by a string. One of the greatest sights the Zoo has ever had to offer followed a heavy fall of snow. Then the otters had slides that really were slides, and they would come down head first, sometimes upside down, disporting like children. When tired of this they would get their head started in a snow drift and wriggle through. They kept up this sport for hours with as much zest as healthy children, and varied it by playing hide and seek with each other around ice cakes, or engaging in mimic wrestling matches.

In the "good old days" of zoos, when we were getting our first specimens, a good healthy otter cost anywhere from $12.50 to $28. We have had no offers of any otters at all in the last four years. This would indicate that they are becoming rare, because of the relentless traffic in their fur. But they are such clever little fellows that we may believe they will maintain themselves as the European otter has done against odds, especially when away from settled communities. The European species, slightly smaller than the American, frequently has been trained as a domestic pet and is sometimes employed to catch fish for its master.

During the Middle Ages the Church permitted otter to be eaten on fast days, under the impression that it was "half fish." In captivity I believe it is almost essential for the otter to have very fresh water. They always seem more thriving when they are living in water that is actually running. They must be fed fresh fish, of which they habitually waste a great deal, so that they are expensive animals to keep. Tame ones develop a taste for bread, and ours are so fond of peanuts that several have died through eating too many, tossed into the pool by visitors. Sányál of Calcutta tells of a common otter which

PLATE 37

Beaver work in the Park.   They have built themselves a ten-foot dam

PLATE 38

The rare Stellar's sea lion which came to the Zoo from a Coney Island amusement park

he had in the zoo that twice escaped, and on each occasion made for the nearest fish market.

Tropical otters do not seem to live so well in captivity in the North, possibly because they are not usually provided with large indoor pools during the cold weather. The zoo at Pará had a beautiful specimen of the Brazilian otter in a large outdoor pool, which played incessantly with a wooden ball in the water. When I revisited the zoo after ten years' absence, I experienced a twinge of sorrow at seeing the cage now rusty, the door open, the wooden ball still lying in one corner. The otter had died years before. We have never had any of these tropical forms at the National Zoo, but I have seen the large South American form very abundant on the Rio Negro in Bolivia. Nobody lives there, not even hunting Indians, and the otters were remarkably tame, swimming around under our canoe, and eyeing us with evident interest.

Mr. Baker has written the account of the establishment of our beaver colony, years ago:

At the time that the National Zoological Park came into existence, live fur-bearing animals were of little interest: the only demand was for their pelts. So when we wanted beavers with which to establish a colony in the Park, no regular channels of supply existed. In time we did secure several from widely different sources but most of these were crippled or otherwise in poor condition when received. Finally we turned to the Yellowstone National Park, and through the cooperation of Captain George S. Anderson, U. S. A., then in charge, made arrangements to procure a supply there. The animals were fairly common in localities suited to their mode of life, but to get possession of them alive and uninjured was not an easy matter. It required knowledge of beaver habits and more than the ordinary trapper's skill and ingenuity. Fortunately, Captain Anderson found ready at his hand the man needed in the person of Elwood ("Billy") Hofer, widely known to sportsmen and naturalists as a hunter and guide, and he was, with some difficulty, persuaded to undertake the capture of the beavers.

By setting nets in their runways and then driving the beavers out of their houses, Hofer finally succeeded in collecting a total of ten American beavers, which were thought to be a sufficient number for the purpose. They ranged from adult and apparently rather old animals down to young of that season.

Shipping crates, carefully designed, were prepared for them, each lined with sheet-iron and furnished with a tank so that the animals could have their bath. Personally conducted by Hofer, they made the long journey from the Yellowstone Park to Washington, all arriving safely. Thus began the beaver colony at the National Zoological Park.

The first site chosen for the beavers was on comparatively level ground near the bank of Rock Creek. An area some fifty feet across was inclosed with a fence of heavy wire netting, below which a barrier of sheet iron extended some four feet into the ground. The newcomers seemed fairly well satisfied with this and took possession to such an extent that soon they were out of sight most of the time. A small artificial pool occupied part of the inclosure but the location was such that the beavers had no chance to build a dam. Not long after the beavers had been established on this site, the development of streets in the immediate vicinity created a demand for a new driveway along the side of Rock Creek. The beavers were squarely in the line of this new improvement and nothing remained to do but remove them to some other home.

The new place selected was in the lower part of what has sometimes been picturesquely termed the "Missouri Valley." Here the grass-covered banks sloped rather steeply to form a V-shaped valley, in the center of which ran a little stream of clear water, fed by springs, which had cut for itself a narrow trench at the very bottom of the valley. We built an inclosure, about a hundred feet wide and nearly two hundred feet long, up and down the valley.

The first thing we had to do in removing the beavers was to catch them, and that proved to be no small task. We found that they had fairly honeycombed the ground of their inclosure with burrows. Not until practically every square foot had been dug over with pick and shovel was the last beaver located and secured.

Their new home seemed to meet with immediate approval and evidently was recognized as better suited to their needs than the first site, for they set to at once to build a dam across the bottom of the valley near the lower end of the inclosure. With this completed to a point where it gave them a good depth of water, they started a second dam several rods above, and the two seemed to satisfy them for some time. At once, on taking possession of the new inclosure, they had proceeded to cut down the few trees that had not been protected, including several small pines. They next investigated a sycamore tree some fourteen inches in diameter which had been protected with a guard of heavy wire netting secured to stakes at the bottom. They succeeded at night in loosening this so that it could be shoved up, and, by the time we noticed their operations, they had girdled the tree and cut considerably into the wood. Since it was then too late to save the tree, we turned it over to the beavers, who cut it down at once. In order to provide suitable food, small saplings and trimmings from larger trees were thrown into the inclosure by the wagon-load. After eating off the bark, the beavers cut up the sticks into suitable lengths for use in the dams. Not very long after the building of the second dam the beavers undertook an even more ambitious enterprise in the shape of a dam crossing the full width of the inclosure and raising the water level fully ten feet at the lowest point in the valley. So extensive was this last dam that the fence had to be moved up the hill on the rear side of the inclosure, and along the front the water occasionally rose to a point where it ran out through the fence on to the public walk. This great dam, which at first bristled with white, peeled sticks, has been overgrown with grass and marsh vegetation so that it now appears only as a rounded, steeply sloping green bank.

Various accidents, some tragic, befell the members of the beaver colony. One individual, more agile or more restless than the others, succeeded in climbing the fence and took up his life in Rock Creek. He was seen, at first, farther up the creek, and then at several points lower down, but always evaded capture. Finally he made his way into the Potomac River and, coming out several miles below on the bank of Four-Mile Run, he encountered a man making hay, who greeted him with a pitchfork and ended his life.

Another beaver succeeded in making a hole in the fence through which he went out at night, cut small saplings on the adjacent hillside, and dragged them back through the opening. Apparently he failed one night to find the opening on his return, and, following down the rear side of the fence, he came at last to the Creek. He eventually found the Chesapeake and Ohio Canal, which follows the Potomac, and when several miles distant from the Park was found on the towpath by a farmer, who killed him with a club.

Young have been born several times, some of which lived to replace the older animals, and several were sent in exchange to other zoological parks.

The beaver is unusual among animals in zoos, in that it can lead in an inclosure a perfectly natural life. To feel perfectly natural a lion would have to have a zebra a day to kill, and the bush pig an acre of African planted potatoes to hoe up, but a beaver can lead his real beaver life with running water, mud, and sticks. Ours loaf in spring and summer, but when winter approaches the dam

PLATE 39

Fur seals from Pribilof Islands, rare in collections

is prepared, new sticks are added, more mud gathered from the bottom of the pond and put in place.

At one time a mother and father built a supplemental dam below the large one, where their three little ones played, and dug tunnels in every direction. Our specimens have their lodge in the bank which they have covered with a pile of saplings. After four in the evening one may see them swimming about for a time, busily working. They are fed grain and vegetables, and sometimes bread. During the summer the night watchman carries some supplementary food which he throws into the inclosure.

To the visitor who sees the sea lion in action before mealtime and feeding voraciously when the fish is served, it would seem scarcely possible that a large percentage of seals and sea lions captured refuse to eat at all. The dealers who handle these animals catch them in large nets and try them out before bringing them into the market. Those which feed are kept for sale to zoos and circuses, and those which refuse to feed are turned out. When they do eat, seals eat ravenously. Ten pounds of fish a day are ordinary rations for a medium-sized sea lion. He is one of the most expensive animals to feed kept in average zoo collections. The walrus, of course, with his appetite for clams, costs a great deal more to maintain, but then he rarely appears in zoos. One sea lion is almost as expensive to keep as an elephant. The fish must be absolutely fresh, for hardy as the animal is, it cannot stand tainted fish, and the entire herd in the pool can be wiped out with one bit of carelessness.

One young showman of my acquaintance has solved the problem of keeping seals by selling fish to visitors. Above the sea lion pool he has placed a large sign:

YOU THROW 'EM—WE CATCH 'EM.

He not only gets his menagerie fed, but derives some profit from the fish.

WILD ANIMALS

The common California sea lion came to us for exhibition in the early years of the Park. The first specimen in the collection, received in October, 1894, was killed by the shock of a dynamite explosion set off in connection with the building of a city sewer through the Park. We replaced it at once, and have never lacked for a specimen since, having shown twenty-eight in all during the last thirty years.

The great northern or Stellar's sea lion, however, is rarely offered, and is reputed to be very difficult to keep in captivity. The Park naturally would have been glad to exhibit such a notable animal but, in view of the experience of other zoos that had tried to keep them, did not feel justified in paying the price that was asked for the occasional one offered. However, a very unusual offer came in October, 1900, when Captain Paul Boyton, the famous swimmer, who had an amusement park called "The Chutes" at Coney Island, wrote that among his herd of common California sea lions there was one of apparently a different species, heavier built and with a deeper voice. As it was the end of the season, wrote the Captain, he was about to close out the entire bunch, and would the Park be interested? The Park was interested, and its representative at once took the night train for New York. At nine the next morning, when "The Chutes" opened, he was at the gate. Captain Boyton took him to the lake, and when the sea lions swam up at call, there was no question but that one was a Stellar's. It was larger and more "stocky" than the others and its voice was entirely different. The Park's representative settled the matter with Captain Boyton on the spot, taking the animal at his figure of $150. It was thoroughly tame, ate well, and had long been accustomed to captivity. Captain Boyton said that it had been captured on the Pribilof Islands, but the U. S. Fish Commission, which had charge of those islands, discredited this statement, and the Park was unable to verify it. The animal lived in the National Zoological Park from October, 1900, to January, 1918, or more than seventeen years, and finally died of a general decline, due apparently to old age. Afterwards other specimens were obtained, but they could not be induced to eat, so soon died.

The true seals, of which we have had the leopard seal (*Phoca richardii*) and the San Geronimo harbor seal (*Phoca richardii geronimensis*) from the Pacific coast, as well as the common harbor seal (*Phoca vitulina*), do very well in captivity, provided they are furnished with well-constructed outdoor tanks in which the water does not become polluted. These seals have progressed so far on the road to aquatic life that they have almost lost the ability to use their limbs on shore. The rear legs or flippers seem to be quite useless out of the water and the animal must wriggle forward awkwardly on its belly, almost as a fish would do. Sometimes when excited it takes spasmodic hops on its forelegs. A leopard seal getting into the water in a hurry will often roll to the edge.

The little harbor seal has usually been represented in the collection. Like its relatives, it often refuses to eat in captivity. Four specimens have lived here five years, two of them six years, and one twelve.

One of the rarest members of this family is the sea elephant (*Mirounga angustirostris*), or more properly speaking, the elephant seal, so called because of its extensible nose. Mr. Baker has contributed an account of our specimens, and also of our West Indian seals:

The largest of the seal tribe, and living on unfrequented shores, the elephant seal could be secured for a zoological collection only by an expedition specially equipped for its capture and transportation. Such an expedition was sent out by the Bureau of Fisheries in 1911, and it secured on Guadalupe Island, off the coast of Lower California, a pair of fine young elephant seals, which reached the Park October 21.

The long journey proved hard on them, and both showed evidence of colds when received, so they were a little slow about taking interest in things. Food constituted a puzzling problem, as they were believed to live on boneless fare. We tried them with soft-scaled fish and with flakes of cod from which the bones had been removed. They took the cod between their jaws, shook it, tossed it, and played with it generally, finally swallowing an occasional piece. In time, however, they settled down to the boneless cod diet and each ate from six to twelve pounds a day.

They seemed quite comfortable in their water pool, and they began to exhibit there a sportive habit, either resumed from their former life or evolved under the stimulus of new conditions. A mouthful of water was taken in and then forcefully ejected, apparently with a definite aim in mind. Many unsuspecting visitors suffered a shower bath before they learned of this accomplishment of the seals.

There was, of course, a very considerable risk in bringing these seals from tropical waters to the climate of Washington just at the beginning of winter. The colds which they seemed to have on arrival gradually disappeared, without leaving any noticeable effects. After a time, however, they began to have a little difficulty in breathing, with some discharge from the nose, and later a cough. Then they lost interest in food, after which, and before many days, the end came, a little more than four months from the day of their arrival.

In the spring of 1897, a representative of Saunders and Company, a big fishery firm operating a fleet of boats out of Pensacola, Florida, called at the Park when passing through Washington. During this visit he mentioned, incidentally, that some of their fishermen had recently reported seeing a few seals on certain little islands near Yucatan. He said that if the Park would care to have some, he would have them caught.

INHABITANTS OF TANK AND POOL

This report at first seemed very improbable, as the seals of the Atlantic coast would not be likely to go so far to the south. Then it was realized that the animals reported might be survivors of the West Indian seal (*Monachus tropicalis*), which was abundant there two hundred years ago, but had long been supposed extinct. So it seemed worth while to try for some of the animals, whatever they were, and the offer was gratefully accepted.

The West Indian seal was first mentioned by Dampier in 1675, in his account of *Two Voyages to Campeachey*, where he called it the "Jamaica seal." The species then existed in great numbers, but, as they were fat and yielded a valuable oil, they were rapidly killed off during succeeding years. Naturally the Park felt much interest as to what, if anything, would come from Saunders and Company, and when, a few weeks later, a telegram was received that two seals were on the way from Pensacola, curiosity rose to a peak.

The animals arrived in excellent condition and were seen at once to be the long-lost West Indian seal. The Park reported its find to other zoos, some of which commissioned Saunders and Company to bring up specimens for them, and naturalists for the first time had an opportunity to see what this seal looked like.

CHAPTER IX

ELEPHANTS GOOD AND BAD

FROM the time they arrived at Rock Creek and so launched the National Zoo as a physical fact, the elephants presented to the United States by a traveling circus made Zoo history. Mr. Blackburne recalls some of the high lights of their career herewith:

The first animals to be quartered at the newly created National Zoological Park were Dunk and Gold-dust, male Indian elephants presented to the Government on April 30, 1891, by James E. Cooper, owner of the Adam Forepaugh Circus. Secretary Langley of the Smithsonian, Dr. Frank Baker, Mr. A. B. Baker, and I visited the circus to accept the gift. Mr. Cooper found it necessary to dispose of the animals because of their vicious disposition. Dunk was an elephant fighter and frequently charged the other male elephants of the show. Separating them was a dangerous task. When we got him, Dunk weighed 6,040 pounds, and his age was estimated at twenty-five years. He was a second-class elephant (grade *dwasala*) and fairly easy to handle except during the must period. Some years before his death he became weak in the hips and joints of the hind legs. Because of this condition he was unable to lie down, and so slept standing up, leaning against the wall. Paralysis of the trunk followed, when it became difficult for him to bring food and water to his mouth. During the early hours of March 30, 1917, while sleeping in his accustomed position, he lost his balance, and fell forward to the floor, breaking his shoulder. He was of such dead weight that the bone protruded through the hide. Normally such a fall would have been prevented by his trunk, but this, of course, was paralyzed. Eight shots in the ear with a 45-caliber Winchester rifle ended his career. During his years of good physical condition he weighed 11,000 pounds, and was eight feet nine inches high at the shoulders.

Gold-dust, a third-class (grade *mirga*) elephant, was somewhat smaller than Dunk, but he weighed over 5,000 pounds. He was of mean and treacherous disposition and a man killer. We exercised Dunk and Gold-dust by chaining them together and walking them along the road. On one of these occasions Gold-dust fell down, and was unable to rise. A derrick was rigged up to bring him to his feet, but he could not remain standing. We covered him with hay, but he died during the night of November 4, 1898. An autopsy revealed catarrhal inflammation of the stomach and intestines, diseased feet, and poor teeth.

When Dunk and Gold-dust arrived at the Park there was not even a shed to shelter them. We chained them to trees for several months, until the octagon house was built. Supplying the huge pair with drinking water presented one of the most difficult tasks in their care. At that time the Park had no supply of running water, so two barrels were loaded on a horse-drawn cart, and hauled to Rock Creek, where they were filled by the tedious process of dipping the water with buckets. Hauled back to the elephants, the water had to be again hand-dipped, this time into two other barrels. This took place twice a day, and as the total was eighty gallons of water it took considerable time to satisfy the elephants' thirst. The men who went to all this trouble were always vexed at the rapidity with which the elephants emptied barrels, in comparison with the time it took to fill them.

The story of our two African elephants is likewise told by Mr. Blackburne:

The National Zoo purchased two African elephants from the Gizeh Zoological Park of Egypt for $1,500 each. Jumbo, the male, was four years old, weighed 1,700 pounds, and was five feet six inches high at the shoulder. Jumbina, the female, was two and a half years old, weighed 875 pounds, and was four feet three inches high. At the same time we bought also camels, cheetahs, gazelles, baboons, and some smaller animals. The animals were crated and entrained for Port Said, where a lighter transferred them to the S. S. *Stermfels*. The voyage through the Mediterranean proved most pleasant, but after passing through the Strait of Gibraltar we experienced a severe change; on the Atlantic the ship encountered fog, wind, rough sea, and cold. All of the animals but the elephants were sheltered in an empty coal bunker, but the latter remained on the poop deck, their crates well covered with heavy tarpaulin which kept out the wind so that even they seemed comfortable. The first two days none of the animals cared for food. They were more or less nervous and worried in their close confinement. By the third day they had become much more nearly reconciled and looked for their food. From that time on they thrived and their condition improved. However, even during the time that they would take no food, all of them wanted water. I carried water from midship to aft deck, and thirty-six buckets to the elephants on the poop deck. The captain took pity on me and had two wine barrels placed near the elephants. These he kept filled with water, which, of course, materially lightened my work.

The crate which held the male elephant had an opening about fifteen inches square in front of the animal's head. Through this Jumbo could poke out his trunk and tusks. I was a perfect stranger to him, so whenever I approached his crate to care for his wants, he would immediately "show fight." Talking and coaxing did no good, and I realized that if I appeared timid at the start, conditions would get worse. We settled our difficulties then and there, and Jumbo caused very little trouble during the rest of the voyage. We became good friends, and in a few days he would put his trunk and part of his head through the opening, and rest his trunk over my shoulder. He seemed perfectly satisfied as long as I remained with him and patted his trunk, but when I left he would trumpet and thunder as long as I was in sight.

Jumbina, the female elephant, was without doubt the quietest animal in crossing the ocean that I had ever handled. One hardly knew she was in the crate. The two crates faced each other, a few feet apart, so that the elephants could see and sympathize with one another and wonder how it would all end.

On August 5, 1913, we landed at Boston, after a voyage of twenty-one days, without loss of a single animal. The shipment reached Washington late on the evening of August 8. The following day the elephants were liberated in separate quarters, where they had ample room to exercise. At first they would not eat oats, a new food to them, but would toss the grain over their backs as they frequently do with sand or water. Finally, however, they learned that the oats were food. Both elephants continued to thrive on this fare.

On June 28, 1916, Jumbo was enjoying a bath in the tank, submerging, spouting water, and having a jolly good time. This was at three o'clock. At 3:30 the keeper informed me that Jumbo was acting rather queerly. I went to look him over. He was pacing about the inclosure, occasionally lying down. There was nothing to indicate colic, but I realized his pain must be severe. That night he died. A post mortem showed a great rupture of the abdomen and peritonitis. This probably was due to overexertion while frolicking in the tank. Had he lived I think he would have been a giant, possibly equaling his old namesake, the original Jumbo.

Jumbina, the female, continued very mild and meek

and liked attention. At Gizeh she had been kept in an inclosure with two African buffalo calves and two pigs. At feeding time she would back away, drawing her hay with her, until she had covered the food allowance of the other animals, which would stand by and watch her eat up their rations. The soil in the inclosure was fine and soft, so that her toenails were not kept worn down on her forefeet. They had grown to a length of six inches or more, and were turned upwards. After her arrival here it took some time to pare her nails and trim the soles of her feet back to normal shape. At first we held up a foot while trimming it. When I got tired I would sit on a box to rest. Jumbina came and stood near me for a few minutes, then quietly lay down beside me and remained there while we sawed, cut, and filed away her nails. She is still in the collection and has never caused the least bit of trouble. She is now eighteen years old, eight feet two inches high at the shoulder, and weighs about 7,000 pounds.

Probably the most famous pachyderm ever kept in captivity was the six-and-a-half-ton African elephant, Jumbo, which had come to the London Zoo as a baby, standing only about four feet high and weighing less than 700 pounds. At first he was rather troublesome but after a short time became perfectly manageable and grew very rapidly. Mr. Bartlett, the director of the garden, attributed this to good food and a daily bath in hot weather. In sixteen years he grew from four to eleven feet in height. Then the London Zoo sold him to an American circus, despite the fact that he had become their prime attraction. The reason lay in the fact that Jumbo was given to fits of excitement and terrified everybody who came near him except his keeper, Mathew Scott, who had extraordinary control over him. It was feared that if Scott fell ill, or was injured by the animal, the creature would be entirely unmanageable, for no other man dared go near him in his house. At night he would tear about and almost shake the house down. After becoming the property of Mr. Barnum, however, Jumbo's temperament seemed to change, probably due to the harder work and exercise which went with the life of a traveling circus. He became quite tractable and was exhibited all over Europe and America. Mr. Blackburne, who is perhaps the only living eyewitness of his fatal accident, tells the story of his death:

Jumbo, an African male elephant, the largest living mountain of flesh to travel the United States since the disappearance of the mammoth and mastodon, arrived in New York in March, 1882. His height was ten feet ten inches at the shoulder, and he weighed approximately 16,500 pounds. He was shipped in a heavily built crate that weighed probably nearly as much as he did. Low wheels of heavy iron were fastened to a truck under the crate and twenty-two horses hauled it from the docks to the old Madison Square Garden, where he was on exhibition for one month. Then, with twenty-four other elephants, he made the trip to Brooklyn, crossing over the Brooklyn bridge. The following week he was loaded in an especially constructed car built for his accommodation at Jersey City. Because of his refusal to go into the car, chains were fastened around each foreleg and drawn through heavy rings that had been made fast to the floor of the car. In this way his front legs were drawn into the car, then two of the largest elephants were placed behind him with their heads to his rump and given an order to push. Jumbo did not like this and resisted by surging back as hard as possible. Finally he was conquered and safely chained. He kept the car rocking for hours and was greatly frightened when the train was moving.

Mathew Scott, the keeper who had charge of him at London, came with him to the United States. Scott had a berth in a small compartment in the car in front of

Jumbo's head. A small door gave entry to Jumbo's quarters and the elephant would not allow it to be closed. Scott found it almost impossible to get any sleep as Jumbo annoyed him constantly by poking his trunk through the open door, to pull off the blanket or sheet, or the pillow from under his head. It was laughable to hear Scott scolding Jumbo. "Give me the sheet," or "the blanket," or "me shoes, you blighter."

The night of September 15, 1885, while the Barnum and Bailey Circus was showing at St. Thomas, Canada, Jumbo met his death. He was struck by the engine of a freight train that came thundering along at the time the elephants were being loaded in their cars. The engine hit him on the rump as he was running along the track, knocked him down, and drove his head under the trucks of a freight car. He died within five minutes after the crash. Ward, the taxidermist of Rochester, New York, undertook the mounting of the hide and setting up of the skeleton. These were placed on large trucks and exhibited about the country for two years, then carried over to London where they proved a great attraction. The mounted hide was then given to Tufts Museum, Boston, Massachusetts, and the skeleton placed in the American Museum of Natural History, New York. Mathew Scott, who had become mentally unbalanced, fell into the habit of visiting the mounted skin of his old charge in the Tufts Museum. He would dust the skin and talk to it. "Jumbo," he would say, "I'll bet the candy concession people miss you. Many and many a dollar you have put in their pockets."

The Grand Trunk Railroad Company, which was responsible for the elephant's death, agreed to transport the circus trains (which were in three sections) from town to town through Canada at a cost of one dollar per train. I never learned the total amount allowed to compensate for the death of the elephant.

Jumbo was about twenty-five years old when he died.

PLATE 40

Dunk, the Zoo's first elephant. An Indian species presented by the Adam Forepaugh Shows

PLATE 41

Jumbina, from the White Nile, a female elephant brought from Egypt by Mr. Blackburne

He was six years old when received at the London Zoological Gardens.

I had an elephant myself once, but I never saw it. One evening at the club in Dar-es-Salaam Swinnerton told me that the game warden at Mikindani had captured a baby elephant, which he wanted to give to me. Mikindani is three days by sea, in good weather, to the south; but the steamer in which we planned to start home was expected shortly, and our animals were being shipped in from their various depots. With so many things to do I could not possibly go after the elephant myself, so we cabled to a boat at sea asking it to stop and take the animal aboard, but the steamer had already passed Mikindani. There were no Government boats available in the harbor. We cabled the Sultan of Zanzibar, asking to borrow or charter his steamer, which earlier sultans would have gladly acceded to, but were informed that it was out of commission.

Then the owner of the local garage offered to go and get the elephant for a hundred pounds. The deal was closed, and he left immediately in a one-ton truck. Swinnerton telegraphed various government officials to aid our emissary all they could on his trip down and back. He also telegraphed the game warden to hold the elephant until our friend got there. That afternoon a deluge of telegrams came in from various government officials, all of them bearing warnings against going to the south; a bridge had burned out, another had washed away, the roads were termed generally impassable. Accordingly we wired the driver that he had better return. In reply, he telegraphed us that he had crossed the uncrossable Rufiji, and was headed south. The next day he was still headed south. Then came a telegram from the warden. The baby elephant had died. We sailed before our automobile friend returned. Perhaps he never returned. I shall always think of him as going over bridges where there were none, and driving through quicksands, headed south.

Many times on *safari* we have heard the curious stomach-rumbling sound of elephants, and each time our white guides, ivory hunters all when they were not with us on live animal work, would start and glance longingly in the direction of the sound. Our first evening in camp on the shores of Lake Meru, we were interrupted at tea by a boy who came running, whispering, *"Tembo,"* and pointing. Alongside camp ran a stream bordered by a row of trees which screened from sight the other side. We waded the stream, and there, in an open flat not more than a hundred yards from our tent, stood a moderate-sized bull elephant. He hadn't located the tent, but evidently sensed something was wrong. He was fanning his ears, moving his trunk about, and walking slowly away. Lyman, who had a license to shoot elephants, and Guy, his white hunter, walked rapidly, following him, and I behind, taking snapshots and forgetting to turn the film roll. Lyman and Guy bobbed their heads at each other, and Guy raised his fearsome 4.50 and shot. He took a brain shot right behind an ear, and I saw the bullet strike—at least the dust splashed. The elephant, instead of falling to his knees, trumpeted, and ran into the bush where he was joined by a half dozen cows. We heard them tearing through the forest, the bull evidently with a sore head, trumpeting from time to time. We could not understand it until one of the natives ran to where the elephant had stood, and picked up from the ground a smooth rifle ball. Elephant shells are expensive, and Guy had had these longer than one should keep them. It was simply a dud shell with enough explosive power to give the elephant a stinging blow, and no more.

Kechil, the Sumatran elephant, a much smaller species, is the bad boy of the National Zoological Park, a mischievous, tricky animal who will, as he grows larger,

become an "administrative problem." He can throw
with good aim rocks which have been tossed into his
inclosure, and has several times hit visitors on the head.
He was bought, with his mate, Hitam, by means of a
public subscription raised some years ago. For several
years the two of them lived together, disporting like two
children in their water tank in the yard. Hitam finally
had to be shot because of sarcoma of the stomach, and
Kechil, who missed her, was meaner from then on.

When the circus came with the white elephant, the
captor and owner of that animal, an Indian authority on
elephants, spent the day with us at the Park, and his
first remarks on seeing Kechil were, "A high-caste elephant—probably mean in temper." One of the marks
of a high-caste elephant is a distinct double chin, and
Kechil has it.

It should be pointed out here that the people of India
divide elephants into three distinct classes: the *koomeriah*
or thoroughbred, the *dwasala* or half-bred, and the *mirga*
or third-rate creature. Sányál quotes from the notes on
elephants by Captain H. Wilberforce Clarke, R. E., the
following "points" for these three types:

The parts of a koomeriah are—
Barrel deep and of great girth; legs short (especially the hind ones)
and colossal; the front pair convex on the front side, from the development of muscle; back straight and flat, but sloping from shoulder to
tail, as a standing elephant must be high in front; head and chest
massive; neck thick and short; trunk broad at the base and heavy
throughout; hump between the eyes prominent; cheeks full; eyes full,
bright, and kindly; hind quarters square and plump; the skin rumpled,
inclining to fold at the root of the tail, and soft; tail long and well
feathered.
If the face, base of trunk, and ears be blotched with cream-coloured
markings, the animal's value is enhanced.
The dwasala class comprises all those below this standard, not
descending so low as the third class.
The parts of a mirga are—
Legginess, lankiness, and weediness; arched sharp-ridged back,
difficult to load and liable to galling; trunk thin, flabby, and pendulous;

neck long and lean; falling off behind; hide thin; head small; eye piggish and restless; and altogether unthrifty, which no feeding improves.

On my first day as an official of the Zoo, I tried obligingly to pose with animals for various camera men. I posed too near Hitam, and the camera man, had he been quick enough, could have got a splendid picture of me in the air jumping to get out of the way of a blow from her trunk. I thought ostriches were safer, and sidled alongside of a male Nubian, who showed such an interest in my eyeglasses, of which I believe ostriches are particularly fond, that I could not obey the camera man's orders to "Look at me instead of at that bird."

The age of elephants is often overestimated. This animal grows old at about fifty years, but there is one now living in the Cincinnati Zoo which is known to have lived for eighty-five years in the United States.

Besides their tendency to "go bad" elephants suffer from nervousness and, occasionally, from unreasoning panic. A large and very tame female Indian elephant at the London Zoo actually died of fright caused by a thunderstorm in the summer of 1855. She was out at exercise when a violent peal of thunder caused her to break away from her keeper. When caught she was in a pitiable state of terror, shaking and trembling with violent, spasmodic twitchings of her whole body. When led back to her stable she continued to show unmistakable symptoms of shock and collapse. She lay down and after a few days, despite all that could be done for her, she died.

Largest of all land mammals, and among the most intelligent, elephants are always favorite attractions in zoological gardens, and have contributed almost as much as all the other animals combined to the folklore of such institutions. From the standpoint of the zoo itself, they are highly desirable because of their longevity, the ease of feeding them, and in general, ease of handling, though older ones sometimes become ill-tempered and difficult. The public comes to know them personally. Three generations of people may feed peanuts to the same individual elephant.

I remember a cartoon seen many years ago, I do not know where, of a tiny girl standing in front of a big elephant, asking, "Please, Mr. Keeper, will it hurt the elephant if I give him a currant out of my bun?" Most people do not ask, and regardless of the sign, throw peanuts continually into his cage. Ordinarily, the feeding of peanuts or fruit does not injure the elephant, but a visitor to a zoo should remember that the proportion of elephants to the public is not the same as in a circus. Our largest circus at present exhibits about forty elephants in the menagerie tent, where a maximum of 40,000 visitors see them in a day. In our Zoo we have two elephants and have had as many as 80,000 people between 9 a.m. and 4:30 p.m. Should all of them feed peanuts to the elephants, we would have fewer elephants immediately.

Practically all elephants seen by the public have been captured wild. It is one of the few beasts that can be tamed when captured as full-grown, or nearly so, and because of this the Indian species has proved well adapted for domestication. In the United States the animal is used entirely for exhibition purposes, except in circuses, where it is most useful for pushing heavy wagons. Before the opening of the gate in the menagerie tent one usually finds an elephant pushing ponderous animal dens into their proper places in the line. On wet, muddy days the cry of "Bring the bulls!" is heard, and the "bulls" (circus for elephants) will, with apparent ease, push wagons out of the mire, where horse teams have been struggling in vain at the other end.

Despite its enormous size and superior intelligence, the elephant is one of the most easily trapped of all the larger wild animals. In India as many as 120 of the beasts have been trapped at the same time, while captured herds of forty, sixty, and even eighty form the rule rather than the exception. The most ingenious and spectacular method of trapping wild elephants makes use of the keddah or stockade, employed by the Government elephant-catching stations. The progress of the hunting party resembles that of a small army moving to the front. In the van are a dozen or two koomkies—the heaviest, tallest, and most majestic domestic elephants, on whom will fall the brunt of the battle—with turbaned attendants sitting astride their necks. Behind them follow as many low-caste elephants, beasts of burden loaded with ropes, axes, shovels, and picks. Then come from one to two thousand natives on foot with horns, tom-toms and other noise-making instruments.

Miles ahead in the jungle a hundred or more skillful trackers have been at work for a week locating a wild herd. At the appointed place the head tracker and catcher meet and as the expedition nears the game all is silence. For a time even the tame elephants are left behind and only the men led to the front. They press forward through the underbrush, forming a circle about a mile in diameter. So silently and quickly do these trained men work that not until almost the last link in this chain has been forged do the elephants scent trouble. Then suddenly, as though springing out of the ground, comes the unearthly din of howls, cries, horns, and tom-toms. This sends the beasts scurrying in the opposite direction, only to run into the same racket again. It meets them in every direction they turn. The animals become more and more puzzled and frightened with each repulse. Finally they huddle helplessly in the center of the circle, and so permit a great stockade of tree trunks, ten feet or more in height, to be built around them.

Then the real capture begins. The koomkies are driven into the arena, each beast bearing on his back from six to ten native elephant catchers. These men cling to their mounts by a network of ropes which enables them to descend to work or ascend out of danger, like so many monkeys. The koomkies, who once roamed the jungle themselves, seem to take a special delight in shoving, butting, prodding, and bullying their former colleagues into submission. It is a curious fact that only very rarely will an elephant attack a man mounted on another elephant. Generally the koomkies work in pairs. Like a pair of animal policemen arresting a prisoner, two of them will sidle alongside a victim, and jostle, push, and worry him, tail first, towards a tree. When near a stout tree or stump the elephant catchers slide from their mounts to the ground, crawl under the ponderous bellies, slip cable slings around a hind foot, and take a turn around the tree. Back staggers the victim, butted farther and farther to the rear. The men take up slack until the great gray leg is tied hard and fast against the tree, where the captive is left, struggling and panting. Thus the herd is fettered, one after another.

Once captured, the elephant is by no means a difficult animal to domesticate. The community life of the creatures and their natural intelligence serve the trainer a good turn and it is not long before they are carrying logs, being trained as riding animals, or being prepared for shipment to some wild animal dealer.

Any adult elephant is apt at certain times to become suddenly murderous, and many give way to frightful paroxysms of rage. Sometimes one becomes a chronic man killer. A famous example was Mandarin, of the old Barnum and Bailey Circus, who killed three men, maimed a fourth, and finally was strangled by a steam winch aboard ship just before the ship reached New York from its trip abroad. The elephant was thirty-five years old at the time, and had been with the show for thirty years. He had grown to large size, and until the circus was touring France had never shown a trace of ugliness.

The first murderous fit came upon him during a performance, when a substitute trainer was trying to put him through his regular act. The man laid himself flat on the ground to have the elephant walk over him, exactly as he had walked over men hundreds of times before, and exactly as elephants walk over men today at every performance of every circus. Mandarin advanced as usual, but when he came to the man he lifted his ponderous foot, held it over him a moment, and then with a shrill trumpet planted it squarely on the unfortunate's chest with all the pressure of 4,000 pounds. Then, trumpeting madly, he started on a run, picked up a hyena cage and smashed it, and broke the back of a mule with one blow of his trunk. He was finally roped and thrown and filled with opiates.

Apparently he had yielded to the treatment. But within six months the madness returned, and this time he seized a stable boy who was cleaning his quarters, and dashed him against the floor, afterwards kneeling on his lifeless body. The circus authorities resolved to execute him and prepared a noose of cable rope with which he was to be strangled by other elephants, but suddenly Mandarin became again a model of propriety and was given a respite. His legs and head were chained, but he gave no trouble until he was on the ship for the return voyage to the United States, when a drunken intruder in his cage teased him. The animal threw his full weight against the man, crushing him against the wall. One of the keepers, a negro, ran up with an uplifted elephant hook only to receive a blow from the upraised trunk, which knocked him thirty feet across the deck, unconscious, and with both shoulder blades broken.

This sealed the fate of Mandarin. The execution took place thirty miles off Sandy Hook by hanging. The animal died without a whimper, holding its breath for the enormously long period of two minutes and forty seconds before he went crashing headlong, breaking an eight-by-eight timber as his great body toppled in a

PLATE 42

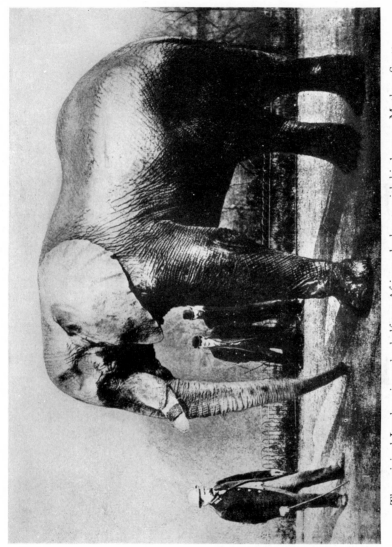

The original Jumbo, six-and-a-half-ton African elephant, with his keeper, Mathew Scott

PLATE 43

Kechil, from Sumatra, a ten-year-old youngster

heap. Then his cage, weighted with 5,000 pounds of old chains and scrap iron, was raised by a derrick and dropped into the ocean.

Ordinarily the execution of a "bad" elephant is not such an elaborate or gruesome affair. A bran mash containing a heavy dose of cyanide of potassium has been used, and Topsy, a "bad" elephant at Coney Island, was electrocuted and dropped like a log when 6,000 volts were sent through her body.

An African elephant, which went "bad" in the Liverpool Zoological Gardens in 1848, was said at the time to have been the finest pachyderm in Europe, but it killed two keepers, and the officials in the gardens were so terrified at the thought of its escape that they set up two six-pounder cannons in front of the elephant house, and then gave the elephant two ounces of prussic acid and twenty-five grains of aconite in its food. This did not have any effect, so thirty soldiers from a regiment were ordered out to shoot it. The first volley of fifteen balls did not kill it, but the second did, and the elephant sank with thirty bullets in his body and enough poison to kill fifty men.

Damon and Pythias have their representatives among the elephants, and Hans and Parkie, presented to the Stadtholder of Holland in 1784, are to be compared to that duo of good friends. These elephants were both about eighteen months old when captured in Ceylon. After their arrival in Holland they were kept for a year at Le Petit Loo, the country residence of the Stadtholder, just outside The Hague. They were great favorites of both the court and the people of the nearby city. They enjoyed complete freedom of the grounds and buildings, and were later removed to Le Grand Loo, the larger estate of the royal family, near Apeldoorn, where there was already a menagerie, so that they might have still more space. The journey involved crossing a wooden bridge over the Rhine at Arnheim, and the elephants were induced to trust themselves to this apparently flimsy structure only after they had grown hungry and hay was displayed on the other side.

From the time of their arrival in Holland one was never seen without the other. Hans would often pull down high branches with his trunk and hold them, in order that Parkie might feed more easily upon the leaves. They were cared for by a keeper named Thompson, for whom they displayed great fondness, obeying his commands and running to him when he called their names.

Ten years later Holland was overrun by the armies of the French Republic. A troop of French cavalry was billeted at Le Grand Loo. Fodder was scarce and it was proposed to kill the elephants so that more hay would be available for the horses. Thompson made a successful plea for his pets with the French commander and provisions were set aside for them, but the rest of the menagerie, one of the most interesting in Europe at the time, was being slaughtered by a representative of the French Republic who found pleasant and easy hunting about the grounds. Thompson, fearing for his elephants, went to the French General, Dejean. This official not only issued orders that the menagerie be preserved, but sent a strong detachment of soldiers to protect the animals. A short time afterwards the creatures were ordered transported to Paris—an order easier to issue than to fulfill in those days of limited transportation.

The transportation of the elephants was most difficult of all. Two large wooden cages mounted on wheels were built especially for them. Hans was induced to enter one of the mounted cages and bars were let down in front of him. For the first time he was separated from Parkie. The big pachyderm smashed through the bars as if they had been made of paper and rushed to join his companion. Four months were required to build another cage, but when the work was done, Hans, with the long memory notable in elephants, refused to be led into it. His faith in men was shattered. Accordingly, a child was employed to deceive him. The boy finally induced him to enter the cage by tempting him with potatoes, which Hans particularly liked. Parkie then was led into her cage without difficulty. They finally arrived at Paris and were taken to the Jardin des Plantes after a journey by land and water which had taken six months. During this time Hans and Parkie had not seen each other. A day or two after their arrival Parkie was let into Hans's cage and the animals rejoiced at being together again by caressing each other with their trunks.

They became the most notable exhibits at the Jardin des Plantes. They were given a special attendant. The elephants were trained to do amusing tricks, upon which they improvised, for the benefit of the visitors. At one time a special concert by sixteen artists from the Conservatory was provided for them in order that scientists from the National Museum could study their reactions to different sorts of music.

A few years after arriving in Paris Hans fell sick and died. Parkie would not be consoled. There was no other elephant available in Europe at the time, so she was given a camel as a companion, but she refused to have anything to do with him, and continued to decline. At last it became obvious that unless a comrade of her own kind could be secured for her she would die. After two years an elephant was purchased for 16,000 francs, but it was too late. Within a few days Parkie died.

The elephant is sometimes in need of the service of the zoo's surgeon. He is usually not a bad patient, and seems to realize that what is being done is for his benefit. In captivity it is necessary periodically to trim the feet and toenails of the elephant. The sole of his foot measures about twenty inches across, and consists of a tough, elastic gristle. An elephant at large in the jungle or doing his day's work in India gets sufficient exercise to wear the soles of his feet to a thickness of an inch, but in the zoo the soles get thicker and thicker until they crack and pick up all sorts of foreign substance, which may work in to the quick. From the soles of one elephant in Central Park, New York, were removed a set of dice, the bowl of an iron teaspoon, the handle of a penknife, and an iron nail. The animal had gathered up these things in six months. The tools for trimming an elephant's feet include a carpenter's drawknife, a rasp for the soles, a horseshoer's knife, and sandpaper for the toenails. Strips of the horny soles are sliced off with the drawknife until the desired thickness is reached, and the surface is smoothed with the rasp. The toenails are then cut and rubbed with sandpaper.

Elephants, particularly on their arrival from the tropics, are apt to suffer from stomach ache caused by the cold. Sometimes they are so severely affected that they roll on the ground. The application of a thick mustard poultice and a dose of gin and ginger usually prove effective. The treatment consists of wrapping a blanket around the body of the animal and plastering it with a thick layer of mustard. Over this another blanket is thrown and securely bound. Soon the heat of the mustard begins to permeate the stomach. The gin and ginger, taken internally, of course, complete the cure. Sometimes elephants who have tasted this drink during their earlier attacks have feigned illness in order to obtain it again. A pachyderm in one American circus was very fond of rolling on the ground in order to secure the coveted tonic. He was not cured of this deception until the treatment was reduced to the mustard poultice alone.

An ugly temper does not necessarily mean that an elephant is "going bad." It may be that his toenails need cutting. This was the case with Big Tom, an unusually tractable and playful animal in Central Park, New York, about twenty years ago. He was a great favorite with the children and was considered an entirely safe playmate.

Suddenly he became vicious and lame at the same time. Otherwise he appeared in perfect health. Upon close examination it was found that his toenails had grown to an abnormal size. For the trimming operation his keepers assembled a special chiropody outfit consisting of a saw, chisel, sharp knife, coarse rasp, and sandpaper and smooth polishers. With the operation completed Big Tom was released from his fetters, cured both of lameness and ill temper.

CHAPTER X

THE WATER HORSE

THE National Park's pair of hippopotamuses came from East Africa, the female in 1911, the male in 1914. It is interesting to note that the male, which came from Tanganyika Territory, was bought for $1,600 in 1914. In 1926, the first day that I was ashore in Dar-es-Salaam, I was offered a young hippopotamus for sale, f. o. b. 110 miles from the nearest railway, at a price $900 greater than we had bought the other one for in New York City. At that time we were frantically trying to dispose, by exchange, of a young hippo born in Washington, so the Hindu gentleman who was acting as middleman went away disappointed.

At Tula, Tanganyika, hippos made themselves a great nuisance; so much so that the game department had sent down a number of game boys, armed with rifles, to reduce the herds in the nearby swamps. The animals would come out at night and create havoc in the natives' plantations. Curiously, they were kept out of cultivated fields by most ridiculously small and fragile fences, and we came upon several of these built by the natives.

A small stream with several large pools in it ran near the camp. We did not want a hippopotamus, but after listening to their roaring grunts at night I was anxious to see one alive. One of the game boys went with me early in the morning, and we hid in a thicket of papyrus at the edge of the stream, directly above a pool perhaps twenty feet across. We waited for some time. A good preliminary exhibition was arranged by a crocodile five or six feet long floating on the opposite side of the pool, and a little pigeon who wanted to drink, but somehow sensed that it should not. It would run along the edge of the pool and the crocodile would disappear. A moment later two bulging eyes would come to the surface, whereupon the pigeon would run a little farther, only to encounter those eyes again.

At the right of the pool stretched a sand bar where some obstruction had caused a little ripple. I watched this from time to time, and presently noticed another ripple to the left. Thinking it curious I had not noticed this second ripple before during our hour of waiting, I studied it more closely and saw that it was caused by an object as large as a frying pan which had come to the surface. Sharper inspection revealed this object to have two eyes, two ears, and two nostrils. It belonged to an adult hippo. I leaned forward and we stared at each other while one might count three, after which the hippo disappeared. A few moments later we heard a heavy body thrashing through shallow water on its way to a deep pool beyond. This was my only sight of a live wild hippo.

Young hippos are caught sometimes in pits, but sometimes in the open by killing the mother. While attempting to capture one by the latter method Gustave Hagenbeck, of the well-known firm of wild animal collectors and dealers, met his death.

The hippopotamus is quite common in zoos; he breeds well, and lives, with proper care, for many years. From our pair have been born five young, four of which we raised and sent away in exchange. From my notes the period of gestation is between 232 and 245 days, and the weight at birth from forty-five to seventy pounds. The one we failed to raise was drowned when the mother accidentally held its head under water. Contrary to popular belief, the hippopotamus cannot live long submerged. Bartlett records fifteen minutes for a young one.

From five to eight minutes is as long as our adults stay under water. An unfortunate incident happened before this baby was born. Someone left open the door to a python cage. One of the pythons crawled out, crossed the room, and entered the pool in which the hippo was sleeping. The night watchman was astounded on entering the building to hear splashing and found an hysterical hippopotamus trying to trample the life out of a ten-foot snake. The latter was removed and put back into its cage but the hippopotamus was nervous for a long time afterward, and to this may be due her carelessness with the new-born baby.

The hippo is ugly. He can't help that, and one resents the slurs cast by visitors upon an animal unusually intelligent despite his uncouth appearance. The story of one of our baby hippos, "Buster," which appears in Volume I, page 88, of this SERIES will abundantly bear out this statement.

The hippopotamus belonged to the group of sacred animals of Egypt. It seems to have appeared first in Europe in the menagerie of Octavius in 29 B. C. Since then many individuals have been recorded, notable among which was Guy Fawkes, a cow by the way, which lived for more than forty years in the London Zoo, where she exemplified the placid life. Year in and year out she grew up peacefully in the garden, alternating between her indoor quarters and a deep tank of water outside. She grew amazingly fat, and like many fat people, had a pleasant disposition. She would open her enormous jaws at a word and allow the keeper to play with her huge, flabby tongue, though why the keeper would want to do so I can not guess.

Obash, the first hippopotamus exhibited in the London Zoological Gardens, once escaped when the keeper left the door of his cage open. Attempts to lure him back into captivity with mouthfuls of hay failed and the zoo staff was in despair when a brilliant idea came to the

PLATE 44

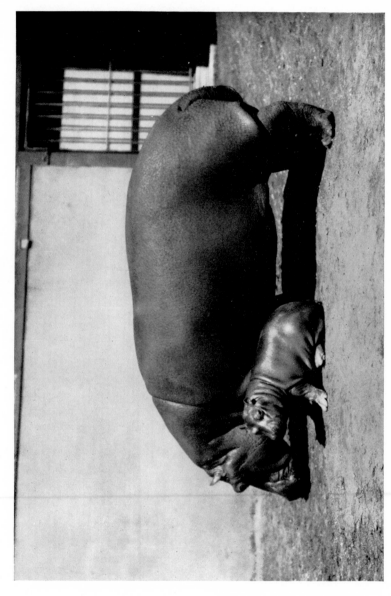

Mom, the East African hippo, and one of the five babies born in Washington. Baby weighed at birth seventy pounds

superintendent. There was one keeper, Scott by name, the sight of whom was to Obash as a red handkerchief to a bull. With his courage sustained by the promise of a handsome bonus, Scott agreed to place himself between the retreating form of the hippopotamus and the open door of its den. At the cry of "Obash!" the brute turned its head, and then catching sight of Scott, wheeled and charged. A hippo can charge with amazing speed for so bulky an animal. Scott fled, Obash lumbering after him, grunting as he came, through the open door of the cage, across the inclosure, and then Scott cleared the fence beyond. The gate was closed on Obash, and so on the incident.

The pygmy hippo, a species known only from Liberia and scarcely larger than a big hog, is a much rarer animal in captivity. It differs, in addition to its smaller size, in the structure of its skull and teeth, and is especially interesting in that it exudes a whitish, latherlike substance from the skin, rather than the carmine-colored secretions which have given the larger hippo the name of "blood-sweating behemoth." Our specimen was captured by an employee of the Firestone Plantations Company in Liberia, and presented to President Coolidge by Mr. Harvey Firestone. He arrived at the Zoo in a wooden box with a little tank built at one end of it. From the beginning he was very gentle and playful, fond of running about aimlessly like a puppy, and snapping at imaginary things in the air. He liked having his gums rubbed, and I did this day after day until I noticed a pair of tusks already over an inch long, so discontinued my friendly offices.

Hippos, in common with humans, often suffer from their teeth and occasionally require the services of a dentist for an extraction or for the more difficult and painful operation of "filing down." The animal has two very prominent teeth, properly called tusks, growing out of the lower jaw. They start in a vertical direction but later bend in a graceful, backward curve. They are most useful teeth to the wild hippopotamus for tearing up the trees and bushes upon which he lives. Under normal conditions these teeth reach about six inches in length. The rough work to which they are subjected by the animal when roaming through the forests in quest of food prevents them from growing unduly. But in the zoo cage, where the owner lives on luxurious dishes of bread, hay, and bran mash, the tusks have no hard chewing to do, so that they sometimes push out to such a length that, if not cut, they would pierce the upper jaw, prevent the animal from eating, and slowly starve him to death. Consequently they must be filed down whenever they threaten to cause trouble. In the front of the mouth, also in the lower jaw, are two other prominent teeth, projecting straight forward. These are not used for biting but for digging up the earth when the animal fancies a tasty root for dinner. These also sometimes must be cut back, although they do not cause as much inconvenience, when too long. The following account of the "filing back" operation, as performed on one of the hippos of a well-known American circus, is given by Mr. Frederick A. Talbot:

To enable the operation to be satisfactorily performed, "Babe" [the hippo] was led out into the arena and placed near a stout iron post which had been deeply and rigidly fixed into the ground. The hippopotamus looked about him quizzically as if endeavoring to divine what move was in contemplation. Chains were passed around his short legs, and fastened firmly to the ground. Babe, not quite comprehending the meaning of this secure hobbling, gave a sonorous grunt, and looked threateningly at his keeper. But at this juncture a loaf was offered to him, and his momentary anger was instantly appeased.

Babe was then enticed to open his mouth by means of further dainties held temptingly high above his nose. At first he refused point-blank, but he finally succumbed to

FIG. 9.   Sketches from an artist's note book.   By Benson B. Moore

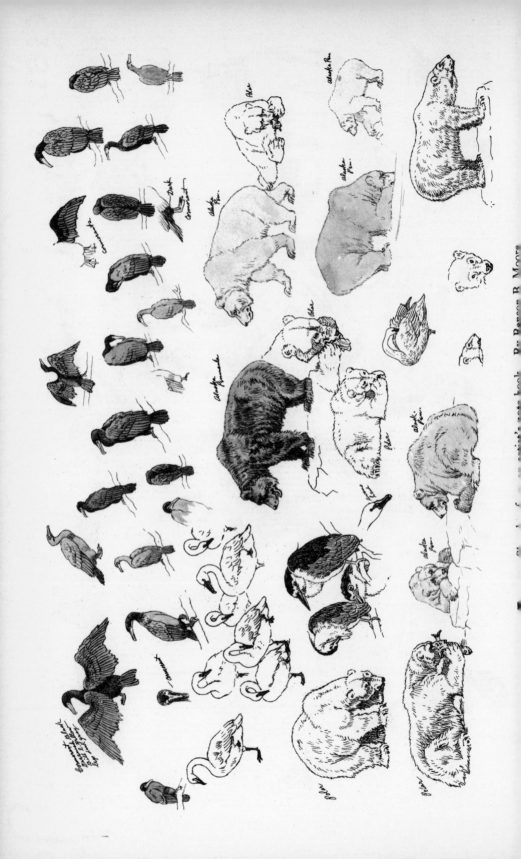

Sketches from an artist's note-book. By Benson B. Moore

the bait, and opened his capacious jaws to the extent of two feet. Immediately, two assistants standing in position dexterously threw two chains over the distended jaws—one over the lower, and the second over the upper—and passed the ends through ringbolts fixed to the post. Babe attempted to close his jaw, but in vain. He was a secure prisoner, bound literally foot and mouth. The keeper then proceeded to perform the necessary operation with all possible celerity. For this delicate dental work the menagerie proprietor has provided a special outfit consisting of a small, finely tenoned saw, three files, one of which is about as coarse as a wood rasp, and the other two very fine and more suited for polishing purposes. The files are only cut upon one side, the other faces being covered with thick and soft leather, so that in the event of the file slipping off the tooth, the brute's mouth would not be wounded in any way.

The front digging teeth first claimed attention. The keeper set to work with a will, merrily filing at the teeth as if he were rasping a piece of wood fixed in a vise. The animal gurgled and spluttered, and large tears, like balls of crystal, rolled from his eyes. He grew restless, and in two or three minutes his struggles became so violent that the operator had to desist.

When Babe had quieted down once more, the dentist again set to work vigorously, and ceased for a few moments every time the hippopotamus grew restless. Probably the animal suffered little real pain, but experienced a disagreeable sensation as the strong steel file rasped over the bone, which proved to be extremely hard. At the end of five minutes, one tooth had been filed down an inch and a quarter, and before a quarter of an hour had elapsed both the digging teeth had been treated and polished.

A curious feature was observed during the operation. The body of the animal appeared to be bathed in blood, and the ground immediately beneath it was dyed a deep red. This was due to Babe's violent perspiring, as the perspiration of the hippopotamus, when excited, is red in color.

The dental surgeon then directed his skill to the tusks. This task was considerably facilitated by sawing off the tusks to the desired length, and then finally grinding the teeth down to the requisite shape with the files. They were then polished, and the unpleasant operation was completed.

Great excitement now followed. Every man, with the exception of the keeper, decamped from the scene of action. The keeper then hurriedly knocked away the chains holding the animal's mouth and also quickly hied him to a safe distance, in case Babe proved obstreperous. The hippopotamus closed his released mouth with a snap, and spluttered viciously with violent anger. He glared at the keeper as if he would have liked to kill his tormentor. He opened and closed his mouth several times, found his teeth more comfortable, and then signified his appreciation for what had been done to him by sniffing about for something to munch. The keeper warily approached him with an appetizing pail of bran mash, which Babe devoured with great zest. The shackles were knocked off his legs, at which the brute gave a grunt of satisfaction. All signs of viciousness had vanished and, quite content, he accompanied the keeper back to the cage, where he lay down and went to sleep.

CHAPTER XI

OLD AND NEW WORLD CAMELS

ALTHOUGH the camel is one of the very commonest animals in zoological collections, it is interesting to note that the average visitor to a zoo, even the hurried one, stops for a moment to look at it.

The "ship of the desert" deserves its name. It is a cargo ship, a battleship, and a passenger ship, and while serving in the latter capacity, can even make the passenger seasick with its steady, rocking gait. Combining the usual characters of the horse, the cow, and the sheep, and with its own peculiar virtue of being able to withstand long periods of drought and hunger, it has enabled man to live in vast areas of the globe otherwise uninhabitable, supplying him at the same time with food, drink, clothing, and transportation.

The camel's ability to withstand drought and hunger has probably been overestimated, although it doubtless excels all other domestic animals in this respect. When compelled to travel for days with little or no food, camels soon break down. This was shown disastrously in the British Khartoum expedition when hundreds of the creatures died of exhaustion because those in charge did not seem to realize that there was a limit to their endurance. The British had a similar experience in the Afghan war, when 20,000 Bactrian camels perished miserably.

My own experience shows that after three days without water a camel becomes even more irritable than at other times, which is the nth power of irritability. In crossing the Sinaitic Desert we were amazed at what they could do on forage which they picked up after the day's journey was over, forage of thorny scrub, so that we jokingly maintained that they could live on kindling wood with shingle nails in it.

The patience of the camel has also been popularly exaggerated. What patience it has is due to stupidity. When made to kneel down and while receiving its load, it utters loud cries of indignation. Nanny, my riding camel, would commence howling as soon as I approached her to mount. Sometimes I would give her a handful of dates, and the noise would cease just long enough for the food to pass the howling portion of her anatomy, when the horrible gurgling grunt would resume. She would go out of her way to bite anybody, even another camel, and the only time I could detect any satisfaction in her bearing was when she had kicked a hole through my suitcase.

The two attempts to introduce camels in the Southwestern deserts of the United States as domestic animals have failed, though it is not definitely known why. The first herd was procured by the United States Government from Smyrna in 1856, and distributed over Texas, Arizona, and New Mexico. During the Civil War all of these animals fell into the hands of the combatants and were used for carrying mails, some of them making journeys of more than 120 miles a day. After the war the remnant was once more taken over by the Federal Government and others were purchased in 1866. These were distributed through Arizona and Texas for breeding purposes, but many died. The remainder were turned loose and every now and then there appears a newspaper account of somebody having seen one. It is improbable, however, that any of them exists at the present time.

In Australia the introduction proved successful, and camels are still used as beasts of burden in the desert regions, though each year to a less extent. In consequence, the dealer finds Australia one of the easiest places to

PLATE 45

Arabian dromedary with the first young born in the Park

procure camels. A few years ago one enterprising animal man brought from there to New York no less than fifty-eight big Afghan camels in one shipment.

The ancestry of the domestic camel is unknown, but neither of the varieties,—the Arabian or single-humped, and the Bactrian or double-humped,—exists any longer in the wild state, though there are some semiwild herds which have escaped from captivity. Wild camels are said to have existed in Arabia at the start of the Christian era and this, coupled with the fact that they do not appear to have been known to the ancient Egyptians, makes it seem plausible to assign to both types an Asiatic origin.

The dromedary, the taller and more graceful, if that word can be applied to a camel, of the two species, is confined to the hot regions of Asia and North Africa. The Bactrian is found in nearly all the desert regions of Central Asia lying between Afghanistan, Turkestan, China, and southern Siberia, where it is as important to the nomad inhabitants of this region as the Arabian camel is to the Arabs. It feeds chiefly on the bitter plants of the steppes, which are rejected by most other animals, and has a curious partiality for salt, drinking freely of brackish water and salt lakes. The young are so helpless at birth as to be unable even to eat for about a week, and they do not attain their full size and vigor before the fifth year.

The specimen in our Park at present was born here. The mother died shortly after, so the baby was brought up on a bottle. Eventually it took to eating hay and grain, and the bottle was discontinued. After several months, for some unaccountable reason, it went "off its feed" and visibly pined. At this time the head keeper got out the bottle and fed it milk again for a week, after which it resumed its vegetarian diet, and has grown into a very fine specimen. This last statement might be open to question in the summer months when it is shedding. Then great patches of hair come off, while others remain to set off the barer places, so that one visitor remarked that that animal was sadly in need of new upholstery.

Our Arabian camel has struck up a friendship with a goat placed in the paddock some years ago, and they appear to enjoy each other's company.

The New World members of the camel family, comprising the llama, the guanaco, the alpaca, and the vicuña, are well known in zoos. They offer no particular problems in temperate climates. Of the four species, two wild and two domestic, the llama is somewhat the hardiest. In our herd one has lived for seventeen years and eleven months, and we have sent away in exchange no less than forty specimens born here. Eleven guanacos have also been born in Washington and sent away to other zoos.

The smallest and most timid of the family, the vicuña, has lived here for over eleven years. It is an extremely light, graceful animal, confined to the mountains of central Ecuador and central Bolivia. It has never been successfully domesticated, but is still hunted both for its flesh and its excellent wool.

The other wild species, the guanaco, is a larger, heavier animal whose range extends from the high mountains of Ecuador and Peru to the plains of Patagonia and the islands of Tierra del Fuego. It appears to have a curious instinct for resorting to particular "dying places" when it feels the end approaching. Darwin observed that on the banks of the Santa Cruz in certain places the ground was white with bones. They did not appear gnawed or broken, as if dragged together by beasts of prey.

Both the domestic species are believed to have originated from the wild guanaco. The larger is the true llama. It was bred by the ancient Peruvians as a beast of burden and a riding animal. At the time of the Spanish conquest it was not uncommon to meet droves of from 500 to 1,000 llamas loaded with silver, all in charge of a single native. Only the males were used as beasts of burden, the females being kept for their flesh and milk.

PLATE 46

When its mother abandoned this baby Bactrian camel, Mr. Blackburne brought it up successfully on a bottle

PLATE 47

Llama and young.   Hardiest of South American camel family

It is estimated that at the time of the conquest as many as 300,000 were employed in the transport system from the Potosi mines alone. Introduction of horses and mules may have somewhat reduced their numbers, but it is still a common beast of burden in Peru and Bolivia, and I was told in La Paz that a dead animal, for its hide, its flesh, and its bones, had as much value as a live one. It is a common sight to see an Aymara Indian driving a small herd of these animals before him and knitting steadily as he walks. Their dried dung is important as a combustible in La Paz. It is sold in great cakes called *takia*, and used in cooking fires. One of the few occasions in La Paz that I remember being unusually warm was in the home of the American Consul before a large open fire of *takia*.

The alpaca, still kept in great herds on the high plateaus, is smaller and not used as a beast of burden, but bred entirely for the sake of its fine wool, sometimes so long that it reaches almost to the ground from the animal's belly.

CHAPTER XII

SOME PIGS

SEVERAL varieties of the wart hog are found over a great part of Africa, and it is one of the commoner animals seen by the traveler. During the day the species lives in holes in the ground, but morning and evening find them foraging and rooting. Generally they adopt a kneeling position as they root, and they have great calluses on the knees of their forelegs, which are of special interest because they are quite well developed on the embryo. Does this constitute an example of the inheritance of an acquired characteristic?

We caught our specimens at Tula. To the native, game is forbidden, because white and native are treated alike under the game law and few of the natives have sufficient money to pay for the necessary license. But certain animals are game to them, among others the wart hog, which, with the bush pig, an even more destructive relative, often creates considerable havoc in the gardens. So our natives of Tula had already had considerable experience in catching them, using nets for this purpose. We would put these nets in place, send the line of drivers around, and then wait patiently to see what came out of the forest. Most often it was wart hog. An adult, with head and tail up, running swiftly toward one is a fearsome sight. Nine times out of ten they would hit the net, go through it, and disappear. Once when I was back of the net one broke through. I ran in front of him with a lariat. He turned, and came at me for a dozen feet before swerving, and the movie man missed a picture of a record high and broad jump, combined, by not having his camera set up at the time.

But several did not get through the net. We hastened up and put a double hitch around the upper and lower tusks with a rope. The first one we decided to put in a large bag we had with us. None of us, not even the natives, had ever put a wild pig in a bag before and after considerable arguing as to how it should be done, we decided to leave it where it was in the net, and in fact to add several more nets for good measure. We carried them home to camp in this way.

Once we put up about fifty feet of net in one place and fifty feet in another, intending to fill in the gap when additional boys and nets came up. While we waited a wart hog suddenly appeared and dashed against net number one, and while we were tying him another from the opposite direction, evidently frightened by the sound of our approaching cavalcade, darted out of the bush and hit net number two, so without a drive we had caught two of them in a very few moments. At another time a large male was tangled in one end of a net and Charley ran up and was tying his mouth, when suddenly a smaller one dashed blindly out, struck the same net and tangled the three of them up together. It was funny after it was over, but not at the time, for the tusks are capable of inflicting bad wounds. In fact, the only serious casualty caused by animals that we had on the entire trip resulted when one of our boys had a large piece taken out of the calf of his leg by a wart hog.

The animals behaved well in captivity. They took kindly to any food that we would give them, and soon lost their nervousness. Aboard ship one day Saidi came into the dining room at lunch time and shouted to me that the wart hogs had escaped and were on the deck. We dashed below to the main deck and found three of our four specimens standing in a group, bewildered at the strange environment of a ship's deck. We opened

the door of their crate and all three trotted in, apparently
well content to be home again. The fourth was missing,
and after considerable search we located him at one end
of a long coal passage, hiding behind a wheelbarrow.
We rigged a crate at one end of this passage for him to
run into, and then threw a rope over the wheelbarrow
and pulled it off quickly, to frighten him down the passage.
But instead of following our plan and going into the box
prepared, he jumped through a small hole into the stoke-
hold. This was thirty feet below us, and reached by three
flights of steel stairway. We heard several distinct
bumps, and I remarked to my companion, "Well, that
leaves us only three wart hogs." Then I shouted down
the hold to the stokers, "Is it dead?"

It took some moments for the reply to be formulated
in English, but it finally came in a disconcerted, "He has
come."

We went down the stairs and found the pig, entirely
unhurt, running back and forth, while the stokers,
Mohammedans who don't like pigs anyway and who
furthermore did not know there were any aboard, having
paid little attention to the cargo on deck, had stopped
their work of feeding the furnace and taken positions up
the sides, where they hung like so many bunches of
grapes attached to ropes. We got a rope over the pig's
head, lifted him up, slipped a bag beneath him, pushed
him into it, and put him back into his crate, whereupon
the stokers resumed stoking and the ship its full speed
ahead.

The four arrived in Washington in October and were
put together in one cage. They took very readily to life
in the Zoo, and lost all fear of visitors. In May the
weather had become warm, and when we opened the big
door that leads to the outside paddock all four pigs
jumped through it and started on a run for home, which
they evidently thought was just around the corner.
They did not notice the iron bars, and all of them were

PLATE 48

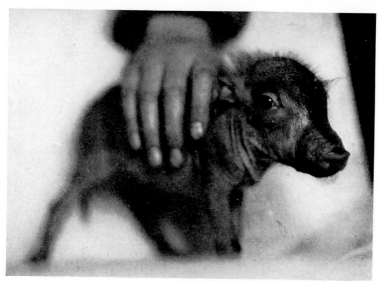

Upper: East African wart hog
Lower: A four-day-old baby

knocked out by hitting them. One died from spinal injuries received in this way. We had to drive the other three into the house, close the door, and put up a big board fence. They soon became accustomed to the fence, and having failed to make home through the iron bars, have ever since been trying to root their way there.

They bred, but the young were born during a cold snap, the mother paid no attention to them, and all five died within a few days.[1]

We have had at various times East African bush pigs, handsome and active animals, which become very tame and friendly when handled.

Of the American pigs, the peccary is common to practically all zoos. It lives well, becomes very tame, and frequently breeds in captivity. I have heard of travelers being treed by herds of these, but I have shot a female out of a herd of fifty or more in Bolivia, caught her young one, and held him, squealing, while I got her in the bush, and yet they never rushed us, though the old ones champed their jaws.

The peccary seems to be capable of attaching himself to an individual. One I knew at Kete Purangi, on the Rio Negro a little above Manáos, lived as one of us, a pleasant pet except for a habit at mealtime of rooting one's leg beneath the table to attract one's attention to the fact that the pig also would dine.

One of our European wild boar lived at the Park for fifteen years and three months. When she finally died, it seemed incredible from the post mortem that the animal could have lived so long with such a diseased interior as she had. The new pair that we have now were born in Detroit.

The pig has always been a much maligned animal. We have heard of a little girl named Mary who was followed to school each day by a lamb. We consider this very doubtful, but if the lamb did follow Mary, he did so

[1]This year four were born and are all alive as this goes to press.

because of an instinctive need of care, of food, or of warmth. But a little pig might have followed her through fondness for her, just as a dog would. Of course if he had, he never would have got into poetry. The incident would have been considered pure comedy.

There is scarcely a farmer's boy who has not at some time or another had a pet pig. Bill Barlow, for instance, a pig that I knew of on a New England farm, was crippled during the first weeks of his life, and was rescued from the hog pen and taken to the kitchen where he was given a warm place behind the stove in a box bedded with hay. He never went back to the sties. For nearly three years he lived with the family, sleeping with a shepherd dog on the back porch. He used to make his own bed, bringing straw in his mouth from the barnyard. He was always at the heels of the farmer's wife, pulling at her dress to attract attention and sometimes following her as much as two miles to the home of a neighbor. But the fate of all pigs is the same. The family finances forced the sale of Bill Barlow, and the butcher, who had no regard for personalities, considered him simply a three-hundred-pound porker.

Someone has said that he never knew what "domestic animal" really meant until he went to Brazil, and one can well believe it, after living in houses where pigs run in and out but in general behave quite as well as dogs or cats.

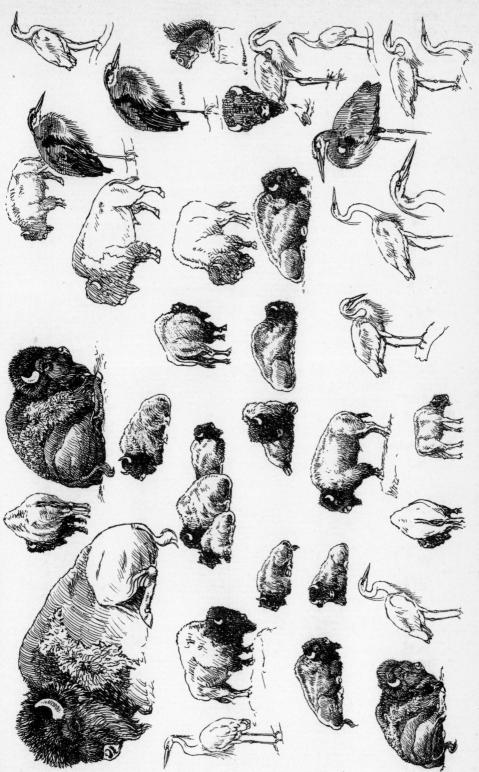

FIG. 11.   Sketches from an artist's note book.   By Benson B. Moore

CHAPTER XIII

WILD CATTLE

WILD cattle as a whole are interesting to the general public because of the use that man has made of them, rather than because of any peculiarity or intelligence in their behavior. There is little individuality among them. One bison is very much like another bison. The behavior of the wild cattle is duplicated largely by that of the domestic breeds. They are among the most docile and the most dangerous of animals, as everybody knows who has stroked the forehead of a gentle old milch cow and has been chased out of a berry pasture by a bull. Twenty or thirty centuries of domestication have resulted in little fundamental change from their wild ancestors, and even today domestic and wild species interbreed freely. They show little capacity to learn from experience, though Dr. William T. Hornaday states that the North American bison did acquire a saving fear of man and some ingenuity in keeping out of his way after they had been slaughtered almost to the point of extermination.

At the time the animals of the incipient National Zoological Park were quartered on the grounds of the Smithsonian Institution, interest in the American bison was becoming widespread on account of the danger of the complete extermination of this typically American animal, and in 1888 our first bison came to Washington, a gift from the Honorable E. G. Blackford of New York City. The records describe it as "Blind in one eye. Both horns sawed off" when it arrived. It had been captured four years before at Ogalalla, Nebraska.

[163]

WILD ANIMALS

The following year Dr. V. T. McGillicuddy deposited five individuals which had been captured as calves in 1883 by the Ogalalla Sioux Indians north of the Black Hills. There were several births from these animals, and in 1897 the herd was augmented by three specimens purchased from Mr. M. Pablo of Ronan, Missoula County, Montana. It is interesting to note that these animals in that day brought a price of $500 per specimen; today the market price is very much less. One of our early bison served as the model for a work of art probably as much sought after as any ever made—namely, the United States Treasury's ten-dollar bill, of which there were 148,958,000 printed. The drawing was made by C. R. Knight.

In later years the Zoo secured several additional bulls and cows from Charles Goodnight's herd in Texas, and in 1904 Buffalo Bill and J. A. Bailey deposited seven males and five females. Some of these were subsequently returned to the owner; others remained here. Specimens of unrelated blood were secured from the Blue Mountain Forest Association and the whole collection was divided into two herds. Between 1890 and 1928 there have been fifty-nine births in the two herds—thirty males, twenty-seven females, and two still-born young, of whose sex we have no record.

In the early days of the Zoo the herds were kept in a large paddock, partly in the hollow along Rock Creek. This part of the Park suffers from a great deal of heavy fog, and many deaths from lung diseases resulted. Since the transfer of the bison to one of the higher parts of the Park, on clay soil, deaths have been only from natural causes, principally old age. They live here contentedly in a large paddock with an open shed, which gives them sufficient shelter in very bad weather, and with plenty of clay to wallow in, in wet weather. They enjoy this, though visitors sometimes write us that we should remove them from the muddy paddock to a nice valley in the hollow along Rock Creek.

[164]

PLATE 49

The model for the former ten-dollar bill of the United States Treasury

Certain precautions are necessary in keeping buffaloes together. The feed pans should be shallow so that when the animal is feeding his eyes project above the top and he can see another one rushing him. We had several casualties when deeper feed pans were used. One nearly fatal accident occurred, when a bull attacked a keeper, knocked him unconscious, and broke several of his bones. Since then we have had a fence of iron piping, three feet high, placed inside of the main fence, so the keeper can duck through when necessary. This is useful not only to keepers but also to calves, for sometimes a bull would rush a young one and kill it against the fence. But now the threatened youngster can get beneath this iron pipe into a safety zone.

In transferring the herd to the new paddock, several escaped in the Park, breaking through a temporary fencing. For two hours the keepers tried to drive them into the permanent corral, but they would not be driven until a nurse girl, wheeling a baby carriage, hove in sight, and frightened them all into their permanent quarters.

At one time two cows calved in two days. One mother died, leaving a day-old orphan calf. The mother of the other did not like the orphan, and would kick him when he came near. But when her own calf was nursing, the foundling would sneak up quietly from behind, avoiding a side kick, and nurse also, nourishing himself in this way against the wish of the cow, at least to the extent of keeping alive until he was able to eat hay and grain.

At present our oldest cow is Pocahontas, now nearly twenty-three years of age, a magnificent specimen, which, however, has never bred. She is descended from the Buffalo Bill stock.

When Cortes and his little band of marauders came to Montezuma's capital in 1521 they saw in the zoological garden of that enlightened Aztec king an animal which was described by de Solis, historian of the expedition, as follows:

WILD ANIMALS

. . . The greatest Rarity was the Mexican Bull; a wonderful composition of divers Animals. It has crooked Shoulders, with a Bunch on its Back like a Camel; its Flanks dry, its Tail large, and its Neck cover'd with Hair like a Lion. It is cloven footed, its Head armed like that of a Bull, which it resembles in Fierceness, with no less strength and Agility.

From this crude description we must conclude that white men had looked for the first time on an animal which existed on the North American continent in such numbers that, in the words of Doctor Hornaday:

Of all the quadrupeds that have lived upon the earth, probably no other species has ever marshaled such innumerable hosts as those of the American bison. It would have been as easy to count or to estimate the number of leaves in a forest as to calculate the number of buffaloes living at any given time during the history of the species previous to 1870.

He estimates that the bull in Montezuma's zoo must have come from Coahuila, 500 miles to the north.

Though bison may have extended over most of the continent, the center of population was the Great Plains region extending for more than 3,500 miles from northern Mexico through Canada; but the great herds overflowed the Appalachians to the Atlantic coast and went high into the Rockies. The North American continent literally was blanketed with them. Their only enemies were the Indians and the wolves.

In 1870 Col. R. I. Dodge drove for twenty-five miles along the Arkansas River through a single herd which stretched as far as the eye could see. This great mass of animals was composed of innumerable smaller herds of from fifty to two hundred, and averaged fifteen or twenty individuals to the acre. The year before had seen the bison definitely divided into two herds by the completion of the Southern Pacific Railroad across the prairies. The southern herd, Hornaday estimates, numbered about 3,500,000 head and the northern herd about 1,500,000.

Then came the slaughter. Ten years later the American bison was almost an extinct animal. The completion of the Northern Pacific in 1880 was a final blow. In October, 1883, was staged the last great bison hunt when about 1,000 animals were killed in southwestern Dakota by Sitting Bull and 1,000 Indians from the Standing Rock agency. Only a few small herds were left in the entire continent. The slaughter from 1870 on has been wasteful, conscienceless, and indiscriminate. Thousands have been shot for their tongues alone, which were considered a delicacy. Hundreds of thousands were slain for their hides, which sold for about two dollars each. The prairies were strewn with carcasses. This wholesale murder stopped only when bison became so scarce that it was profitable no longer.

It was not until 1902 that Congress took the first steps toward the preservation of these animals by appropriating $15,000 to establish a bison reserve, under fence, in the Yellowstone National Park. In 1907, there was a "tame" herd of 846 animals and a wild herd, seldom seen by anybody, estimated at about 125 individuals, in the Yellowstone area. Since then four other reserves have been created in the United States. These are the Wichita National Bison Preserve in Oklahoma, which now has 197 animals; the Montana National Bison Range founded in 1909 by the National Bison Society, which now has 540 animals; the Wind Cave Preserve in South Dakota, with 139 animals; and the Niobrara, Nebraska, National Range, with 69 animals. All these herds are increasing constantly.

In Canada the Buffalo National Park was established near Wainwright, Alberta, in 1911 with 918 bison, which in 1925 had increased to 8,231, altogether too many for the grazing space. As a consequence 1,634 animals were shipped north in the summer of that year to be released in Wood Buffalo Park just south of Great Slave Lake and in 1926, 2,011 were added to this number.

Aware of the imminent extinction of these animals, the Smithsonian Institution in 1887 sent an expedition under

Doctor Hornaday, then chief taxidermist of the National Museum, to Montana to secure both living and dead specimens for exhibition. This was the foundation of the bison herd in the National Zoological Park. The expedition captured one calf, two or three weeks old, which had been abandoned by its mother because it wouldn't keep up with her in her flight, and it was easily tamed. Says Doctor Hornaday:

The one captured in Montana by the writer, resisted at first as stoutly as it was able, by butting with its head, but after we had tied its legs together and carried it to camp, across a horse, it made up its mind to yield gracefully to the inevitable, and from that moment became perfectly docile. It very soon learned to drink milk in the most satisfactory manner, and adapted itself to its new surroundings quite as readily as any domestic calf would have done. Its only cry was a low-pitched, piglike grunt through the nose, which was uttered only when hungry or thirsty.

These animals are at their best as exhibits in November and December when the new coat of hair has reached its full growth. They begin to shed in March and look very shabby in April, May, and June, when old hair clings in ugly patches to the body. They are almost naked through the summer. The calves are born in April or May and before this event the mother always should be removed to a separate inclosure. In the wild state, the female always separates from the herd and hides her calf for a few days. Afterwards the calves are kept together near the herd, the mothers coming to them to let them nurse. They are devoted mothers but in the old days, it is reported, would abandon their offspring at the approach of man. Colonel Dodge recorded one instance of a half dozen bulls surrounding a calf to protect it from wolves.

The bison breeds freely with domestic cattle and produces fertile hybrids which tend, however, to return to the wild type. Several efforts have been made to breed in a bison strain in the hope of producing a hardier domestic animal, but without permanent success. As early as 1843 Robert Wycliff of Lexington, Kentucky, was experimenting

FIG. 12. Sketches from an artist's note book. By Benson B. Moore

successfully with bison as draught animals. He told Audubon: "I have broken them to the yoke, and found them capable of making excellent oxen; and for drawing wagons, carts, or other heavily laden vehicles on long journeys they would, I think, be greatly preferable to the common ox."

New types of draught animals, however, hardly are pressing needs of the country just now and the ox itself is rarely met with.

The other American animal which may be included in the cattle family is the Arctic musk ox, occasionally seen in captivity. Hornaday states that he gazed upon each living musk ox in captivity with wonder, as if it were a creature from another world. These creatures live entirely within the Arctic Circle. The Indians of northern Canada credit them with supernatural powers and say they can understand human speech. Surely the capacity of these curious beasts to obtain sustenance in the world's sparsest pastures is little short of supernatural.

Musk oxen are still rare in captivity, but are extremely hardy animals, easy to keep in good health in a temperate climate. The first to appear in Europe were captured by a Swedish explorer on Clavering Island, off the east coast of Greenland, in 1899. These two males were sold to the Duke of Bedford who placed them in his acclimatization park and attempted without success to produce various crosses with them. The first to come to the United States was a female calf, about eighteen months old, captured in 1902 about thirty miles inland from Lady Franklin Bay by Captain H. H. Bodfish of the whaler *Beluga*. This was presented to the New York Zoo. In October of the same year Robert H. Peary, the future discoverer of the North Pole, captured a young male in northeast Greenland which he presented to the same collection.

"The musk oxen," says Casper Whitney, "are stupid, mild creatures. In one little band of eight which we had separated from the main herd and killed, a yearling calf ran against my legs, seemingly seeking protection from the dogs precisely as a young sheep would." Adults, of course, would be extremely difficult to capture and transport. They go in herds of from fifteen to fifty, which gives them a better chance to defend themselves against their one enemy, the Arctic wolf, and also gives them, through close contact, warmth and protection against the wind. They are remarkable appearing creatures with outer hair a foot long in winter, big chocolate-brown eyes, and purple lips and tongue tip.

We have had only two African buffaloes in the collection. One, from East Africa (*Synoceros neumanni*), lived three years, and the other, from South Africa (*Synoceros caffer*), has now been here for a year and a half and is still immature. Judging from its appearance and the ease with which it can be kept in captivity, ten years is not an unusual age for cage specimens. The African buffalo is not common in collections, because of the difficulty of capturing them.

Our one attempt to capture a young one came close to ending in disaster. George and I were walking a hundred yards back from the edge of Lake Meru in Tanganyika. The shores between us and the water were swampy and covered only with short grass. To our right was an area of scrub about up to my chin, and beyond this, 200 yards distant, a forest.

I heard something snort, and George said, "Look at the buff!"

I looked for a buffalo, but told him I could not see it.

"It!" he exclaimed, "There are two hundred of them right against the forest."

And there, sure enough, was a large mass of them, standing in the shade of the forest at its edge.

Suddenly George said, "I am having a go at the cow on the right. She has *mtoto*." *Mtoto* is the East African word for young animal.

WILD CATTLE

At the very edge of the herd I saw a cow with a little calf beside her. George raised his gun and shot. It was the horrible 5.75 single-barrel that he carried, which always terrified me when he used it. Looking at the herd I saw two hundred necks stretch out and four hundred ears come to the front, and then a surge of the mass toward us.

George shouted, "Look out, they are charging!" and started running, with me after him, though I could not see any use in doing so, as there was no shelter to run to. Anyway, we made a record for a hundred-yard dash in mud shoe-top deep. We stopped eventually and listened to the thunder of a herd of heavy animals. They came about fifty yards in our direction, and then broke into two herds, one of which went up the lake and the other down.

According to the picture drawn by an artist 10,000 miles away, and reproduced in the press at the time, it was a very thrilling adventure; and had I seen this picture before the event, I should certainly never have allowed George to fire into the herd.

George was sure that he had killed the cow, or at least wounded her, so we scouted about until dark—very cautious scouting it was, our boys climbing trees and scanning the territory below. But it had evidently been a miss, for we found no traces of either mother or child.

Lyman, on his previous trip, had secured much game, but had had bad luck as far as buffaloes were concerned, so he particularly wanted to get one. As we were coming one day into the hunting region, George and myself walking a couple of hundred yards ahead of Lyman, a bull buffalo emerged from the forest and stood in the open as though waiting to give Lyman, who was hobbling along with a large blister on his heel, a shot. We waved and he hurried forward, but just before he came up the buffalo turned slowly and disappeared into the forest.

After we had had our set-to with the herd, we told Lyman about it, and he immediately moved camp farther up the lake in the vicinity in which we had seen them. He told me afterward that he had been afraid to shoot, that buffalo were sprinkled all through the forest, and he feared a charge if he hunted them. His fear was well founded for the buffalo is, without exaggeration, the most dangerous of all the larger animals; dangerous, in that instead of making a blind charge he will stop and hunt out his enemy as a dog will a rat, and will even resort to skillful trickery when coming upon him. George told me of wounding a female buffalo, failing to locate her, and then, as he was walking a trail a quarter of a mile away, of being suddenly charged by the same animal from the tall grass. She had evidently trotted ahead and waited for him alongside the trail.

Buffaloes are considered pests in some parts of Africa. Where they are much hunted they are likely to charge at any time. When I was given a "meat license"—a permit to shoot certain game as food for ourselves and native boys—officially but one buffalo was permitted, but the warden informed me privately that in the Meru country there was no limit. Since then I have heard that the buffalo has been declared a pest in certain parts of Tanganyika, and can be shot by anyone.

There was a time when it seemed that the species was doomed. Rinderpest spread among the herds and where thousands had wandered only dozens remained, but it is a prolific breeder and a long-lived animal, and has re-established itself naturally throughout most of its former range. In captivity they breed readily, and will cross with domestic cattle. I heard of two of them being used as plow animals by a planter in Rhodesia, but judging from the disposition of the youngster that we have in the collection now I should hate to plow behind that planter's pair.

We have never had a specimen of the European bison,

PLATE 50

African buffalo bull, reputed to be most dangerous of African game

PLATE 51

Bull yak or grunting ox. This species is native to the high plateaus of Central Asia

which abounded in western Europe in Caesar's day and was still killed occasionally in Germany during the Middle Ages, but which never attained to anything like the numbers of its American cousin, and which still exists, although on the verge of extinction. Its fate since the war is uncertain. At the 1925 meeting of the International Society for the Preservation of the Wisent, as the European bison is called, it was reported that there were sixty healthy animals in Europe, mostly in zoos and private estates, and ten or fifteen still wild in the Caucasus. During the period of hostilities the creatures were killed off purely for meat and leather with no thought of the fate of the species.

Before the war there were two preserves where the few remaining animals were rigidly protected. One was the vast hunting grounds of the Grand Duke Sergius Michailovitch on the northern slope of the Caucasus, comprising an area of nearly 2,000 square miles, where they could be hunted only by the duke himself. The other was the Bielowitza forest in Lithuania. In both these preserves young animals occasionally were captured and presented to European zoos. The Caucasus herd, containing about 700 individuals in 1914, was said to be the best. It ranged from high alpine pastures to deep wooded valleys along the water courses of the Bielaja and Malaja Laba Rivers where there were numerous sulphurous springs. These animals varied widely from the American species in their food habits, feeding largely on the bark and twigs of elms and on young ferns.

An interesting instance of the capture of one of these animals is given by A. Yermoloff, former Imperial Minister of Agriculture, in the Smithsonian Institution *Report* for 1906. The pregnant cows, M. Yermoloff says, leave the herds of from four to fifteen animals just before the birth of their calves and hide in impassable masses of rhododendrons, from which they emerge, followed by their offspring, after six or seven days. They have such an intense fear of humans, however, that they will abandon their little ones when a man approaches. Yermoloff wished to introduce some of the blood of the Caucasus herd among the smaller, less hardy Lithuanian animals, and took advantage of this shortcoming of the mothers.

Bison from the Lithuanian herd, which numbered 727 in 1914, found their way more frequently into European zoos because they were more easily captured in the marshy country which they inhabited. Animals of both these herds were found to breed freely with domestic cattle. The Lithuanian herd was given stricter protection and was in charge of a staff of keepers employed by the Government, who patrolled the Bielowitza forest to guard against poachers, kept the creatures supplied with rock salt, and with hay and grain during the hard winters. In the Caucasus only rock salt was provided and the bison were entirely wild. Even the moderate protection given in Lithuania resulted in a weakening of the animals, which were smaller than their southern cousins.

The yak, or grunting ox, is another most useful animal, making travel possible in the high mountains of Central Asia where it is found both as a wild and as a tame animal. It is difficult to see how the natives of these desolate mountain valleys could do without this creature, which feeds on the coarsest pasturage up to an elevation of 20,000 feet, climbs through difficult passes as sure-footed as a goat, swims icy torrents, and traverses glaciers that would be impassable for almost any other beast of burden. The yak's one great drawback is that it will not eat grain, which it could carry on its back, and consequently forced marches are sometimes necessary to prevent the animal's perishing from hunger.

The yak does exceedingly well in captivity, even in low altitudes, and our own herd, which has been in existence since 1898, has no specimen in it that ever saw Tibet. We received our earlier specimens from the Zoological Society of London. From them numbers of young were born, some were sent away, some were kept in the herd. In 1921 new blood was added in the form of a fine bull, sent to us by the Canadian Government through J. B. Harkin, the Commissioner of Dominion Parks. In Canada the yak is being raised successfully. Like most of the cattle family they are stupid and uninteresting animals in captivity, but they deserve a conspicuous place in a zoological collection because of the important part they play in human economics.

CHAPTER XIV

THE TREE BROWSERS

OUR experience with the giraffe in the National Zoological Park has been exceedingly meager and even more disappointing. On our recent trip to East Africa the animals most desired were a pair of giraffes. Accordingly, I went to Tula in southeast Tanganyika, where they are abundant, and because of the strict protection given them by the game department, unusually tame.

The best possible way to catch giraffes is to run them with horses and lasso the young ones, or to drive them into a compound. We were unable to use either of these methods, and had to depend on our natives and our nets. We worked far from camp so as not to frighten those nearby. The first day we succeeded in surrounding a young one, which ran back and forth in a circle of boys, who waved spears at him and shouted valiantly. However when the baby (it was really a very small one) made a determined rush through the line, the nearby natives, instead of catching him as they should have done, simply brandished their spears at him. So he got away and I could see him run for a half mile, until he rejoined his mother from whom he had been separated in the drive.

Our first capture was made by surrounding one about seven feet high, and then grabbing and throwing it. We sent to a nearby native house for a bed, a contrivance of rope woven on four sticks. By piling this high with grass it made a comfortable stretcher on which to carry the animal to the house. We were living in a thatched native house containing three rooms, into one of which we put the giraffe. He tamed remarkably quickly, and the following morning had apparently lost a great deal of his fear of us, drank milk from a basin, and ate acacia leaves. The giraffe has three styles of kick: with his hind feet, a cowlike swing; with his forefeet, a chop kick like a horse; and also a straight-out football-player boot. The small one that we had in the house used the football kick on the walls, punting them repeatedly during the night. Though not very secure, the house was the best place we had for him, and in addition we posted a native guard to keep constant watch, but he didn't, and the giraffe got his head and shoulders beneath a pole not more than three feet from the ground, and wormed his way through. The last we saw of him he was going into the scrub, and I hope he rejoined his herd in the vicinity.

The third specimen, captured in the same way, was likewise caged in the house, while I, resolving to have him in a crate at once, dashed down to Dar-es-Salaam and sat out the entire day on a chair in the shop of a Hindu carpenter until the gigantic crate was made, and then shipped it up the railroad. When it reached the station there was no truck large enough to carry it eighty miles to the giraffe at Tula, so the giraffe was brought to it, held by natives on a truck. The railroad carried him safely in his crate to the harbor. There we placed him at the Government veterinary station, in the shade of a big mimosa tree, where he seemed contented and healthy.

A month had passed since I had communicated with Washington, because I had nothing to tell, but on this occasion I cabled to the Smithsonian, "Captured giraffe." An answer came by return cable, "Cable age, height, sex of giraffe, all particulars. School children in Washington holding contest to name it."

To know that my baby giraffe was causing such a commotion in Washington filled me with apprehension. We were going to do our best to bring it home alive, but—. So I replied by cable, "Giraffe delicate animal, eighty miles from railroad. No guarantee its arrival Washington."

A few hours later came, "Is our giraffe a boy or girl?" signed, "Children of Washington, care *Evening Star.*"

The only thing I could do was to reply, "Boy," then flee from the vicinity of the telegraph office.

While the natives were naming him "Mfaume," which means *a princely emissary*, the contest was going on, on the other side of the world. One evening while at dinner, Saidi, our head boy, dashed up and said, "Bwana, the giraffe is in the bottom of his cage, kicking." We grabbed rickshaws and got there as soon as we could, found him standing up and chewing mimosa leaves. We stayed with him most of the night, but could see nothing wrong with him. The next day at two o'clock, however, he dropped dead. A post-mortem showed acute pneumonia.

I had already telegraphed to my companions in the field, instructing them to bring all their animals to Dar-es-Salaam that we might sail for the States. Personally I could not come back without giraffes. So I arranged passage for them, and resolved to stay another month myself, just for giraffes. Swinnerton, the chief game warden, suggested that I cable to the Sudan to see if the game department had any for disposal. In reply to the cable I was informed that they had a pair of giraffes that they could let me have.

The pair was loaded at Port Sudan, and put first on one side of the promenade deck until the weather became cool in the middle of the Atlantic, when they were let down into the forward coal bunker. Having seen Mfaume drop dead, I had no confidence that I would have any luck bringing home giraffes. Each morning when I awoke, Saidi would be standing at the door with the latest news on their health. They were very sensible animals, and during some heavy seas we had they lay down in their crates and avoided the risk of breaking their necks or legs. Eventually they arrived in Washington,

PLATE 52

The giraffe arrives at port by rail

and we found that the school children had named them "Hi-Boy" and "Dot," and for a time they were Washington's leading citizens. Their arrival was the outstanding event in the history of the Zoological Park. A christening ceremony was held, in which the little boy and girl who had given the chosen names received their prizes, and all records for the number of visitors were broken during the next two months. Two gentler, prettier creatures were never in captivity, and the boys and girls of Washington will long remember them.

Because I was not certain I would ever get any giraffes home alive, I had not told about number two until a day out from Boston, when I had to wireless about it, so that quarters would be ready. The newspaper contest had gone on furiously, and the first giraffe named "Hi-Boy," and then the tired manager of the contest had to go all through another competition to get a name for Hi-Boy's mate. When I met him his first remark was, "Thank goodness, you did not bring home three."

We constructed a cage for them at one end of our bird house, where they had plenty of room to move about, and Mr. Blackburne, who during his thirty-eight years at the National Zoo had been without giraffes, stepped into the cage with them. He petted one, and received a vicious kick in his ribs. When he came out of the cage I asked him if the kick had hurt, but he replied, "No, it is a pleasure to be kicked by a giraffe in my own zoo." Kidney diseases, with complications, took both of them off in less than two years.

Besides the giraffe that lived twenty-eight years in the circus, making an American record for longevity, many have lived for a long time in American zoos. There is one in the Cincinnati Zoo, still alive, born there seventeen years ago, and a number have been born in the New York Zoological Park.

The number of ways which a giraffe can find to injure himself is remarkable. One in the zoo at Calcutta reached up to get a leaf from a tree in his inclosure, caught his neck in a forked branch, and hanged himself.

It is singular that giraffes live as well as they do in captivity, because they are among the most specialized feeders of all animals, subsisting in their native state entirely on the leaves of the mimosa, whereas in captivity they must be fed on hay and grain.

Mr. Blackburne recalls the difficulties of caring for giraffes in the old circus days:

During the years 1882, 1883, and 1884 the Barnum and Bailey Circus carried with it the largest number of giraffes ever seen together in this country. It had ten fine specimens that were kept while on exhibition in a small square tent (marquee) with a heavy cord mesh front. These animals were led around the hippodrome track in the grand entry, with such animals as Jumbo; Columbia, the first baby elephant born in the United States; its mother, Hebe; and twenty-four other elephants, plus yaks, zebras, llamas, camels, and so on.

The giraffes were generally somewhat frisky and often displayed their awkward dancing, kicking, and striking. These animals were not kept in a cage as they are at present in traveling shows, but each animal was blanketed and led from the show grounds to the railroad, and there loaded into a specially constructed car, heavily padded on all sides to prevent injury while the train was in motion. This loading and unloading presented the most difficult problem in the handling of giraffes. The unloading was particularly hard, as they would stand and look from the car door for some little time before they could make up their minds to risk coming down the gangplank, and when they did come, no one knew just where their feet were going to land.

The herd gradually decreased through an occasional death. Several were deposited in the Central Park Menagerie, where they eventually died from lack of proper quarters. In the end only one of the lot was

Fig. 13. Sketches from an artist's note book. By Benson B. Moore

carried with the circus and it was confined to a cage, with a small pen erected at the rear end to allow the animal a chance to exercise and get on the earth during show hours. This seems to be the best and safest way to handle giraffes.

Judging from the records, giraffes have always been rare in captivity. Only one was included in five shiploads of wild animals—lions, leopards, buffaloes, and monkeys—brought to the Egyptian Queen Hatasu, of the Eighteenth Dynasty, from "the country of the Somalis." Rameses the Second, of the Nineteenth Dynasty, owned one specimen. The first seen in Europe was obtained from Alexandria by Julius Caesar and exhibited to the crowds who expected, from the name "camelopard," to find a combination of the size of the camel and the ferocity of the leopard. Pliny, who described it, echoed the public disappointment. "It was as quiet," he wrote, "as a sheep." Doubtless a few more of these animals found their way to Rome through Egypt, but the records are obscure.

After the fall of the Roman Empire the few giraffes seen in Europe were gifts from Eastern sultans and pashas. The prince of Damascus gave one to the Emperor Frederick II in 1215. The Sultan of Egypt presented one to Lorenzo the Magnificent, which became the pet of Florence. It was allowed to walk through the streets and take presents of fruit and cakes extended to it from the balconies. Then the giraffe drops out of European records for five centuries and many persons must have considered it a fabulous monster akin to the dragon and the griffon. It did not reappear until 1827 when the Pasha of Egypt sent one each as gifts to Constantinople, Venice, England, and France. The Parisians went wild with excitement over the Pasha's present. It had spent the winter at Marseilles and throve there on the milk of four cows which the Pasha had sent over from Egypt for its use. The prefect of Marseilles had the arms of France embroidered on its body cloth. It entered Paris escorted by a Darfur negro, an Arab, a Marseilles groom, a mulatto interpreter, a professor from the Jardin des Plantes, and the prefect himself. Around the creature's neck was a band of parchment upon which were written several passages from the Koran, designed as a charm against all illnesses and mishaps, particularly those due to malevolent enchantment.

It was the sensation of the year. Troops were called out to hold back the crowds. All Paris came to see the animal. Artists painted it and poets wrote verses about it. Clothing designers copied the delicate markings of its coat. *La robe à la giraffe, le chapeau à la giraffe,* and *le peigne à la giraffe* appeared in the stores. The animal even became a factor in politics. The opposition party struck medals bearing the figure of the giraffe and the words, "Nothing is changed in France; there is only one more beast." Parisians gradually became accustomed to this animal, which survived for nearly twenty years.

CHAPTER XV

ANTLERS AND HORNS

TWENTY-SIX species of deer have been exhibited at various times in the Park, and literally hundreds of specimens born here. Practically all our deer are kept in outdoor paddocks, even tropical species such as the sambar, one of which lived for sixteen years out-of-doors, the axis, and the Indian swamp deer or barasingha. A Japanese deer, the head of the herd, which has been living now for twenty years and seven months, holds the record for this family here.

Gentle in disposition throughout most of the year, in the fall the males often become so fierce that it is necessary to dehorn them. At one time our elk bulls started on a rampage and killed a number of females and calves. We had to rope and dehorn five bulls in one morning.

Though the handling of the deer family in captivity consists mainly of routine work, it is not altogether uneventful. It was the ordinary European red deer that kicked the head keeper in the face, removing most of the skin, when he was tying the animal to dehorn it. There was an interested audience outside watching the operation, so the keeper, whose circus experience had told him that "the show must go on," kept at work with one eye useless from blood, and dehorned the animal before leaving for first aid.

The first male Virginia deer in the collection came to the Park as a gift. There was no place ready for him, so he was put in the beaver inclosure, out of which he immediately jumped. The head keeper decoyed him halfway across the Park and into another inclosure by giving him nibbles of fine-cut tobacco from time to time. To-bacco seems as choice a tidbit to deer as it is to bears, and apparently, in small quantities, does them no harm.

Our herd of red deer had a curious origin. An English sportsman in the Northwest had unwittingly violated a game law. The warden, no respecter of persons, seized his equipment, and the local judge fined him heavily. He came to Washington to protest at the Embassy, and during his stay visited the Park and noticed the absence of European red deer. When he returned to England he sent a pair as a gift to the Park. Often, as we gaze at an empty cage, we long for another Englishman to abuse.

The Philippine have proved the most interesting of the tropical deer. One of these was captured in the mountains of Abra Province by Igorrotes with nets, and another one, from Luzon, which had been a mascot on the Battleship *Iowa*, was presented by Rear Admiral R. D. Evans, U. S. N., in 1904, and lived for thirteen years.

We have always had specimens of the most beautiful of all of the deer, the axis, which although it inhabits the warmer parts of Asia, does very well out-of-doors here.

Our herd of the Indian hog deer was started from speci-mens that had been raised in the New York Zoological Park, and for twenty-one years has increased in numbers.

Two Panama deer did not do so well. The little Brazilian brocket requires a heated house, and even with this our longest-lived specimen has barely exceeded two years.

Roe deer have never done well at our Zoo. The Euro-pean fallow deer thrives.

The Park's present thriving herd of American elk was started in 1888, when the Honorable W. F. Cody, "Buffalo Bill," presented a trio. Four years later four pairs were captured in the Yellowstone National Park and sent to us by Captain George S. Anderson, at that time superin-tendent. Five years later the Captain sent a number of other specimens. From this original stock no less than 110 young have been born at the Park and sent away in

PLATE 53

Inyala from Rhodesia. At present unique in collections

exchange at various times to other zoos, game preserves, and private parks. The American elk is no longer in danger of extermination. Even in small inclosures, and with reasonable care, it can be depended upon to increase in number.

It has always been a dangerous animal in the park. I remember at the London Zoo a large sign warning visitors that the male elk on exhibition was a particularly dangerous animal, and this is true. At the same time it is the most magnificent of all its family.

Even fiercer than the American elk is our specimen of Kashmir deer, which is descended from a pair presented to us by the Duke of Bedford in 1916. No animal in the Park shows such concentrated, venomous hatred as this animal during the fall and winter when the velvet is off his horns. It seems a pity to have to dehorn him each year, because he bears the most magnificent antlers of any specimen in the collection. His snort of hatred seems to come from his very soul, and during the mating season he emits a roar not unlike the snarl of a leopard. At home he lives at elevations as great as 12,000 feet during the summer, but he does very well in our climate.

The Bedford deer has been with us for ten years, though it has not proved a good breeder. Four arrived in 1916, and the herd now numbers only five.

The only thoroughly domesticated deer is the celebrated reindeer, which in legend draws the sleigh of Santa Claus, and in reality the sleighs of the Laplanders, and whose peculiar qualities have made possible human habitation in large areas on and above the Arctic Circle. Though familiar to all of us from early childhood, it is only within recent years that there have been large importations of these animals into the United States, principally for the purpose of providing Christmas atmosphere in department stores and city streets during the Holidays. The remainder of the year they are deposited in zoos, where they do not, as a rule, live well. No animal seems more plagued by stable flies than they, and the average specimen that comes in is already badly infested with warbles. Our herd came direct from Norway five years ago, at that time about three years old. They were placed in a rangy paddock on a slope with a moist area at the bottom, and at first fed on hay, grain, and reindeer moss, which was secured from Maine. The moss has proved unnecessary for these animals in captivity, and since we have discontinued feeding it our herd has done quite as well. Two have been born here. One died of acute indigestion and one as the result of an accident.

The reindeer's close relative, the Newfoundland caribou, the only species we have had, has been represented in our collection a half dozen times. One, secured through the United States consul, Martin J. Carter, at St. John's, Newfoundland, lived nearly ten years.

Of all the ten American moose that the National Park has had, none has lived more than two years, and most of them have died the same year they were received. It is regrettable that such a magnificent and apparently hardy animal should be so delicate in captivity, but it is so, even when provided with a pond and given birch browse as food, and I do not believe that the moose should be considered a fit animal for a zoo. Of course an occasional specimen, under special conditions, has lived longer. The difficulty of obtaining its natural food can hardly be surmounted outside of its own country.

We frequently get inquiries as to whether we can furnish surplus specimens of the Japanese or Sika deer. People with private herds, as well as other public parks, want fresh blood in their herds. To this we always reply that there is no herd of Sikas in America that does not have the blood of our herd in it. The Japanese deer, one of the most adaptable of all its family to captivity, has been represented in the National Zoological Park since 1905, when a pair was secured. Two years later an

PLATE 54

European red deer presented by an English sportsman

PLATE 55

Upper: Kashmir deer, from the Duke of Bedford collection. So fierce
he has to be dehorned every year

Lower: Axis deer from Asia, most beautiful of his tribe

additional female was bought, and from this trio and their descendants have been raised upwards of sixty young.

Many of the casualties among the Park's deer have been caused by dogs, a subject on which Mr. Blackburne has some vivid recollections:

During the early days of the Park the boundary fence consisted of oak palings and there were no gates at any of the entrances, so that intruders had access at all hours. Back of the Park grounds were some scattered shacks inhabited by people who owned many dogs. The latter frequently paid visits by night, and amused themselves by racing around the deer inclosures, barking, and causing the deer to dash about their pens and run into the fencing, sometimes breaking their necks or their legs.

On one occasion a pack of dogs dug their way under the fencing and got into the Virginia deer inclosure. The following morning two of the deer were found dead, one with a broken neck, the other hanging by one hind leg in the fencing, disemboweled by the dogs. Three other deer were unable to move, owing to compound fractures of the legs, and had to be shot.

At another time a large bulldog dug under the fencing and got into the Sika deer inclosure. He maimed a couple of the females and then attacked the buck, who at the time had a good pair of sharp spiked antlers, which he proceeded to use. One of the prongs penetrated the dog's belly, and he was so weakened that he was unable to make his escape. He was found lying in the ravine, quite helpless but ready to fight. We dispatched him without sorrow.

One day about noon a male mule deer, of which we have several from Arizona, became frightened and leaped over a seven-foot wire fencing which surrounded his quarters. Keepers were gathered and the chase began. It led through the wooded section now occupied by the Bureau of Standards, and towards Chevy Chase Circle. Without exertion the deer outdistanced the keepers and at dark the chase was given up. Four days later, on New Year's Day at 12:30 a. m., a street-car conductor discovered the deer making his way into the Park.

The board boundary fencing was eventually replaced by a Page wire fence, gates were placed at all entrances, and the watch force increased. Only occasionally now a dog gets into the Park, and the invaders have caused no serious accidents recently.

The prong-horned antelope, native to the plains and hills of the Western United States has many superficial points of resemblance to the true antelopes, yet it differs from the latter so essentially that it has been placed in a separate family. This interesting animal has come very close to extinction, and its preservation constitutes a most difficult problem. It is an animal of the wide open spaces, and of herds, and apparently can survive only under these conditions.

The *Report* for 1927 of the American Bison Society gives an account of a herd of ten of these antelopes purchased in Alberta and placed in the Wichita game preserve in Oklahoma. Shortly after their arrival six of them died, so in 1922 six more were purchased. Five of these died a few days after their arrival, leaving a total of five. In 1924 three pairs of twins were born and four of the old animals died. In 1926 ten fawns were born, so that in 1927 there was a total of seventeen head, a total increase over the original accessions of only one in five years. These figures show clearly that the preservation of this animal is a difficult problem, and it is obvious that zoological gardens can do little to help, since the creature certainly will not remain long alive in small inclosures.

We have never had much success in maintaining the prong-horned antelope in Washington. The first herd we

PLATE 56

Upper: American pronghorn antelope.   Does poorly in zoos
Lower: Young Philippine deer from Luzon

PLATE 57

Female Indian antelopes or black bucks.   Their pose betrays their nervousness

received consisted of three males and three females, sent by the superintendent of the Yellowstone National Park on December 10, 1896. The last of these died April 25, 1902, making a record of a little over five years for this species. Altogether we have had thirty-six in the collection, six of which were born here. One of them broke its leg during its life at the Zoo. This was put in splints, and apparently healed, for the animal lived for two years afterward, until a mule deer in an adjoining paddock leaped over a fence and gored it to death.

A number of young ones have come to us from Nevada, where they had been caught and raised by hand. They are usually gentle and tame, feed well and appear hardy, yet for some reason they have never thrived. Pneumonia has carried some off, but for the most part accidents have been the cause of death. They are very nervous, and a number of ours have jumped into the fence and died from the resultant injuries.

It is considered necessary to keep these animals in a dry paddock and away from green grass. Under these conditions they may do quite well, but on the whole they are very unsatisfactory to have in the collection.

The black buck of India, a medium-sized antelope, on the other hand, makes a most successful exhibit. Specimens of this antelope are nearly always in the collection, and they live remarkably well out-of-doors in the climate of Washington. Twenty-one of them have been born in the history of our Park, but curiously the most prolific pair of parents that we have had always refused to take care of the young, and would either butt it or kick it, so that most of them were killed before we could take them away. One that we succeeded in rescuing in time was raised on a bottle, and is now a fine adult male. The first specimen we ever received came from the zoological garden at Philadelphia in 1897, in exchange for four beavers.

The white-bearded gnu abounds throughout most of Tanganyika. With our file of boys we had marched from

Umbugwe, on the flat, arid plain, to a mimosa forest, and then three hours through forest and swamp, when we emerged suddenly on the open shore of the most delightful lake in the world, Lake Meru. Every traveler discovers the most wonderful lake in the world, and there is no reason why he should not, because each has its own particular charm for the traveler at the moment of discovery. So Meru, thirty miles long and four miles wide, so shallow that one could wade clear across it in many places, and with heavily saline waters, is to me the last word in African lakes.

As we came out of the woods, there jumped up in front of us three wart hogs, and then to the left we saw a small herd of kongoni, and beyond them a group of about 150 white-bearded gnu. The kongoni disappeared into the woods. The gnu started ahead of us on the shores of the lake, and from then on until we arrived at our camping place, Magi-Motu (hot springs) with its springs of hot and very sulphurous water coming out of the mountain side, we were never out of sight of herds of these animals. They would run along in front of the *safari*, zig-zagging back and forth. Two or three old males, guardians of the herd, hung behind, and they would prance toward us, brandishing their horns and waving their tails, then turn around and gallop toward the herd, shortly to repeat the threatening gestures.

One evening, as we came back toward camp from the hunt, this herd, running ahead of us, turned along an estuary of the lake and ran perhaps a quarter of a mile into a copse of wood. We were at the bend and saw them, and it occurred to us that if we could get them separated we might have a chance at one of the several young we had noticed, so George and I, together with six natives, squatted behind a bush. The other boys made a big detour through the woods, came out behind the herd, and suddenly charged at them, shouting. They ran in our direction, almost in a mass, which, by the time

PLATE 58

Upper: White-bearded gnu in Africa, when captured
Lower: After two years in Washington, a dangerous animal

PLATE 59

Aoudad, or Barbary sheep.   Father and son

they reached us, had become a thundering charge. When they were a hundred yards in front the eight of us jumped out at them with loud shouts, and the herd broke into 150 parts. Most of them whizzed by us. Since then, after seeing more of the gnu in captivity, I have wondered why one of the males did not horn us incidentally in passing. They were within eight or ten feet of us, and the gnu is no coward. Yet no one was hurt. Some broke to the left and went into the water, and we cut a yearling off from the shore. He started swimming toward the other side of the bay, making better time than we could, and disappeared into very thick cane. But he had to beat it down as he went, so that by taking advantage of the opening he had made, we soon came upon him where he had paused to rest, and dropped a lariat over him. He was tired and I ordered the boys to stand back until he had rested a bit. He recovered remarkably quickly, and the next thing we knew he was charging in my direction, with a pair of four-inch, perfectly straight, sharp horns pointing at my middle. With what I consider great presence of mind, I sat down in a foot-and-a-half of water, and he passed over me. Then we seized him. Four boys took him on their shoulders, carried him into camp and picketed him to a tree until they could build a small corral.

Our movie man had stayed in camp this day, and when we told him of the wonderful charge of the herd he was all for having a picture of it, so the next day we went out to repeat the performance. We left him hiding in the place that we had occupied the previous day. Then we made a long detour, hoping to round up the herd as before, but they would have none of it, and after many miles of walking, attempting to get in back of the gnu, we gave it up.

At night our captured gnu barked a number of times, and we could hear the nearby herd answering. The corral was not too strongly made at first, and he kept breaking through nearly as fast as we could piece it up, but in a day or two he appeared to become entirely reconciled to camp life, lost his fear of us, and while never very tame, could be readily handled.

At the end of the *safari*, when we got ready for the long trip back to where our automobiles were parked, we constructed a hammock for our gnu, an affair made out of burlap sacking fastened to two long poles and with four holes punched in it for his legs. Four boys carried the poles, and another one stood at his head. He looked uncomfortable at first, but as we walked along, sometimes on soggy ground, sometimes where it was rough, and always with sharp grass that would cut our bare knees, we often envied him riding in luxury in his hammock.

As we journeyed down the lake shore on our return to Umbugwe where our automobiles had been parked, this same herd kept running in front of us, zigzagging back and forth until at the end of the evening they had covered many times the distance that we had, walking in a more direct line, and they were tired. Suddenly, from their position perhaps a quarter of a mile ahead of us, they decided to get back between us and the lake. They turned around and came thundering toward us. There was a universal shout of *"Mtoto"* from our boys, and they raced in the direction of the herd, which in turn went into the lake. There was mud six inches deep, and ninety boys mingled with 150 wildebeeste splashing in the muddy water offered a wonderful sight. The grand finale saw the herd, now on shore again, get together and gallop madly away, while five little groups of boys in the water each held a live, kicking and bawling baby gnu. This is one of the times when an animal collector's heart is almost frothy in its lightness, while the movie man's heart is bowed down in sorrow. At the first cry of *"Mtoto"* all our baggage had gone skyrocketing into the air, cameras, tripods, and other photographic paraphernalia with the rest. It was several days before I had the nerve to look

PLATE 60

Upper: Rocky Mountain sheep or bighorns. Father, mother, and yearling

Lower: Mother and child

PLATE 61

Rocky Mountain goats from Banff, Canada

into the box that contained a portable typewriter. The camera man hurriedly got his apparatus together and had the camera set up just when everything was over and I was sprawled on the last gnu, tying him.

We had used up our available ropes on the first three. The fourth I had tied with cloth, hurriedly bargained for from the native who had considered it a suit of clothes up to that time, it being the least rotten rag that any of our boys wore. For the last I was using my belt, and just had it affixed to one foreleg, when I heard a plaintive, "Get some action in that, Bill" from the camera man. I let the antelope get up so that I might throw him again for the benefit of the film, but he legged it away, and the last we ever saw of him or my belt was as they both passed over the top of a little ridge in the direction of the herd.

One little gnu, separated from the rest, got beyond his depth in water and struck out swimming, our boys after him, but he kept ahead of them, and made a semi-circle, which we estimated at considerably more than a mile, and rejoined the others on the beach far beyond our reach, giving a most extraordinary exhibition of swimming power for a young antelope.

During the rest of the *safari* we picketed the young ones outdoors, where they grazed and gave no trouble at all. At Umbugwe we put them into a native house until we made crates, and then took them by automobile the 203 miles to Dodoma, our base camp, where we rented the back yard of our next-door neighbor for them until we started home.

One of them had been severely horned in the flanks, probably by one of the younger bulls of his herd, and despite veterinary treatment on the part of the Government doctor, he died. The other three at first lost flesh, due to entirely new diet.

The first thing to do with a young antelope is to get it in good condition, but these refused any native grains that we could buy. Finally we discovered that they would eat an American brand of oatmeal which comes to Africa in sealed tins, so for a month each was fed a tin of this a day. They became fat, eventually took to eating matama, and arrived in Washington the thriftiest of all our antelopes.

A pair of them have since lived out-of-doors for two years and developed into unusually handsome specimens. The male, though still not adult, is one of the most vicious individuals in our collection. We use a fairly light wire mesh rather than bars in these paddocks. Most antelopes let it alone, but Husky has developed a habit of charging the visitors, and incidentally ripping up the fence, so we had to put a heavy metal bar inside to keep him from it.

Recently, while at a committee meeting, I was informed by telephone that Husky had seriously gored his keeper, and hurrying to the hospital, I found the boy there. The gnu's quarters are so arranged that we can lock the animals either in the building or in the yard, depending on which is being cleaned. The keeper in this case was in the shed. The gnu was a hundred yards away in the yard, apparently asleep, so he took a chance and got eight feet into the yard, and the next thing he knew the young antelope was upon him. The wound afterwards proved to be not serious, but we know that in a year or so more we will have to double the strength of the inclosure for Husky.

The gnu is a heavy feeder, and on the voyage home, when I had become very much depressed at the small amount some of the antelopes were eating, I could always cheer myself up by sitting in front of one of the gnu crates and watching the antelope store away great portions of edibles. The gnu is a grazing animal and thrives on hay and grain.

We have had all three species, the white-bearded, the brindled, and the white-tailed. One of the latter lived for thirteen years in an open paddock with only a tight unheated shed for shelter in winter. Even in his declining years he would occasionally have wild fits of leaping about and barking in his paddock and fighting the bars or his keeper. He had the common vice of most antelopes in captivity, of working on the front of his cage with his horns, wearing them down or breaking them off. Our brindled gnu has broken off one of his horns in this manner. Our lechwe from Rhodesia has worn his down to a third their natural thickness. So general is the habit that I have seen few antelopes in cages that have not mutilated one or both of their horns.

One evening after the day's work at Tula a messenger came in from the railroad, bringing a pile of letters from home. There was one from Mr. Baker with news from the Zoo, all good news. Congress had approved a new building for our birds; a collection of nice things had come in from the East Indies as the gift of a naval officer; and we had finally exchanged the baby hippopotamus, which had been very much surplus (he was in the way because there was no place to keep him). In a foot-note at the bottom of the letter I read, "I do hope that you can secure some impallas, for I have always remembered them as the daintiest and most graceful of all antelopes." It so happened that that morning we had captured five of them for the first time after many attempts. As I read the letter they were all inclosed in a tight corral we had made by driving stakes in the ground and roofing them with nets.

Impalla hunting with nets is most exciting. Time after time as we sat behind the line, waiting to see what the boys would drive out of the woods, impallas had appeared. Nine times out of ten they would break through the line of boys and disappear with flying bounds. Sometimes they would come head on, and then gaily sail over the net. But this morning five jumped too short, got tangled, and were ours.

The delicate legs of the impalla, which are so easily broken, make it a difficult animal to transport, and we had no confidence that we would get any of these home alive, but the boys put them on their shoulders, and we returned to camp.

The natives love to dance. We liked to have them dance, as it showed they were in good spirits, and as the African dance at Tula is the only dance that I was ever able to learn, I used to join with them. On this occasion, just as we came into the camp, they started a wild celebration. The capture of five antelopes in the course of a half hour was almost too good to be true. They knew there would be some extra presents distributed that evening, and they broke into spontaneous gaiety. Those who had no spears robbed the nearest corn patch of its stalks, and waved them instead. It was all very gay until I suddenly noticed that even the boys who were carrying the impallas were dancing. It is not good for a delicate, newly-caught animal to be danced with, and I tried to make them stop. My knowledge of Swahili is not too good. They kept on dancing, and when I finally lost my temper, stamped, and waved my arms, they thought that was merely another kind of dance and kept right on. However, we finally got the antelopes into the *boma*, where to our great surprise they were comparatively quiet.

The following day they fed, and we eventually crated them and brought them home, arriving at Boston with all five of them. Two are still with us, contented and thriving, despite their very great nervousness. Because of their high-jumping abilities we have not been able to give them open paddocks, having no fence in the Zoo that they could not jump over.

In the field the impallas may always be counted on for a surprise movement. One sees them grazing and the next instant they will start off, making prodigious leaps in the air as they go. Apparently this is a great waste

PLATE 62

Arizona mountain sheep after eleven years in the paddock.   Thought to be a record for longevity in captivity

PLATE 63

The gemsbok, one of the handsomest of the African antelopes

of effort on their part, and yet it probably saves many of them, because they are exceedingly difficult to shoot. George had twitted me about a miss I had made, and a half hour later he tried for an impalla, which is, incidentally, one of the best eating game that we found, and also missed, so when I returned to him the sarcasm he had given me, he replied in explanation, "Well, there is an awful lot of space around an impalla."

The day a native brought in our first and only reed buck, a thin baby antelope, we were in the field, and every container we had was full. So all we could do was to picket him to a tree, where for three days and nights he tried to break his neck on the rope. He afterwards became a camp pet, and during the voyage home we put him in the crate with one of the younger impallas, a thing one should never do, by the way, because they are very likely to cut each other with their hoofs in any excitement. However, these two lived amicably. Their feeding habits presented a striking contrast, the reed buck eating largely, while for days it seemed that a leaf or two of alfalfa was all that the impalla would eat. We kept them in the same cage in Washington for about a year, when the reed buck, having developed neat little horns, took to charging the other, so we had to separate them.

Perhaps the most magnificent of antelopes are the East African eland and Livingstone's eland. The latter has been represented in our collection by six specimens. The Duke of Bedford presented the Park with two pairs from his herd at Woburn Abbey, England. Of these a female lived for ten years and a bull for nine, and this pair produced two young, one of which was sent to the zoo at Philadelphia. We have had three specimens of the East African eland, two of which were received from Henry Tarlton of Nairobi, British East Africa, in 1909. Our third specimen we brought back from East Africa in 1926. It was caught young and took six bottles of milk a day—two in the morning, two at noon, and two at night—when captured. It lived only six months in Washington.

Our experience with elands has not been strikingly successful, but in other zoos, and especially on large private estates, they have done well. Even in parts of Africa where the species has disappeared in the wild state, it is still preserved in small herds on farms.

The dainty chamois, which occurs in the Alps, has been represented by seven specimens in the history of the Park. In 1909 five of them were given by the Swiss Government to the United States Government, and two were born from these.

Practically every zoological garden exhibits the aoudad, or Barbary sheep, often in large herds, and it makes a most desirable addition to the collection because of its grace of form and its tremendous beard. It breeds almost as readily as domestic sheep. We have had specimens since the early days of the Zoo. Twelve to sixteen years are not unusual periods for the species to live in captivity.

If possible even better fitted than the aoudad for captivity is the tahr. This inhabitant of the Himalayas takes to confinement almost as readily as any domesticated animal, and a zoo which has started with a pair of these always has them upon its list labeled "surplus."

An interesting variety of domestic sheep, the Barbados, a species clothed with hair instead of wool, was long exhibited in the Park, having been received as a gift of the United States Department of Agriculture from their experimental farm at Bethesda, Maryland. Many were born, some were exchanged, but as is often the case among a little herd of animals in a zoo, the race finally died out. The last survivor was a male that had been sent out to be used as food for animals in 1911. He lived until 1925, when he died of old age.

The Rocky Mountain sheep, commonly called the bighorn, usually does not do very well in captivity, but we have had singular success with a small herd kept on a high dry hilltop, sheltered in inclement weather only by a roof, and fed, of course, on hay and grain. The paddock is divided by a wire with an opening at either end, through which smaller ones may escape when pursued by the others. This makes it impossible for one to corner another, and we have had no casualties, so that at the present time our herd consists of ten, of which seven were born in the Park, and four are grandchildren. One male, the father of five young in the Park, lived a little over seven years, finally dying of old age. Another one lived seven and a half years, coming here as an adult specimen, a gift of the Canadian Government, through Mr. J. B. Harkin, Commissioner of Canadian National Parks.

Our record for longevity in the bighorns was held by an Arizona mountain sheep (*Ovis canadensis gaillardi*), a ram from the Colorado Indian reservation, which was captured when about eighteen months old by an Indian and sold for ten dollars. He lived from September 18, 1917, to May 2, 1927, when he died of double pneumonia and pleuritis. He showed his age, with his horns badly worn from butting into the inclosure posts, but at the same time he was a gentle animal, friendly with his keeper and with visitors.

Besides these we have had the Mexican mountain sheep (*Ovis mexicana*) and Nelson's sheep (*Ovis nelsoni*). We have succeeded in keeping neither of these species longer than two years. Hornaday has described the mountain sheep as "of ruminant animals the philosopher-in-chief." In nature it inhabits high mountains in grass belts just above the timber line and formerly was hunted very much by the Indians for the sake of its fleece. It is now protected throughout practically all its range, so there is no danger of extermination. At Banff it comes down into the settlements, and I understand that the specimens which the Canadian Government sent us were trapped there.

The mouflon (*Ovis europaeus*) is the only member of the wild-sheep family inhabiting Europe. It is confined to the islands of Sardinia and Corsica, where it has been hunted almost to the point of extermination. However, the mouflon in captivity breeds readily, and it runs no danger of extinction. It is reported that occasionally wild mouflons desert their own kind to live in the herds of Sardinian shepherds, and sometimes a motherless domestic lamb has been known to seek companionship among a flock of mouflons. Handsome animals, they are popular in zoos, though it is a fearsome sight to see the old ram charge his keeper. When his horns hit a bucket held out as a protection, they make a sound which reverberates around the whole Park.

The mountain goat from our Northwest as a rule proves very delicate. Of the twelve we have had in the Park, most of them gifts of the Canadian Government, few have lived over two years, but the two males still living have been here now for six. One born here, whose mother died immediately after its birth, was raised on a bottle, and it lived for four years, dying at the end of that time from pneumonia. It is curious how pneumonia attacks such animals as these, accustomed in nature to withstand all the rigors of a high mountain climate.

Our males are very fond of climbing to the top of a big pile of rocks in their paddock, and one will remain motionless for long periods of time, so that visitors, noticing his absence, have asked whether we have removed the statue they had seen there on an earlier visit.

The Alpine ibex generally does well, and our specimens have bred, but so far neither of the young has lived longer than six months. We do not know why.

The other ibexes we have not had in the Zoo, though I once obtained a pair of specimens in Sinai. It is singular how these animals have persisted on the limited mountain

PLATE 64

East African water buck

ranges of this part of the world for thousands of years, without any protection other than their ability in mountain climbing and their furtiveness. They are still killed from time to time by the Arabs, and on our trip we had no difficulty in obtaining plenty of horns, but we did not come upon any live animals ourselves, despite days of climbing from one mountain crest to another. An Arab brought in two little ones, selling us one, but insisting on keeping the other to kill and eat, as he stated the meat of a young ibex would cure his fever. Usually one has, or should have, a certain sympathy for the beliefs of people among whom he is living. Though this was years ago I am still glad to know that the meat of this dainty little animal did not do him any good. The specimen we had was unable to stand the jolting of a long camel ride. It died about a week after we had secured it.

The habits of most of these sheep and goats in captivity are very much the same. They eat, stroll around the paddock, climb a pile of rocks if one is provided for them, and the males from time to time try to butt the keepers. The sheep in general are hardier than the goats.

CHAPTER XVI

SOME RHINOS THE PARK
HAS NOT HAD

THE history of the rhinoceroses that we have had at the National Zoological Park is very short. The temporary deposit by the Forepaugh Circus of its animals at the National Zoo afforded an opportunity for the only time in our history of exhibiting a Sumatran rhinoceros (*Dicerorhinus sumatrensis*). Later on, an African black rhinoceros (*Diceros bicornis*) was purchased. It was never in good health and died after a year and seven months at the Zoo. A post-mortem showed an abnormal structure of the teeth and jaws, as well as the intestinal trouble which had caused its death.

The rhinoceroses that we have not had, but have tried to get, make a longer story. Year after year we have sought one from our Congressional Committee. This is no fun at all, but in Africa we had the most pleasant though most disappointing part of our trip while on the trail of the black rhino. After finishing a day's hunt one evening, George and I were returning to our camp on Lake Meru when a messenger came to us from Lyman, who had moved up the lake to a separate camp in order to hunt buffaloes to better advantage. The message he sent us read:

S. O. S. Rhino. Have just shot a female rhino and are trying to capture its rather sizable young. Come at once with ropes.

We started off at once accompanied by the guide to the other camp, only stopping in our tent for a moment to spread cheese on bread and smear jam on top of that for a quick lunch. We ate this as we hastened along what was at first a trail but afterwards petered out into a succession of elephant pug marks. During the rainy season when the ground is soft, the feet of the elephants naturally make deep impressions in the trail, which later on may dry out leaving ugly places to fall into as one hurries along a trail. Our guide cheerfully kept telling us that we were almost there now. It grew dark, and the trail got worse. Something snorted once in the high grass ten feet from us, and galagos chattered incessantly. We reached Lyman's camp at eleven at night. It had been a twelve-mile walk, and at the end of it we found that he had shot the rhino just twelve hours previously and the little one had disappeared into the bush. Early in the morning we started out and spent hours beating the bush in an attempt to locate the youngster, but never found him. Perhaps a lion got him during the night.

The district commissioner at Mbulu had told us of an area on the Masai Steppe that was "stiff" with rhinos, so when I returned to the base camp with two truckloads of animals I went ahead into this district where I was to join George as soon as possible.

Coming back we secured additional natives at Mbulu, and started on a four-day *safari* to where George was supposed to be, but at the end of the first day we met him coming back. In a week he had seen only four rhinos, and none of them had young. Mando, our head boy among the natives, told us of the Ja-Aida swamp country, where there were "*faro mingi sana*," which means "very much rhino," which corresponds to the Spanish "*hay mucho*," which really means nothing.

Two days' *safari* took us to the swamp. We camped at one side on an elevation, and near a plain three miles wide and perhaps seven or eight long, that was teeming with antelopes and zebras. As we came into camp on our first night's march, a rhinoceros darted out of a clump of bush on the other side and fled. On *safari* next day a white-ant hill in front of us suddenly jumped up, and with tail up and head down charged off in the form of a 5,000-pound rhinoceros.

Once in camp we started out to follow day after day the trails made by the animals whose young we hoped to secure. We encountered during three weeks sixteen of them. Six times we crawled to within thirty or forty feet of them in the bush, attracted at first by the loud *zaa-zaa* of the rhinoceros birds, which the books say warn the rhino of his enemies. In the scrub it was necessary to get close to see if any young were there. George would usually whisper reassuringly, "When it charges, jump off the path," and invariably there was an aloe with sharp spines pointing at me from the only available place to which to jump. However, we were charged none of these times, thanks to keeping in the right relation to the wind, and finally after I had concluded that the rhinos were systematically practicing race suicide in this part of Africa, we came upon one with a baby. We peered into the bush, and George, who saw the *mtoto* (baby) first, made a grimace and elevated his palm, indicating that it was a very large one to attempt to catch. But we were getting desperate. This was the fourteenth rhino that we had seen and the first one with young, and after all, it gets tiresome spending day after day on trails followed 200 yards behind by a group of sixty boys—trained rhinoceros catchers (trained by ourselves at play in camp each evening after dinner, Mando being the rhinoceros and the other boys surrounding and roping him. This was a sort of drill which we hoped would be useful in case we ever did come across a young one). One of the boys carried a hammock. The thought of this hammock of burlap cloth on two poles—made especially for the rhino we did not catch—being carried patiently day after day over what seemed at the time like the whole of Africa, still fills me with sorrow. Anyway, there was a young one here. We saw the mother

PLATE 65

Baby African black rhinoceros, the National Zoo's only specimen

facing us. She did not see us, and we waited until she swung to one side, and then fired, taking the neck shot—eight inches back from the ear, and down. She fell to her knees, and then we discovered—a most hurried discovery—that it had been a family party of three, father, mother, and child, with the male asleep some twenty feet back of where the cow had been standing. He woke, jumped up, and charged, the young one following him. And so ended our one chance to get a young rhinoceros.

This *safari* was terminated suddenly by one of the rhinos that we did not get. This animal, as every one knows, is stupid and nearsighted, and when one is on his way to a water hole and suddenly finds himself surrounded by tents and native boys, he will charge through blindly. Our peaceful nights were interrupted four times in this way—the heavy rumble of a ponderous animal rushing into camp, and boys yelling, "Hia! Hia!"; one leaps out of his cot and into the open so as not to be caught in the same tent with the rhino. The boys, on the other hand, come rushing up to be near the white men and the guns. No harm was done until rhino number four came up. One had come through camp about eleven at night, and between two and three in the morning another, perhaps the same, came back. It was just as before, boys yelling and rhino charging, but Le Mesurier, awakened by the noise, saw his tent waving. A boy had tripped over one of the ropes, but Le Mesurier didn't know that. He jumped out and met a half dozen boys coming in, with the result that he was thrown down, caught his knee on a tent peg, and we had to break camp and take him to the Government station to get a doctor to perform a minor operation to save his leg.

One might truly say that the most magnificent animal in any zoo is an adult Indian rhinoceros, but few zoos have them. Magnificent in size, armor-plated with great folds of skin, it is as fantastic as the mighty animals of the prehistoric Carboniferous swamps. From the standpoint of the zoo, it is also one of the rarest of all large animals in collections, and at present little short of impossible to obtain. There are three living in America, but none have been in the market in the hands of dealers for many years, and even the largest circus has been unable to obtain one to replace the historic specimen which lived and traveled with the show for more than twenty years.

Unlike the hippopotamus, rhinos do not breed readily in captivity, though they have done so once or twice. They have long been known in captivity, but never very many at one time. Always objects of superstition and fear, it may be that we see in the rhino the origin of the fabled unicorn. Its picture is found in ancient Chinese hieroglyphics. In the Roman arena they were pitted against lions, but we have no records of the results of these contests.

In 1517 a rhinoceros and an elephant were brought to Lisbon and presented to King Manuel. There was much discussion in the court and on highways as to "which could lick which," so the king decided to put it to the test. A city street was closed with palisades, the rhinoceros concealed behind a curtain, and the elephant brought in, whereupon the curtain was raised and the rhino began tugging at his chain. The attendant, an East Indian, loosened this, and the rhino advanced slowly toward the elephant with his horn lowered. The elephant stood still, watching his supposed enemy advance near him, then suddenly lose confidence in himself and flee, butting his head against the barrier. The elephant turned and went back to his stable.

John Evelyn, in his *Diary* (1684), records that he "went with Sir William Godolphin to see the rhinoceros, or unicorn, being the first that I suppose was ever brought into England. She belonged to some East India merchants, and was sold (as I remember) for above £2,000."

SOME RHINOS THE PARK HAS NOT HAD

At this time rhino horns were in great demand, due to the ancient superstition that a drinking cup made from one of them would reveal the presence of poison. A writer in 1762 stated that when wine is poured into a rhino horn, it will rise, ferment and seem to boil, but when mixed with poison it "cleaves in two." Evelyn saw in Italy a fountain kept free from poison by a rhino horn. This superstition prevails today, and accounts for the rarity of the animal throughout India. I have been told that a good horn from the Indian rhinoceros would bring as much as $1,000 in China, where it is used, also, in the preparation of certain very valuable, very Chinese remedies.

African rhinos are captured by shooting the mother and then seizing and tying the young one with ropes. The small ones tame very quickly, and with proper care may be transported successfully.

Charles Mayer, well-known animal collector, describes a method used in trapping the adult Indian rhinoceros. The first step is to dig a pit about six feet wide, with sides gently inclining to the bottom. Rhinos particularly delight in wallowing in mire, so after the pit is concealed by a covering of boughs and branches, a coating of mud is laid and allowed to dry. When this has baked hard a pool is made. Care must be taken to give this as natural an appearance as possible, for the rhinoceros is a suspicious animal. After stepping on the trap, he slides to the bottom without damage to himself. Coolies then start a cage of rattan ropes, just large enough to hold the rhino, while others are building an inclined road towards the animal's head. This road is just wide enough to permit the cage to slide down on round logs. The door of the cage is raised to allow the entrance of the animal. A thin wall of earth has been retained between the end of the road and the rhino. When the coolies begin to push this wall into the pit on top of the animal, he rushes into the cage, and the door is dropped.

The rhinoceros is reputed to be one of the most dangerous of animals, although some of the Javanese variety
are so docile that natives saddle them and ride them
like horses. A. D. Bartlett states that when very young
and small they have been known to toss and roll a ball
about their paddock for hours, pushing it with the part
of the head where the horn will be formed. Mr. Bartlett
bore witness, however, to the ferocity of adult rhinos.
The Indian animal in the London Zoo, he said, would
have fits of rage during which it would dash its head
against the walls of its paddock, sometimes tearing off a
horn and leaving that part of the skull bare. The male
is especially intractable. The female sometimes remains
docile throughout life in captivity.

The horn is a mass of agglutinated hair which sometimes causes serious trouble to the animal. Mr. Bartlett
tells of one instance where he was obliged to saw off the
horn of a female which had grown forward so that it
projected beyond the nose, making it impossible for the
animal to get its mouth to the ground to eat. This beast
would allow the veteran keeper to stroke its head through
the bars of the cage, keeping its eyes closed during the
petting. For several days he tried her out, patting her
forehead just above the eyes with one hand and practicing sawing upon the horn with a walking stick with
the other hand. On the morning of the experiment he
went to the cage with another man, armed with a saw.
The keeper started stroking the eyes while his companion
sawed off the horn. Never once did the beast open her
eyes and she remained perfectly quiet during the operation.
The horn of another rhino grew back until it threatened
to pierce the skin. This creature was not so docile. Its
front feet were fastened by ropes to the bars and the
sawing process started but three saw blades were snapped
by the beast's struggles before the horn was ampu-
tated.

Mr. Bartlett's most thrilling experience with captive

FIG. 14. Bull moose calling. Courtesy of Carl Rungius

FIG. 15. Sketches from an artist's note book. By Benson B. Moore

rhinos came one winter morning when the female mentioned above broke through the ice which covered a pool nine feet deep in the elephant paddock. The poor beast was struggling helplessly to gain a foothold on the steep and slippery bank. The entire zoo force at the time, twenty-six men, were hastily summoned. A rope was tossed around the animal's haunches and all started to pull. They succeeded sooner than they had expected. The rhino, with the help of the rope, managed to get out of the pool. It had been agreed that as soon as she secured a foothold which she could keep the men were to drop the rope and run. A narrow gate was open behind them. The first to reach it was a fat man who stuck fast in the narrow opening, thus penning his fellows in the inclosure with the excited beast. The animal, however, did not chase them. She seemed grateful to them for saving her life. If she had lost her head some of the men almost certainly would have been killed. The rhino, once it starts a charge, continues relentlessly in a straight line and jabs its horn into whatever it encounters, whether this be a man or a tree. It attacks with no more volition than a cannon ball, incapable of changing its course until it comes in contact with some exterior force. For this reason it is so dreaded by hunters and by natives.

While the rhinoceros shares little of the intelligence of the elephant, it is subject to the same paroxysms of rage which sometimes make that animal one of the most dangerous in captivity. The "bad" rhino is an ugly customer. A notable example was "Smiles," an African black rhino cow at the Central Park Zoo in New York. She was purchased from a circus. For ten years she had been cooped in a cage which was too small for the animal to turn around, traveling 5,000 miles a season. The real viciousness of the creature came out in the spacious stall provided for her in the elephant house—a viciousness hardly to be wondered at when we consider the conditions under which she had lived. At first the slightest noise would excite her to a frenzy and she would rush like a mad bull, driving her fourteen-inch horn through the two-inch sheathing of her stall, and knocking the plank into splinters. In time, after the stall had been lined with sheet iron, she calmed down. She lived for nearly twenty years in her new home, but at any time during this period it would have been suicide to enter her stall without first roping and tying her. Early one morning her keeper was alone in the elephant house, forking straw into a corner of her stall. The rhino was straining furiously against the fetters around her neck and head. Suddenly one of the ropes parted. The man tried to make a rush for the door, but with a mighty twist of the head, the animal broke the remaining ropes. The keeper saw that he was not only headed off but cornered. The beast rushed with lowered head, horn tilted forward to run the man through the body. With a yell for help the keeper threw himself against the wall. About eight feet from the floor was a horizontal joist. With a frenzied effort he jumped for this, reached it and drew himself up in the nick of time. The rhino's horn caught his trousers leg and ripped overalls, breeches and drawers from ankle to hip. The skin, however, was not scratched. Other keepers had arrived by this time. The infuriated cow was driven off with pitchforks and iron bars and the man rescued from his perilous perch.

Visitors to the National Zoological Park used to wonder to see in one of the cages the curious combination of a young African rhinoceros and a goat. The rhino was pining away with loneliness when this companion was furnished him. They became very good friends, perfectly harmless to each other. The larger animal, however, could not be reared to maturity.

CHAPTER XVII

THE HORSE FAMILY

THERE have been few more important developments in the progress of man than the domestication of the horse sometime before the dawn of history. By subduing the horse to his will man obtained an instrument for conquering distance which he was unable to improve upon for thousands of years. Until early in the nineteenth century a human being never had traveled faster on land than a horse could run. Its value was discovered all over again during the Boer War, and Kipling pointed out to the British army that four legs are better than two.

We do not know definitely what species was domesticated. Of the wild relatives of the horse still extant—Prejvalski's horse, the wild asses, and the zebra—none fills exactly the qualifications which the ancestor of the domestic type must have possessed and neither does the extinct forest horse of Europe.

The specifications for an ancestor of the domestic horse are most closely approximated by Prejvalski's horse in Central Asia. This was discovered in 1880 by the Russian army officer and explorer from whom it takes its name, and the zoologists are more or less agreed that it is at least a close relative of the domestic horse. Prejvalski brought back only one skin of the wild horse, from which the species was described, but a few years later two other Russian travelers, the brothers Grum-Grizimailo, brought back four of these animals alive, depositing them in the zoological gardens at St. Petersburg.

In 1889 Frederick Edward Falz-Fein, a wealthy German who had established a wild animal preserve of nearly

2,000 acres on the Dnieper near the small city of Perekop in Russia, conducted noteworthy experiments in acclimatization and domestication, as well as hybridization, using these horses, zebras, and the domestic horse of Russia as subjects, but he met with indifferent success. It is said that one of his wild horses was domesticated to the point where it could be ridden by Cossacks, but this does not mean a great deal. There are many Western mustangs that can be ridden by cowboys which I should hesitate to call domesticated.

All of the Prejvalski's horses now living in collections are descendants of an original herd captured by the German animal dealer, Hagenbeck, and brought to Europe in 1899. The hunters arrived in the field at a fortunate time, about the middle of May, and on the steppes which surround the little city of Kobdo at the foot of Mt. Altai were able to capture fifty-two colts by running the herds until the young ones, out of breath and exhausted, would drop behind. With thirty natives employed to care for the captives, the expedition made its way overland for fifty-nine days from Kobdo to the nearest station on the trans-Siberian railroad, and after eleven months returned to Hamburg with twenty-eight of the colts still alive.

Whether or not Prejvalski's horse is the ancestor of the domestic horse, certainly the prehistoric drawings in Spanish caves show outlines of horses strikingly like our specimens.

The quaggas, a species which is now extinct, striped like the zebra, but without bands on the legs, with short ears and tufted tails, once roamed in great herds over the South African plains, but were gradually killed off for food by the natives and the early settlers. Some attempts were made to domesticate them. South African farmers are reported to have sometimes kept quaggas with their cattle as a protection against hyenas, which the wild horses would kill with their hoofs. As a result of indiscriminate slaughter, the only known quagga lived

PLATE 66

Grevy's zebra.   Presented to President Roosevelt by King Menelik of Abyssinia

PLATE 67

A pair of famous hybrids.   Grevy zebra by Morgan mare, and Grevy
zebra by domestic ass

in the London Zoo years after all the other specimens had been wiped out.

The mountain or true zebra, with distinct donkeylike ears and tail, would have followed the quagga to extinction, had not the government of South Africa given the few remaining herds in the mountains strict protection. Until 1875 the mountain zebra existed in great herds, but it is now reduced to a few small troops frequenting the wildest and most desolate spots in the high lands. Occasionally it comes into captivity, and we are fortunate in having a beautiful pair at the Park from which we hope to raise successors.

The finest of all zebras is the Grevy's, which is also the largest species, with much finer stripes than the others. One famous specimen in our Zoo was presented to President Roosevelt by the King of Abyssinia in 1904. It had walked a distance of 150 miles from the capital to the coast at that time, and arrived at Washington in company with some magnificent young lions and two ostriches. The zebra lived here fifteen years and was loaned to the U. S. Department of Agriculture for experiments in hybridization with the domestic ass and with the horse. The results of these experiments are Juno, our Morgan mare-zebra hybrid, and a zebra-ass hybrid, both of which are still living at the Park.

Though the hybridization of these two species has proved successful, the resultant mules are not especially desirable as work animals. It was hoped that crossing the zebra and the ass would result in a hybrid immune from the horse disease of Africa and so useful as a work animal in the areas infested by the tsetse fly. But the hybrid has proved not very tractable, and it lacks the power and stamina of the domestic horse, so that breeding for utilitarian purposes has been abandoned. However, one sees the mules from time to time, and one of the American circuses had a team of six which drew a wagon in the parade.

Burchell's and Chapman's zebras are the two species found much more frequently in collections. The colored man's description of the zebra as a "sport-model donkey" is not too bad, but not nearly so funny as the description appearing on the circus program of a performance of a group of eight of these skittish animals in one of our circuses. The menagerie tent just before this act was to come on represented a bedlam, keepers being dragged around, kicked, and bitten. Finally the little troupe were led, herded, pushed and otherwise maneuvered into the center ring of the big tent, where they trotted around the ring three times, and then stopped. Then to a long "*Zaa-a-a-a-a*" by the band, about half of them put their heads over the shoulders of the adjoining zebra, when they were hurried out and tied again in their temporary stalls. It was amusing to watch their tails. A troupe of horses would have performed mechanically and without much show of emotion, but every zebra's tail in this troupe kept doing a St. Vitus's dance. The program's description of this performance read as follows: "Number 18. Herds of performing zebras in the center ring will astonish you with their feats of almost unbelievable intelligence."

One of our Chapman's zebras, startled by some unusual sound, jumped into the fence and broke its neck. We got another pair which arrived at the Zoo one evening, and were placed in the paddock. The following morning a small stick of dynamite was set off at the other end of the Park. The zebras started, and one of these also broke his neck on the fence.

The Chapman's zebra abounds in Tanganyika. It is so common that in some districts it has been declared a pest by the game department, and can be killed at will. Natives are fond of the meat, and on some *safaris* it forms the staple food for the porters. We collected ours in the mountains beyond Mbulu. Getugenah, Sultan of the Wamburu, had come to our camp with eighty men.

THE HORSE FAMILY

In the days of German control Getugenah had had some experience in collecting animals for the white traders, and he volunteered to help us get some zebras. The best way, of course, would have been to run them down on horses and lasso them. But there were no horses, nor could any live there on account of the disease-carrying tsetse fly, so the only thing we could do was to run them down by man power.

Getugenah took us to an area of hilltops. It was a very foggy morning when we started out, so that we could see little, but later on the fog lifted suddenly, and before us we saw a herd of about four hundred zebras feeding in and among herds of native humped-back cattle, and paying no attention to the herdsmen. Getugenah had earlier placed little groups of men all about the hilltops and they commenced running the zebra herd, which broke up into numerous small lots of a dozen or so each. There were a number of young among them. The herd would gallop a half mile away from a group of shouting and gesticulating natives, suddenly to come upon another group of the same, turn, gallop another half mile, and again meet more of their harassers. It ended by some of the younger ones dropping behind, whereupon we, accompanied by Getugenah and a group of men who had been resting, dashed up, surrounded them and got lassos over the necks of the youngsters. One was about two-thirds grown. She had slipped in a muddy place, and we were able to put a halter on her before she got up. It was surprising how easy it proved to handle these freshly caught animals, partly, of course, due to the fact that they were very tired at the time. We let each one rest, and gave it water.

On the larger animals we arranged two ropes, diverging, with natives at either end to pull against each other when the animals cavorted, and by this means we managed to lead all of the animals back slowly, with occasional disturbances on their part, to camp. We put them into a mud-and-thatch house and kept them from food until noon the following day, when they all ate, the little ones drinking quantities of tinned milk. Our largest prize became fairly tame in a short time, and her juniors would follow her about, so when we made our long march down the mountains to our animal depot, she took the lead with the others after her.

Tomasi, our cook boy and best animal man among the natives, had been the first to grab this animal. He was proud of her and asked me, rather beseechingly, "Him name Mary?" thereby exposing an affair of the heart that he had had at a nearby village. We teased him about this affair, and he denied it, but afterwards he married Mary, even though he had to change from Christian to Mohammedan to do so. The change seemed very simple. He drew some of his salary and bought a fez, and stopped eating pig.

CHAPTER XVIII

THE POUCH BEARERS

THE marsupials provide a curious and valuable educational exhibit for the zoological garden.

It would almost seem that there exists in nature special niches for various types of animals—the mole, the bear, the squirrel, the cat. Throughout most of the world the placental animals developed into types to fill these niches, but where they were not present, in Australia and the neighboring islands, the isolated marsupials developed and produced approximately the same results. So, among the marsupials we have animals strikingly like the sloths, wolves, cats, moles, and flying squirrels. They develop similar physical forms and exhibit similar behavior, though actually the relationships between the slothlike native "bear" of Australia, the koala, and the South American sloths, and between the thylacine, or Tasmanian wolf, and our prairie wolf are far more distant than that between the latter and the elephant.

Marsupials are in general inferior in intelligence to similar forms among the placentates. Most of them are timid, harmless animals, usually nocturnal, and on the whole not well fitted for captivity. Exceptions include various types of kangaroos, the dasyure, or native cat, wombats, Tasmanian devils, and phalangers, all of which have been kept successfully at our Zoo. The latter have bred several times.

The Tasmanian devils which we have had here have not lived up to their reputation. One, which we had for five years, became quite tame, and would come to the front of the cage and even endure furtive taps and scratches by way of caress. Probably its fierce appearance and its voracious hunting and feeding habits have given it the reputation it bears.

In recent years the Australian authorities have tightened their restrictions on exporting the rarer of the native animals—wisely, because some of the most interesting of all the species are in danger of extermination. We have exhibited twenty-seven species of Australian marsupials at various times, including a number of kangaroos, several phalangers, and in times past even the rare Tasmanian wolf now approaching extinction and practically unknown in collections outside of Australia. Of the five specimens we have had, one lived for seven years and one month.

While kangaroos normally thrive in zoological gardens, there is a curious disease called puff mouth, the nature of which is not very well known, which sometimes creates havoc in the collection, and which has on several occasions completely wiped out the kangaroo herds in our zoological parks.

Not all marsupials are restricted to Australia. One of the common duties of a zoological park director in this country is to write letters "thanking you for the kind offer," but refusing to buy American opossums from numerous captors. This animal is brought in so frequently and lives so well that zoos are usually well stocked with them. Besides, they do not make an attractive exhibit.

On the other hand, some of the smaller South American species are beautiful little animals. Once, in Bolivia, an Indian brought me a mother of one of the tiny species, with her family of five young. The mother herself was no larger than a mouse, and the babies, red in color and hairless, were grouped about her waist. I put them in a small Mason jar and tied a piece of cloth over the top. They lived here for some weeks until an assiduous servant, in cleaning the house, turned the jar over and

PLATE 68

GLEESON

Thylacine wolf and pups from Tasmania.   Tail of young can be seen protruding from rear of pouch

THE POUCH BEARERS

forgot to turn it up again, so the mother bit a small hole in the covering and crawled through, scraping off her family, which were left in a little cluster in the bottom of the jar. All I could do was to gather them up with a teaspoon and pickle them for the Museum.

In Australia, one of the great questions for argument, of less importance only than politics and the price of wool and mutton, is whether the young kangaroos are born in the usual way, or whether they are born in the pouch. Australia is divided into two schools over this question, and there exist tales of lifelong friendships which have been riven by a difference of opinion on this subject. Baby kangaroos are very tiny, and after they get into the pouch they attach themselves to the mother's nipples and remain there. So it is quite natural that early bush naturalists in Australia would assume that they had simply grown *in situ*. Recently the birth of the young and their unaided journey through the mother's fur to the pouch has been observed in both the kangaroo and the American opossum. Mr. Blackburne's notes on this subject are of interest:

Several great red kangaroos (*Macropus rufus*) and rufous-bellied wallabies (*Macropus billardieri*) have been born and bred in the Park. No one here has ever been present at a birth, and so we can not say from personal experience how the young one reaches the pouch.

A great red kangaroo bred July 2, 1916. Life was first noticed in the pouch September 6, 1916. On December 3, 1916, the head of the young could be seen peering over the edge. From that time until February 21 the baby was in and out of the pouch, but after that date the mother refused to allow him to crawl in again. However, for several months thereafter she did permit the young to put his head into the pouch to nurse. I have frequently seen a youngster nursing in this manner while the pouch was pretty well filled with another young one.

A young female rufous-bellied wallaby for some reason

[219]

discarded her first baby. The youngster was very much frightened at being dropped so suddenly, and made repeated attempts to crawl back into the pouch. The mother loosened the draw string, leaving the pouch wide open so as to make it impossible for him to get in. For a few minutes he jumped about the cage, and then crawled into the pouch of his grandmother, who was at the time carrying a youngster of about the same size in her pouch. She seemed perfectly satisfied to care for both babies and the two made an amusing picture, poking their heads out of the pouch. As they grew older and bold enough to venture out for hopping exercise, both would frequently become alarmed and dart back to the pouch at the same time, each scrambling to get in ahead of the other. Many authorities, among them E. S. Joseph, an Australian animal dealer, have told me that they never knew of a wallaby having twins.

PLATE 69

Upper: Tasmanian devil, which, like the kangaroo, carries its young
after birth in a pouch.   Reaches a length of three feet when adult
Lower: Yellow-footed rock wallaby from Australia

PLATE 70

Great red kangaroo from Australia, with young in pouch

CHAPTER XIX

OTHER MAMMALS

PEOPLE frequently ask which is the rarest animal in the collection, a question easy to answer in our Zoo, because that position is filled by the South American bush dog (*Icticyon venaticus*), which at the present time we believe to be the only specimen in captivity, and a species which comes into collections very rarely indeed. It is known to the Indians as *perro con cola chuta* ("dog with the short tail"). It inhabits the wet forest and is nocturnal in habit, so that, as people do not go into the marshes at night, the dog is not seen.

Major E. A. Goldman, of the U. S. Biological Survey, while collecting in Panama, shot at a running object hidden in the bush, and one of these dogs rolled out.

Our specimen was obtained in Rio Janeiro by Mr. W. L. Schurz, the commercial attaché at the American Embassy there, and kept as a pet until he returned to America on a visit, when the animal was presented to the National collection. On arrival at New York he appealed particularly to the newspaper writers, and for weeks accounts of him were broadcast in the press. He was described as a dog with webbed feet, a bobbed tail, and a voice like a bird, and the description is correct. To this may be added that he has tiny ears and a strong, weasel-like smell. He has lived here now since June, 1924, is very tame, and will come to the bars to be petted at any time. He wags his short tail as any dog will do, and while being petted emits a curious whining sing-song. We once took our specimen to the Smithsonian Institution to form part of a temporary exhibit there. When our specimen came back to the Zoo, the first thing he did was to bite his keeper for the first time.

The mongoose, existing in many species in Africa and India, is well known in captivity, both as a pet and as a zoo animal. It deserves attention not only as a traditional enemy of venomous reptiles, but also because of its incessant activity in or out of captivity.

The Indian species (*Herpestes griseus*) is prohibited from entering the United States, and wisely prevented, for wherever it has been introduced it has become a fearful pest. Jamaica furnishes a classic example, as well as Fiji and other localities. Not only does it kill snakes, but any other small things it can get to, such as lizards and birds, and it becomes an able, persistent enemy of the poultry yard.

Years ago, while in Fiji, I was especially anxious to obtain specimens of the native frogs, a distinct species, and especially interesting because of their occurrence in such remote islands. Eventually I did secure some. Formerly they must have been very abundant, as I found four different names for frogs among the natives, but when I asked about them in the vicinity the reply was always the same:

"There used to be lots of them, but they are gone—mongoosi."

I have heard that a friend of mine brought in a pair of this species as "Egyptian weasels." The customs man could find nothing in the book about Egyptian weasels, so these took their places as household pets, and eventually went to a zoo.

One of the most spectacular African forms is the East African white-tailed mongoose, which has an enormous long-haired, whitish tail, quite as long as its body. The specimen that we captured lived only a few months, but we succeeded in bringing in several pairs of the banded mongoose.

[222]

One of these, aboard the ship on the homeward voyage, showed remarkable intelligence. We had made our shipping boxes as best we could; each of them had a footboard which could be raised for purposes of cleaning, and sometimes these were not securely fastened, so one of our mongoose specimens got loose in the hold. It is not pleasant to have a mongoose alive and loose among a hundred cages of birds. We immediately put out traps, caught him that evening, and put him back into the box. He escaped again the following day, and having become acquainted with the type of traps we had, would not go into one. But he could not get into the bird cages, and after a day apparently missed the meals that came regularly into his old home. We had driven a nail into the footboard to keep his mate from getting out, and our escaped mongoose actually worked this nail loose, lifted the footboard, and got inside the cage, where we found him next morning.

Interest in the crab-eating mongoose from India lies in the fact that it is partly aquatic in its habits, swimming easily and feeding chiefly on crabs and frogs. It is a restless, active creature, and does not do well in captivity, even in India. I have never seen one alive in America.

The mongoose is apt to bite, and when talking to the keeper in a zoo it may be best not to mention Kipling's Riki to him, because he is quite likely to have been recently bitten by the local specimen.

The water mongoose (*Herpestes paludinosus rubescens*) of East Africa belongs to the rarer species of this genus. On the first evening of our first *safari* we had found beneath some débris near camp a white-tailed rat, and had put him into a cage improvised from a hurriedly emptied food box. The following day as we were walking near the lake shore, a boy shouted "*Mtoto!*" and pointed to a small animal loping along the beach. While we were on *safari* our boys, knowing that we were after young animals, and that the boy who should see a young one first would receive baksheesh, applied the name to everything we saw. For business purposes a forty-year-old elephant would have been a *mtoto* to them. At first we thought this particular *mtoto* to be an otter, because of its undulating manner of moving. We ran him down on foot, and grabbed him by the neck. He seemed to be a fairly powerful animal, and we shouted for something to put him in. The box with the rat was brought, and we popped him into that, and closed the door. The next thing we heard was a steady *"Crunch, crunch."* Ten minutes after being captured he had killed and completely eaten his box mate.

We carried this mongoose around with us in a crate made of heavy twigs bound together, for a month, until we finally got him back to camp and into a proper cage. He became fairly gentle, made no attempt to snap, and appeared to take an interest in his keeper. At home in the Zoo he was always well behaved and friendly, but consumption carried him off at the end of three months.

The largest of the civets is the East African. We have had two specimens. Usually in captivity it is strongly nocturnal, though occasionally a specimen will adapt itself somewhat to zoo life and become active during the day. It is almost omnivorous, and fairly easy to keep. We secured several specimens in Tanganyika. A native brought one to me while I was in a hotel there. I boxed the animal and left him in the courtyard for the night. Sometime after midnight I was awakened by most terrific howls. For a time I did not understand where they came from, but eventually located them in the civet box. I was afraid of being put out of the hotel, so I went out and scolded him to quietness, then returned to my room. There I enjoyed about five minutes before the howling commenced again. The rest of the night I had to sit alongside the box, keeping the animal cowed in the corner, while the mosquitoes fed on me until

PLATE 71

Elephant shrews from East Africa, about eight inches long, not counting the tail

PLATE 72

Wolverine from Cordova, Alaska.   Sagacious, quarrelsome, and gluttonous

daylight came. This animal has a strong musky smell, not unpleasant when not too strong, which it can emit at will.

The Indian civet, although differing in appearance, has about the same habits as the East African. In captivity both are fed on meats, fruit, and eggs.

Any boy who has ever read Olive Thorne Miller's *Four-Handed Folk* feels the crying need of a pet kinkajou in his life. Personally I was unable to get that need out of my soul until many years after reading the book, when I did secure one. The kinkajou, sometimes called "night monkey," though not a monkey, and apparently never called kinkajou except in the books and on zoo park labels, inhabits the greater part of tropical America, occurring in several varieties. As large as a cat, with a long, prehensile tail, rather bearlike feet, soft yellow fur, large eyes, and usually of gentle disposition, it is an altogether handsome and satisfactory pet.

The first one I had came from the zoo at Pará, Brazil, and was given to me in exchange for a dead scaly-tailed rat from the upper Amazon. The zoo carpenter was engaged to make the cage, and he did it in two days of hard work; it was the most beautiful box I have ever had, each bar of hardwood, carefully rounded and inserted in a hardwood footboard. During the day the *jupara* (that is what he is called in Brazil) slept, but in the evening he would climb around the steamer as far as the cord to which he was tethered would permit. He had the most voracious appetite for his size of any animal I have known. Though smaller than a cat, three or four bananas were considered a light lunch.

Two other kinkajous were given to me in Honduras. I left them in my room at the fruit company's headquarters, caged in a heavy wooden box. On a shelf on the wall I put a dozen bananas. When I returned in the evening, the floor was strewn with banana skins, and the two kinkajous were coiled up together sleeping on the shelf. They had clawed their way out of the box. The kinkajou has long, sharp canine teeth, and sometimes does use them. A specimen in the collection once bit through the hand of one of our keepers.

It is often far easier for American zoos to obtain rare animals from obscure corners of Africa and from Asia than from our own continent. Thus, for twenty years there was not a single specimen of the Alaskan wolverine in the National Zoological Park. Recently Dr. Will H. Chase of the Alaska Game Commission, who is in touch with hunters and trappers in that part of the world, succeeded in getting a nice trio of them. These were caught in steel traps, caged in very stout boxes metal-lined, with iron bars, and shipped to Washington. We liberated them in a large outdoor cage. For a time they were fierce animals, charging the visitors and the keeper, but very soon they tamed down, and became ideal animals for exhibition. They are playful, fond of romping around the cage, and appear to be fond of each other, for they will sleep together, though they do a great deal of snapping and jangling among themselves. One has shown a special liking for climbing a tree in the inclosure. He lies on his back in a crotch and does crude gymnastics.

When one of our wolverines looks one over in a not unfriendly way through the bars of his cage, it is hard to imagine how this largest of the weasels acquired his reputation as the meanest as well as one of the cleverest of warm-blooded creatures. But that he will follow a line of traps through the snow and devour the captured animals is a well-established fact, and he commonly seeks out and destroys the food caches left by hunters and trappers. One of the most inspiring bits of profanity I have ever heard came from a couple of visitors, undoubtedly Alaskans, who were standing in front of the cage discussing the inclosed trio.

Because of the demand for its fur, for use in aviation costumes, the wolverine is becoming scarcer and may

PLATE 73

Malay or saddle-back tapir, one of the half dozen species known

PLATE 74

Giant anteater from South America, which lives in the Zoo on a diet of milk and eggs

eventually become extinct. The Detroit Zoo has a splendid collection of eleven of the animals living together in an open-air pit. So far they have not bred, though I believe a breeding pair of the European species once lived in the zoo at Copenhagen.

The interesting European wolverine, or glutton, has appeared more often in captivity than the American species. He was exhibited in the menageries of the Romans and appears from time to time in the accounts of the royal animal collections of the Middle Ages. One animal kept in the Jardin des Plantes was termed "the animal vulture" by Buffon. He ate a great deal, more than four pounds of flesh a day, if indulged, but when deprived of food was not importunate. In drinking he lapped like a dog. He moved with a kind of leap, and after eating covered himself with straw in his cage.

The ratel, or honey badger (*Mellivora capensis*), a large, badgerlike animal, lives throughout most of East Africa, where no other animal inspires more fear in the natives. It is fearless, and, for its size, one of the most powerful mammals. The one we secured was brought to us at Dodoma by the Wagogo. We put it into a box but that night it scratched a hole in the side and walked out. After considerable effort we got it into another, heavier box, through which it also walked, so we eventually got some tin and lined the cage, and by substituting sheet metal for the tin later, we managed to keep it boxed until it arrived in Washington. Since then it has spent all of every day sleeping beneath a pile of hay.

Sometimes the ratel becomes diurnal when kept in a menagerie. The specimen in Philadelphia is awake through the day and is a comparatively tame animal, allowing itself to be petted to some extent; but ours has remained strictly nocturnal and always very savage.

On a recent occasion a correspondent offered us the "first albino gray squirrel that had ever been captured" for two hundred dollars or "what will you offer?" and we could only reply by stating that "these are such quarrel-some animals that should we put this one in with the three we already have, they would probably fight." The albino is not at all uncommon.

The black squirrels in the National Zoological Park are simply melanistic forms of the gray. Some years ago a half dozen pairs were brought from Ontario and liberated in the Park, and now between fifty and a hundred are living here.

Lack of quarters has prevented us from maintaining collections of exotic squirrels, though some of the most brilliantly colored of all small mammals are the squirrels of the East Indies.

In the London Zoo there is a house given over entirely to squirrels. I noticed the favorite with the public was the ordinary American gray squirrel.

Of the half dozen species of tapirs known, only two regularly come into captivity. These are the saddle-back or Malay tapir (*Acrocodia indica*) and the common South American tapir (*Tapirus terrestris*). The former is the handsomer animal and rarer in American collections.

Until recently we had three species in the collection, but the Malay individual died after a fourteen years' residence, leaving us with the South American and the rare (at least in captivity) Baird's tapir (*Elasmognathus bairdi*) of Central America. The latter species has appeared in the United States a number of times, but usually the young will not live.

In Honduras I made friends with a man who had a small zoo in his back yard, and I talked so convincingly of the need felt by the great American people to look at a Baird's tapir that finally, mellowed by this talk and by certain influence imported from England, he gave me the animal. It had been feeding entirely on bananas, and I had difficulty at first to get it to eat anything else. Before we reached New York, however, it was eating a few boiled potatoes, with which we had mixed bananas. It

PLATE 75

Armadillo from South America with his jointed armor plates

PLATE 76

South American two-toed sloth in his favorite pose

is still living, and has grown from a weight of 186 pounds, including the crate, to a net bulk now of about 500 pounds. This is probably the largest of all the tapirs, and is said to attain a weight of 1,200 pounds, though I have never seen any approximating that size.

When the U. S. S. *Wilmington* made its notable voyage up the Amazon in 1899, Commander Todd purchased from the captain of a river steamer a young male South American tapir and presented it to the National Zoological Park, where it lived for eighteen years. A female was secured two years later, and from the two of them were born, between 1903 and 1909, seven young, six of which lived to maturity. The period of gestation ranged from 392 to 401 days.

The specimen now in the collection was received from the Municipal Zoological Garden of Buenos Aires in 1911, when about two years old. Since that time he has been living out-of-doors, with only an unheated, though well-constructed, shed for the winter time. There is something incongruous in the spectacle of this tropical animal plowing through the snow and apparently enjoying itself during Washington winters.

The smallest of all mammals are the shrews, and one of the smallest of the shrews occurs wild in the National Zoological Park itself. This is the least short-tailed shrew (*Cryptotis parva*). We have had specimens several times, keeping them in glass jars and feeding them earthworms and nuts. They are so tiny as to be difficult to exhibit, but in East Africa we secured a number of elephant shrews (*Elephantulus ocularis*) and succeeded in bringing a pair home, feeding them alternately on fruits and meats. The elephant shrew is about eight inches long, not counting the tail, and has a very long snout. They became fairly tame. Their most peculiar characteristic was the exceedingly swift movement of the mouth in feeding.

The next-door neighbor to the shrew is the hedgehog, most uninteresting because it sleeps rolled into a ball all

[229]

day, usually under a pile of hay, and comes out only at night. A white-bellied form (*Atelerix hindei sotikae*) was exceedingly abundant in East Africa, and we collected a great many, but succeeded in bringing home only a few. We put in the box with them each day a large saucer of ground-up raw meat mixed with egg, which they always "cleaned up." But they died one by one, and at the end of the trip, when we had less than half of the number we started out with, I found they still cleaned up, so that it occurred to me that perhaps some of them had died from not having had enough food. They must be tremendously voracious feeders in nature.

Among the animals seldom seen in zoos is the Solenodon (*Solenodon paradoxus*), though we had a pair of them in the collection in 1910 and 1911. These were brought to us by Mr. and Mrs. Franklin Adams, who collected them in Haiti. One lived for six months. The Solenodon is the largest of the insectivores, with the exception of the tenrec (*Centetes ecaudatus*), a pair of which, by a curious coincidence, were in our collection at the same time. Since then we have been offered these animals once or twice, the last letter, from a gentleman in Santo Domingo, offering to deliver one to the port nearest him for $30,000. Of course there was nothing for us to do but refer this letter to the United States Treasury.

Although bats are extremely interesting and fairly common throughout a large part of the world, most of them are not at all suitable for exhibition. They develop sores in confinement, and soon die. The exception is the fruit bat, or flying fox. In a high, shady, and cool cage he will live very well. Throughout the day he hangs head downward, but in the evening he will crawl about the cage and feed voraciously. We have had only two of these, the Indian fruit bat, in the National collection, though I have seen them often in other zoos.

The flying fox has a very strong, musky smell. Years ago in Fiji I collected a number of these by lying beneath a mango tree on a moonlight night and shooting them as they came to eat mangoes. My object in collecting them was to secure some of the strange parasitic flies which live in their hair. After collecting all of these parasites that I could by the light of a lamp, I put the bats on a newspaper in a corner of my room. The room belonged in a series which formed the headquarters of a sugar plantation, and the next morning, not only my room but the adjoining ones were reeking with bat perfume. My British hosts said nothing, but all during breakfast I could hear them thinking.

Our experience with monotremes has been limited to four specimens of *Echidna aculeata,* the spiny anteater of Australia. None of them lived longer than five months. I once brought one up from Sydney but it died a day before we reached Vancouver. The classic example of longevity for this animal is in the Philadelphia Zoo, where it has lived for more than a quarter of a century in a small cage, the floor of which is covered with earth. It sleeps in a box during the day, and emerges regularly each evening to eat egg and milk.

The spiny anteater's close relative, the duckbill platypus, or ornithorhynchus, belongs in the class of animals impossible to maintain alive. Only one has ever reached the United States alive, brought from Australia by Ellis Joseph, the collector, and it lived but a few weeks in New York. Even in Australia they do very poorly in captivity.

CHAPTER XX

WINGS

Birds are among the popular standard exhibits of a zoological garden, and include hundreds of kinds that are easily kept in captivity, the bird house being always a favorite with zoo visitors because of the attractive colors and constant activities of its inhabitants. The National Zoological Park in its new house for birds, just completed, and its various outdoor cages, has on exhibition regularly more than three hundred species of birds from all over the world, and is constantly augmenting this number so that the student can find here dozens of kinds that he can never hope to see alive in any other way, while the visitor without special knowledge will be delighted by the talking mynah, the strange shoebill, the brilliant lories, and many other strange and beautiful birds.

In 1904 King Menelik of Abyssinia presented to President Roosevelt a collection of native animals, among others a magnificent male Somaliland ostrich (*Struthio molybdophanes*). The express shipment arrived in Washington late in the evening, and was brought out at night to the Zoological Park. This ostrich was the most forlorn specimen that ever came into a collection. He looked as though everybody he had encountered on the trip from Abyssinia to Washington had taken at least one feather from him, so that he arrived a completely plucked bird, six feet high. I don't know whether or not this treatment should be recommended for all ostriches, but the fact is that he grew another coat of feathers, and for the past twenty-four years has been one

PLATE 77

Upper: Female rhea from South America
Lower: Sclater's cassowary

PLATE 78

Inside the great flight cage in summer

of our thriving specimens. Some years ago he lost his sight, so when we moved most of the collection to the new bird house, it did not seem advisable to shift him, as he was so well acquainted with his old quarters.

There were two ostriches in the shipment from King Menelik, the second being a Nubian (*Struthio camelus*) that lived here for seven years. He was very large and aggressive, a really dangerous animal. On one occasion he had two of the keepers sprawled out on the floor, helpless. With an old broom Mr. Blackburne managed to keep him away long enough to allow the keepers to make a quick exit.

Before leaving Abyssinia these two birds had been hobbled with rope tied above the knee joints, sufficiently long to allow them to walk, to make the trip from the estate where they were kept to the steamship, a distance of 300 miles. At sea each was put in a separate crate and the hobbles removed. On their arrival here their legs were in a sorrowful condition, with the flesh worn away exposing the bone, due to the friction caused by the rope hobbles. We had to give them daily treatment for several months before the wounds had healed.

Our South African (*Struthio australis*) and Nubian ostriches occupy a paddock with only an unheated shed for shelter. They have laid a number of times, but none of the eggs have ever been fertile.

The ostrichlike American rhea is one of the commoner birds in zoos. We have had specimens which lived for over thirteen years in the Park. Some young ones that we secured on the Bolivian pampas near Reyes exhibited a most wayward behavior. Their one ambition seemed to be to get out of the courtyard in which they were safely housed, and into the village street, where the Indians' dogs continually awaited such an opportunity. When one did get out, it was so obstinate and did so much ducking about that we could not drive it back, but had literally to run it down and carry it home bodily.

One of our emus (*Dromiceius novae-hollandiae*) has been in the collection now for nearly twenty-six years, and is still an active, healthy bird, though somewhat vicious toward its keeper. It makes a deep booming sound that reverberates throughout the bird house at night.

Cassowaries in general do well, and they should be a delight to the zoo manager's heart. The baby cassowaries are very difficult to identify as to species, and the price on them is low, so that buying one is like buying stocks in the market for a rise, with no risk at all. If it grows up into a different species from what you already have, it is a valuable addition to the collection, while if it proves to be the same, it is worth three and a half times as much as a baby. In this way we purchased a young cassowary for $150 and when it grew up and attained its full color it was found to be *Casuarius philipi*, or Sclater's cassowary, a bird so rare that even its native habitat is not definitely known, though this is supposed to be New Guinea.

Most curious of all the birds in the primitive flightless groups is the apteryx or kiwi, from New Zealand, with its long beak and the nostrils at the end for smelling the subterranean worms which form its main diet. Our only specimen, *Apteryx mantelli*, presented to us by the New Zealand government, lived for two years and three months. It seemed to prefer hiding in a box during the daytime, but would come out in the afternoon to feed on strips of beef cut worm-shape and size, and buried in a pan of earth. The habit of kicking forward viciously and quickly was another of its singular traits. Specimens have lived in England for ten years or more, when given a large run and fed on chopped raw meat, boiled potatoes, and soaked bread.

We have never had much success with penguins. Of six Humboldt's penguins (*Spheniscus humboldti*) from Chile, none lived longer than two months, as they were all affected with aspergillosis, a fungus disease of the lungs, when they arrived, and had lived for a week or so previously on an unnatural diet of bread and water. A rock-hopper penguin (*Catarrhactes pachyrhynchus*) from southern New Zealand lived for one year and five months. We found it a gentle, quiet bird, feeding readily and living on fresh fish. In other zoos penguins have lived a number of years, and have frequently bred. They are sometimes kept in the same inclosure with sea lions, with whom they seem to get along quite well. I had seen this combination in several other parks, and once put our own rock-hopper in the inclosure with a leopard seal. Never did a leopard seal move more quickly—after the bird. The rock-hopper dived into the water, sped like an arrow to the other side and out again. The whole experiment took less than three minutes, after which the penguin was caught and returned, alone, to his own cage.

The loons and grebes do not do well in captivity. The longevity record in our Park was made by a pied-billed grebe (*Podilymbus podiceps*), which lived here for two years.

The great flight cage contains, in the summer time, a large assemblage of fish-eating birds. Among these are the various pelicans, of which four or five species are usually represented. For years we have had no proper accommodations to house them for public view in the winter time, and as many could not stand the winters of Washington in the open, we have had to put them into small pens in the storeroom at the rear of our bird house during all of the colder months. Even with this treatment they live astonishingly well. A European white pelican (*Pelecanus onocrotalus*) has been with us for twenty-five years, and an American white pelican (*Pelecanus erythrorhynchos*) for thirty-one, and both are just as ready as the younger birds to open their foot-and-a-half of beak when they see the keeper approaching with food.

Mr. Blackburne writes of some experiences with pelican appetites:

During the early winter of 1913 several European pelicans were housed for the winter months in a large indoor cage, in company with a lot of other aquatic birds, including half a dozen wandering tree ducks (*Dendrocygna arcuata*). One day a keeper reported that one of the latter was missing. He felt positive it had not escaped, since the birds kept away from the door while the keeper was entering or leaving the cage. I suspected the pelicans, and decided to investigate. When pelicans are frightened after eating they generally disgorge their food. This the pelicans attempted after I had trotted them around the cage several times. Some brought up partly digested fish, but one, after much exertion, ejected two brown feathers. No food was given this bird for two days, and during the afternoon of the third day he disgorged the duck, badly decomposed. Later on he ate his ration of fish and seemed to be none the worse for his experience.

We once kept some American white pelicans in one of the lakes in the Park. One evening they were seen chasing a common water snake. One would pick up the snake and toss it several feet, where another could get it and do likewise. After several birds had amused themselves in this fashion, one of the pelicans caught the snake and swam off with it, eventually swallowing it. For a while he pressed his bill close to his body in an effort to retain the snake, but in a few minutes it had crawled up into the sac of the lower part of the bill, where it wiggled so much that the pelican seemed glad to open his bill and let it escape.

One of these pelicans once attempted to digest a bamboo cutting fifteen inches long with four small branches, each four inches long. One of the keepers noticed two inches of the sharp end protruding at the lower end of the bird's body. The bird was caught and the bamboo drawn through the hole it had made in the pelican's body.

PLATE 79

American white pelicans on parade

PLATE 80

Snapshots in the Flight Cage
Upper: South American stone plover and trumpeters
Middle: East African crowned cranes
Lower: Snake bird or Anhinga, and white ibis from Florida

He soon recovered, apparently without ill effect. Evidently a pelican is willing to try anything. We took a piece of wooden window-screen frame, eighteen inches long, with tack heads sticking up an eighth of an inch, out of another bird's throat. He could neither swallow it nor disgorge it, and it proved difficult to draw out, as the tack heads seemed to catch in his throat. We finally removed it, however, and the bird recovered. The stick was probably thrown into the lake by a boy visitor.

The great flight cage in the open air also contains various herons, gannets, snake birds, and the ibises. The sacred ibis has been with us for over twenty-five years, and a snake bird, or anhinga, for over sixteen. A black-crowned night heron with an equal record is still living in the cage. This species of heron is a native of the National Zoological Park, and during the breeding season in the early spring wild birds make their nests in the vines growing up the outside of the cage while the tame birds use the same vines on the inside, so the captive and wild species are almost within touching distance of each other. The wild birds envy the others at feeding time, for fish and frogs are becoming scarcer and scarcer on the outside of the cage. The mother heron apparently has no nerves, for the continual *clackety-clack* of the young ones whenever there is food about, and whenever there is not, would drive anyone else frantic.

Some of the same birds are kept in winter time in the great flight cage in the bird house. Others stay there the year round, among these being the South American boatbill, who is the National Zoo's one-hundred-per-cent optimist and spends hour after hour and week after week standing by the drainage pipe of the water pool with his head poised on one side, waiting for the fish that has never yet come through and probably never will.

The flamingos, American (*Phoenicopterus ruber*) and

European (*Phoenicopterus roseus*), with their impossibly long legs and necks, and scarlet wings with black tips, also live in this cage. We have never had much success with the American species, which have lived scarcely more than a year, but one European or Egyptian flamingo lived for twelve years and eleven months, when it was killed by an Australian black swan in the same inclosure.

The tropical spoonbills and the scarlet ibises likewise reside in the inside cage. Their brilliant colors soon fade unless a liberal quantity of fresh shrimp is included in their diet.

This flight cage, with a rock pile at one end over which water runs, a large swimming pool in the middle, and an arid area in the far end, contains the greatest assortment of species of any cage in the Zoo. In addition to the birds mentioned there are a pair of Java jungle fowl, a flock of the brilliant decorative nutmeg pigeons from Nicobar, vulturine guinea fowl, crested European ruffs, lapwings, Eyton's tree duck, white-faced, and black-bellied tree ducks, South American stone plovers, white-necked storks from West Africa, Bahama pintails, Nanday paroquets (one of the few species of the tribe that will live at peace with other birds), and even three East African crowned cranes. The last we secured in Tanganyika when they were the size of chickens. Of the five we brought home three live peacefully with all the other birds in the cage. The other two are so pugnacious that they must be kept in separate cages, each by itself. These, with a laughing gull or two, East Indian gallinules, and various and sundry other specimens added from time to time, make up the collection in the cage. It is necessary to choose birds that will live together peacefully. Usually, when a new bird is put in the cage, the others take considerable interest in it, and sometimes annoy it, chasing it around, but in general, after they have spent one night together in the cage, the new one is more or less accepted as a member of the family.

PLATE 81

Abu Markub (father of 'bills), a shoebill from the Sudan. One of the rarest of birds in captivity

PLATE 82

European flamingos.   They winter indoors

WINGS

Occurring only in sparse flocks in remote marshes in the Sudan, the shoebill (*Balaeniceps rex*) is the only member of its family, which is related seemingly to both the storks and herons. Abu Markub ("father of bills"), as the Arabs call the shoebill, has been seen in American collections only since 1926, when one specimen came into the New York Zoo just ten days before we brought ours to Washington. Since then four more have been imported. It is doubtful if many will come into America in the future, for they are difficult to obtain and very rigorously protected by the game department of the Sudan.

While in Ceylon we had telegraphed the zoo at Khartum to ask if they had any animals that we could have in addition to the giraffe already promised us, and a cabled reply stated that they had a shoebill. Effendi Skandar Armenius, who brought him to us at Port Sudan, told us that he should be fed with fresh fish, served to him at the end of a long stick. So we secured fifty pounds of fish from the market and had it put in cold storage. But Abu did not eat fish once during the voyage. For four days he ate nothing. And yet it was plain he needed food. He stood nearly four feet high, with long legs and a short neck, pale yellowish eyes, and a tremendous broad bill, sharply hooked at the end, which has somewhat the appearance of a wooden shoe and gives the bird his name. He would look at us reproachfully and shake his head from side to side when we offered him food, opening his mouth savagely when we approached and then throwing out the fish we had hurriedly deposited there. It was a very distressing situation, for we knew that up to that time no shoebills had been seen in American zoos; moreover, he had cost a great deal of money, in addition to the fifty-dollar export tax charged by the Government on each of these birds.

The fourth day out we had butchered a steer for meat, and the shoebill accepted a piece of fresh lung offered him and swallowed it. We thought our troubles were over, but the next morning he refused lung. He finally took to eating white meat of chicken and during the last seventeen days of the voyage devoured the white meat of three chickens per day. We got him successfully to Washington, where he lived only eighteen months, dying of a ruptured liver, cause unknown.

We obtained another specimen the following year. This one is still thriving. He eats each day four or five fish as large as a man's hand. Sometimes Abu will take a fish from a basin of water. At other times he insists on "service" with his meals, and then a keeper must hand the fish one at a time on a pointed stick. He is very friendly, will let his head be scratched, and will come to the front of the cage. He has a curious habit of hanging his head and shaking it from side to side, so that when we feel humorously inclined we can ask him, "Do you like ladies?" or "children?" or "Congressmen?" depending upon whom we are conducting through the Zoo, and he will reply very decisively in the negative. When feeling especially friendly he will accompany the head-shaking by gutteral grunts.

The wild-fowl lake, where we have about a 700-foot sweep of water backed in by a dam from Rock Creek, usually harbors a collection of some fifty species of geese and ducks, which live amicably together. It is here that we find the greatest records for longevity, ten to twenty years or more being frequently attained by its denizens. With so many together there is not a great deal of nesting, but now and then one of the birds will steal into a secluded corner and produce eggs. Foremost in importance among these is the blue goose (*Chen caerulescens*), which has very rarely before been raised in captivity. A pair of them have produced fertile eggs from which young have been reared for three years in succession. This constitutes a record.

Rarities in the collection include the emperor goose

PLATE 83

Wild fowl in winter.   North American ducks and geese

(*Philacte canagica*), which we received through the Biological Survey from Alaska, and the maned goose (*Chenonetta jubata*) from the upper reaches of the Amazon. The latter can not endure very cold weather and must be housed during the winter. There is a pair of the almost extinct Hawaiian goose (*Nesochen sandvicensis*), an upland form that does not frequent water but lives instead in the valleys of extinct craters. Possibly less than half a hundred of these interesting birds still remain in Hawaii.

The flight cage for the eagles and vultures houses the American bald eagle, the golden eagle, the wedge-tailed eagle, and a variety of vultures from Africa, Asia, and South America. Visitors have protested at seeing the vultures roosting on perches above the symbolic eagle. One of our bald eagles has been with us for more than thirty years, while the longest record we have on the golden eagle is eleven years and eight months.

Our pair of cinereous vultures, an African species, each year make a huge nest of sticks and then patiently sit on the eggs for about forty days. After this we decide they are not fertile and take them away to the Museum.

Above this cage, and on the trees outside, are always to be seen flocks of the turkey vulture, a scavenger bird common in this part of America. From fifty to a hundred of these birds make their headquarters at the Zoo, coming at night to roost, and during the hard months of the winter receiving the scraps offered. Frequently people notify the keepers that some birds have escaped, while other visitors notice pathos in the expression of these wild birds as they gaze at their well-fed relatives in the inclosure.

The highly ornate tropical king vulture is quite properly the finest of the American vultures. One of the two that have lived in the Park for so many years would perhaps shudder if it knew its own history. Twenty-eight years ago Mr. Blackburne was visiting the famous Bostock

Trained Animal Show in Baltimore, and noticed a king vulture in the collection. Mr. Bostock had bought this bird from a ship. Mr. Blackburne arranged to trade him a young kangaroo for it. A few days after the exchange was made came the Baltimore fire, which destroyed Bostock's entire collection, so that our specimen is the sole survivor of one of the most interesting traveling menageries ever organized.

While the Andean condor is called the largest bird that flies, there are records of California condors of equal size. Formerly abundant in California, the California species is said to have been destroyed by eating poisoned bait intended for wolves and coyotes, though some doubt may be expressed as to this statement. It is estimated that not more than between forty and one hundred of these magnificent birds still remain in remote sections of southern and Lower California.

We have the only specimens now in captivity in eastern parks, a trio procured from Mr. W. B. Whitaker of Peru, California, one in 1901, the other two in 1903. They had been taken from the nest and sent to Washington while still in the down, and at that time were fluffy white birds the size of a large hen. Their call is a whistling note like that of a young chicken. The first of our specimens to arrive was very tame and fond of attention, and enjoyed untying the shoestrings, poking his bill up the pants' leg and pulling down the sock of the head keeper, or hiding his head in the keeper's hands, tricks which interested the late Secretary Langley so much that he insisted upon having them done for him whenever he came to visit the Park.

Each year the condors lay usually one egg, though on two occasions the first egg was followed after an interval by another. The value of the egg in oological catalogues is placed at $750 per specimen, so that an occasional egg laid by a condor is always a matter of public interest. We have tried each time to hatch them, sometimes under

PLATE 84

California condors, largest flying bird of America.　Now nearly extinct

the mother bird, but up to now she has invariably broken them. We put several others in incubators, and placed others under faithful hens, but apparently they were not fertile. Unnoticed by the great majority of the Zoo's visitors, these birds are the center of attraction for many bird lovers, who appreciate them not only for their rarity but for their interest and coloring.

The finest of all of the eagles is the fierce and beautiful and most powerful harpy eagle of tropical America, the monkey- and sloth-eating eagle. He rarely comes into collections, and we have had but one in our history. He was secured by Commander C. C. Todd, U. S. N., commanding the U. S. S. *Wilmington* on its famous trip up the Amazon in 1899, who received it as a gift from the Governor of the State of Amazonas. It lived for seventeen years and eleven months in our Park, at one time attaining a weight of nineteen pounds, though at the time of its death it had shrunk to only eight.

The various hawks and owls make especially hardy cage birds, living well and contentedly in captivity, and even the tropical species stand Washington winter weather very well. The owls are fed with strips of beef placed on the branches of their trees late in the afternoon, and when dusk falls they fly out from their box shelters and eat. One wonders how many rats pay for coming into their cages at night.

We have wild owls in the Park, too, chiefly the little screech owl, but sometimes the barred owl and the great horned species. All of these from time to time have taken toll of captive birds in the collection. We once lost a number of Australian grass paroquets from a large outdoor cage. Some of them slept clinging to the mesh, with their heads so exposed that the screech owls could dart by and pull them off.

The curassows, guans, and chachalacas, which with the tinamous and a few quail make up the land game-bird fauna of South America, are nearly always represented in the collection. Usually large, striking specimens, they live well and become very tame. In South America they are frequently found living among chicken flocks of the Indians, and I have been able to pick up many of them while traveling. At Humayta, on the Rio Madeira, I secured a pair of razor-billed curassows from a native and turned them loose on the ship on the voyage home. I presume they did find something to eat, but on the whole trip the only food that I actually saw them take consisted of two pumpkin seeds.

A fine creasted guan, or penelope, from Rurrenabaque, Bolivia, was our camp pet for many months. When we moved from camp to boat he would ride on the shoulder of an Indian, and then sit on the baggage for the day's journey. On clear nights we put up no tents, but only mosquito nets, and this guan would roost on the framework of my net, waking me early in the morning with his complaints. His lack of intelligence was amazing. When we were staying in a native house he would fly to the roof and sit there in the rain, complaining. He has remained tame, and now when I come to the cage, goes through a peculiar ceremony, elevating his crest, expanding his throat, and indulging in a plaintive, whining song, which ends with a sharp squeak.

American wild turkeys, a magnificent game bird, have lived at liberty in the Park as long as six years and eight months. The last one has now disappeared, probably the victim of a vandal.

The various guinea fowl provide some striking specimens, especially the vulturine guinea (*Acryllium vulturinum*) of East Africa, the head and upper part of the neck of which is naked cobalt-blue skin, while its plumage combines blues, blacks, and whites. All these guineas are natives of Africa, and the ancestor of the common domestic "keet" still exists in the wild state from Senegambia to the Niger. Among the handsomest may be included the Grant's crested (*Guttera granti*) and

Reichenow's helmeted guinea fowl (*Numida mitrata reichenowi*), the former having a thick tuft of feathers on top of the head. I secured a dozen and a half of these in the market at Dar-es-Salaam, but on the voyage home they were attacked by the old-fashioned chicken disease, roup, and only one survived despite everything that we could do to cure them. On the other hand, out of thirty-six Reichenow's helmeted guinea fowl, also from Tanganyika, only four perished, and we arrived in Washington with a flock of thirty-two. Some of these have been sent West in an attempt to domesticate and raise them, for they would make a nice addition to our rather small list of domesticated edible birds.

The guinea fowl is the great game bird of Africa, and on *safari* served us as the stand-by. Often they will not take to the wing, but have to be potted, and when they do fly, it is in a straight line, so that it requires only fair shooting ability to supply the mess. Sometimes a flock will go into a tree, and with a small-caliber rifle one can pick off a day's supply before the others become alarmed and leave. Guinea makes a good food, though of course one becomes tired of it after seeing it twice a day for a month or more. We grew especially tired when Abdul, our second cook, would try to make chicken *à la* Maryland out of an ancient cock. Abdul had been a deck hand on an East African coast steamer, and his ideas of cooking had come to him from peering through the galley window. We would hang the birds a day or so, and then when boiled sufficiently they were very good food, but Abdul showed a partiality for selecting an elderly and very freshly killed one, dipping it in flour and frying it faintly before serving. One evening I lost my temper completely after trying to make an impression on a leg cooked in this manner, and hit Abdul on the ear with it, a thing one should never do. Next evening I had cause for repentance, however, because Abdul had stayed in camp the entire day making dough of flour and water, rolling it between the palms of his hands, and boiling it. It was a horrible looking mess when served, and when I asked what it might be, Abdul beamed so proudly as he told me, "Macaroni, Bwana," that I simply had to force down a helping that must have weighed pounds, the gratified cook standing at one side the whole time, ready to replenish my dish.

The grouse family does not live well. We have had few in the collection. The Oriental pheasants, on the other hand, provide some of the most popular and beautiful of birds for exhibition purposes. The commoner species, the English, Mongolian, Reeves, ring-necked, and Lady Amherst's, are usually present in the collection, and some of them have lived a number of years. The argus, one of the larger and more beautiful of the family, has recently been added. Two of them in the great flight cage appear to be thriving. They spend a great deal of their time in a tunnel beneath the rockwork, a refuge reeking with moisture. The peacock pheasant, with the ocellated plumage which suggests its name, was represented in the collection by a cock for a period of ten years and four months. We kept it out-of-doors for a time and it roosted on a branch instead of in the straw provided for it to keep its feet warm, with the result that one foot was frozen and afterward came off. For many years it hobbled about on one foot and the stub of the old one. We could never bring ourselves to put it out of the way because it seemed so cheerful and happy. The proper place to keep pheasants, of course, is in a properly constructed pheasantry, of which we have only plans.

Various partridges and quail live happily in the collection. One specimen of California valley quail has lived in the Park already for more than nine years. Our migratory quail, the quail of the Old Testament, were purchased in Egypt, chiefly as food for various small mammals we were bringing home, they being among the cheaper meat supplies of North Africa. The few remain-

PLATE 85

Harpy eagle, most powerful South American bird of prey. Eighteen
years in the National Zoo

PLATE 86

Australian silver gull with newly-hatched young

ing at the end of our voyage were caged with a group of assorted African weavers and have done remarkably well. The singular migratory habits of this quail deserve mention; some of them summer in northern Europe and winter in Africa; others make the trip from north to south Asia. During the migration they fly, of course, high in the air, but when they settle down into their summer or winter homes, they become again secretive birds, frequenting sheltering grasses and undergrowth.

The little jungle fowl of India merits a place in the collection, because it is probably the ancestor of our domestic breeds of poultry. Zoological parks occasionally maintain a collection of the various domestic breeds of fowl, some of which are very striking, especially the Japanese form, the Yokohama fowl, in which the tail of the cock grows to a length of ten or fifteen feet; and the Araucanian fowl of western South America which lays eggs distinctly blue-green in color. A Chilean scientist once presented a single hen to our Park, and it proceeded to lay blue-green eggs at once. A newspaper account of this resulted in requests from all over the United States for a setting of these blue-green eggs.

The ordinary peacocks need not be kept in cages, and a couple of dozen of these live at liberty in the grounds about the Park, adding greatly to its appearance. Males in full plumage from June to December seek every occasion to show their plumage to the females, from which trait they have the reputation, perhaps unjustly, of being the vainest of birds. In the spring the hen will wander off in the deep woods and reappear some time later with a brood, usually five or six, so that the flock maintains itself very well, though on account of mortality among the young, caused by wild predacious mammals, birds, and small boys in the Park, it has never increased very much. One peacock, a magnificent bird, developed a habit of attacking its own reflection in any shining surface, choosing preferably new automobiles.

So many protests came in from the owners of these cars that we had to send him away. Then one of our white peacocks resented, by jumping and using his spurs, small boys' attempts to steal his tail feathers. After the third casualty had been brought to our attention for first aid, we put the peacock into the large flight cage, where small boys can not go.

At Easter time it is usual for the President of the United States to receive from various admirers newly-hatched chicks which have been dyed various shades of purple, green, vermilion, and scarlet. These often reach the Zoo and create as much attention as a real species. The most remarkable example of this sort of thing we have ever received was a turkey, originally white, that had been skillfully colored red, white, and blue. It finally shed its feathers and became perfectly white. For several years thereafter visitors would inquire what had become of it.

The kagu (*Rhynochetos jubatus*), said to be related to both the herons and the bitterns, belongs in a family by itself. It is found only in New Caledonia, but the presence of its portrait on the early stamps of that country has made it well known. The males are pugnacious, though several of ours have been very timid. They are usually silent, but on occasion can make a violent hubbub, for all the world like a puppy with glorified vocal cords that has had its tail stepped on and at the same time is barking at something else. The last time our kagus broke loose vocally there were two in the cage. When one stopped, perhaps for a rest, the other would take up the chant where he had left off. We fled to the parrot room for quiet, and found the very parrots looking subdued and inferior, for this squawking was even more efficient than theirs.

Among the rails the most interesting that we have had are the weka or flightless rail of New Zealand (*Ocydromus australis*), Earl's weka (*Ocydromus earli*), and the short-winged weka (*Ocydromus brachypterus*), heavy-set birds with very poorly developed wings and villainous dispositions, so much so that we have never been able to keep more than one in a cage. They are exceedingly hardy birds, and two of our specimens have been with us now for nearly eleven years. The great size of the egg in proportion to the bird is remarkable, as it weighs about one-third as much as the mother bird. Numerous other rails have been in the collection and have lived very well.

Perhaps the most ornamental of all of the larger birds are the cranes, of which we have exhibited thirteen species at various times. Among these, again, we find records for longevity. An Australian crane still in the collection has been here now for more than twenty-four years, and an Indian white crane over twenty-two. The whooping crane, now practically extinct, we have had on three occasions, one specimen for a little over twelve years. Some time ago an animal dealer telephoned me in the evening, saying that he had just secured a white crane three feet high. Next morning we hurried to his quarters, expecting to find a whooping crane, but he had mistaken a heron for one.

When I first came into the Zoo, I was worried about the quarters for these cranes. They had no shelter, and the sight of birds, some of them normally tropical in habit, standing or sitting in a sleet storm filled me with misgivings. But the head keeper, in answer to my suggestion that we build sheds, told me of his many years of experience with cranes. They do not like sheds, and usually will not go into them. They live with obvious comfort through the nastiest parts of our winter season.

In addition to being ornamental and living satisfactorily in captivity, cranes also indulge in weird dances, bobbing their long necks, elevating one wing after the other, and stamping or hopping grotesquely about the inclosures.

Related to the cranes are the trumpeters which come from tropical America, naturally the tamest and most gentle of all this group, but wicked with other birds. I have been told by several people in Brazil that when a hunter shoots a mother trumpeter, her flock of young will follow the hunter home and take up their abode voluntarily in the chicken yard. Whether this be true or not I do not know, but it is a fact that one commonly finds trumpeters among the domestic chickens in South America, where it is said that they serve in driving away enemies of the fowls.

The gulls do best when provided with plenty of flying space in large cages, and under these conditions live almost indefinitely and breed freely. A flock of Australian silver gulls, which was brought into the National Park's collection a little over six years ago, has bred regularly and increases annually.

It seems a pity that such striking birds as the skimmers, shearwaters, and puffins do not do well, but we have never had any particular success with them.

The various doves and pigeons are among the most admirable of all birds for aviaries. We have had some forty species in the collection. The most noted member of this family in America was the last survivor of the famous passenger pigeons, so amazingly abundant in the early days, which lived for twenty-eight years in the zoological garden at Cincinnati, long after its species was extinct elsewhere. When it died it came to the National Museum to be preserved. An Inca dove (*Scardafella inca*) and a zebra dove (*Geopelia striata*), still alive in the collection, have been here for more than twelve years.

Some of the most gorgeous birds in this group are the Polynesian and Malayan pigeons, equaling in brilliance of plumage the gaudy parrots of the same region. Fiji is especially notable for this type of bird. None of them do very well in captivity. Out of thirty-six green pigeons I secured in Ceylon on the way back from Africa, only

PLATE 87

Marabou stork, or adjutant, a native of India

PLATE 88

European white stork on its nest

six survived the voyage to Boston, and all of these died within a few months. Some, especially the larger fruit pigeons, have been hunted a great deal, though at present they are rigidly protected by the Government.

I once had an exciting hunt for a large species on the island of Ono i Lau in Fiji. The native captain of our cutter invited me to accompany him on a pigeon hunt. He had an antiquated single-barreled shotgun and two cartridges. We sailed across to a small, uninhabited island nearby, and soon flushed three of these birds. They flew to the other end of the island, and we sneaked carefully after them. When within a hundred yards, the captain stopped and carefully slipped a cartridge into the shotgun, whereupon the birds flew back to the other end of the island. The captain unloaded the gun, put the cartridge in a little bag he was wearing, and we soft-footed it back to where the birds had flown. The same process was repeated and would have continued, I suppose, until we dropped. But at the end of several hours, having walked dozens of times from one end of the island to the other, and having entirely lost my appreciation of the care the captain took of his firearm, my taste for pigeon hunting was glutted.

A related species frequented the island of Kandavu, and we shot them for food a number of times. We were astonished to find their crops full of wild nutmegs so enormous that I do not yet understand how the birds managed to swallow them.

Another favorite in zoos, the touracos or plantain eaters, a small family of brightly colored birds inhabiting Africa, are singular in having nonwashable feathers. The color is a chemical one, due to a peculiar pigment called turacin, once supposed to be a true metal. This is so soluble in water that when the birds get wet the color actually comes out of their feathers.

Nearly a hundred species of the parrot family have been exhibited in the National Zoological Park. One can usually find upwards of fifty species at any time. The first bird ever to come to the Zoo was a sulphur-crested cockatoo from Australia, which had spent five years in the home of a Maryland family before it was presented to the National collection. This occurred in the old days when the Zoo was still down on the Smithsonian grounds. The first bird to come to the Park on its establishment, after an interval of nearly thirty-eight years it was also the first bird to be transferred to the new bird house. From all observations it is still a young, healthy bird in good plumage, and can hold its own in squawking with any bird in the parrot room. When a friend or visitor approaches it will often come to the bars, opening and closing its mouth for all the world as though it were telling him a secret.

For zoo purposes the parrot family may be divided into two categories, the seed eaters and those which live on nectar and fruits. Among the latter are the lories of the Indo-Malaysian region, which thrive on a diet of bread soaked in milk, fruits, and regular rations of honey.

Most parrots are tropical species which require artificial heat in winter, though some thrive outdoors throughout the year. At the head of this list is the kea or mountain parrot of New Zealand, a powerful bird, noted in its native habitat for its practice of killing sheep. It is said to have developed this habit from eating fat from sheepskins exposed to dry about the sheep camps, and later learned to attack live sheep. The keas caused such damage to sheep that bounties were offered for their extermination, and today they are comparatively rare in collections. Our three specimens live in a large open cage, and are chiefly interesting on account of their curious dances, hopping sideways on the ground about the cage. Sometimes they give vent to a long-drawn-out "K—ee—a," the call which gave them their name.

The sulphur-crested cockatoo and the roseate, likewise

from Australia, also live outdoors in Washington through-out the year. Three of the former species escaped some years ago. They have never left the Park, but return daily for seed, which is left outside the cage. We have never captured them, nor made any serious attempt to do so, because they are quite an attraction at liberty, though the gardener comes to the office frequently and requests with tears in his eyes that they be killed, as he claims that they are destroying the forest. One of them has formed the habit of taking off great strips of bark from the trees. Recently they have taken to biting away pieces of the frame structure which shelters their former mates in captivity, and threaten to demolish the shed.

Some of the cockatoos are strikingly beautiful, for example the rare and expensive Leadbeater's from South Australia, whose general plumage is white, while the fore-head, front and sides of the neck, breast, and abdomen are tinged with rose. The crest is crimson at the base, yellow in the center, and white at the tip, and is elevated on various occasions, while the bird waves its head enthusiastically.

The great black cockatoo from New Guinea contrasts sharply with the great white cockatoo from the Moluccas. The former has an enormous crest of blue-black feathers and great pale rosy patches on its cheeks. One of our specimens was captured by Mr. Frost, a noted bird collector, who brought it from New Guinea to London, whence it came as a pet to an American home. Each time I heard it utter a squawk or two, I remarked, "That is one squawk nearer the Zoo," whereat the lady who owned it would remonstrate that pretty Josephine would never so misbehave as to have to be deposited with us. However, the family took the cockatoo with them to a summer home in New York State, and one day a telegram came, asking for someone to come and bring the bird away before it drove the family insane. Steam rollers were at work on the road in front of the house, and their racket inspired the bird to fearful lengths in competition.

The macaws, perhaps the gaudiest of the larger parrots, have few superiors in hardihood among the birds of the collection. A hyacinthine macaw of the central provinces of Brazil, immediately catches the eye appreciative of beauty. The plumage is nearly uniform cobaltlike blue relieved by bright yellow skin around the eyes. In its own country it haunts the inland ponds of the dense interior forest, where it feeds on the fruit of a certain palm, crushing the heavy seeds in its powerful black bill. Next to nuts the macaw loves to bite wire, and we had to take our hyacinthine out of its regular cage in the bird house and place it in a small cage which can be renewed from time to time as the bird destroys it.

The yellow and blue macaw (*Ara ararauna*), which ranges from Panama to Bolivia, and the larger and even more brilliantly plumaged red and blue and yellow macaw (*Ara macao*) are well-known zoo birds. They sometimes become attached to their keepers, but like all other macaws give way to violent fits of screaming.

The only one of the parrot family really indigenous to America north of Mexico is the beautiful though noisy Carolina paroquet, a small yellow, orange, and green bird which formerly extended northward as far as New York and Wisconsin, and whose brilliant plumage has resulted in its extermination. Occasionally still a rumor arises that some have been seen in the extreme southern States, but it is doubtful if any now remain alive. The Park has had three during its history, one of which lived for over fifteen years.

Occasionally a Mexican species, the thick-billed parrot, wanders north into southern Arizona, and so has been given a place on our list. It occurs more commonly in Mexico, where most specimens are captured.

The hawk parrot of South America has a glorious crown

of feathers on its head which it can elevate at will—its own will, not the keeper's, for no one can make him perform.

The tropical American group, and especially those from the Amazon, are blunt-tailed parrots of which more than half a hundred species are distributed over South America. They are all easily tamed and make highly prized pets because of their facility in learning to repeat words and even to whistle and sing tunes. There is the old story of Humboldt in South America, who met a parrot which had belonged to a tribe of Indians that had become extinct, and from the bird he obtained all the words of the tribal dialect that are known.

We once secured a specimen of the large green mealy parrot of this group from Indians who came in to Huachi. Huachi is the metropolis of the upper Middle Beni, and consists of two palm shacks. Every two years these Indians would come on a twelve-days' march from their abode to the village, in order to trade flat bird skins for salt. They had with them on this occasion the mealy parrot. A handful of salt bought it, and after five years it is still living comfortably in our Park. These Indians, by the way, were the most uninterested folk I ever encountered. They stayed about our camp for a day. Moving-picture machines and various camp equipment and impedimenta received not the slightest attention. They wanted salt and nothing else, and when they had traded bows, arrows, and bark-cloth costumes to us for a sufficient supply, they wrapped it up in large leaves, tied it with fiber, and disappeared again into the forest.

Among the dainty members of the parrot family are the love birds. There exist ten species of these, all from Africa and Madagascar, eight of which are seen in captivity. Their quiet notes make them much more attractive as household pets than the little South American paroquets of the raucous voices, and they will do very well even in small cages, where they make nests and raise young, sometimes with great regularity.

[255]

Equally small and beautiful, yet much more delicate, are the tiny upside-down or hanging lories (*Loriculus*) from the East Indies. They grow scarcely larger than the canaries, and have brilliant plumage. Unfortunately they do not live very long in captivity even when supplied with bread, milk, fruit, and boiled rice, which they take in preference to the usual birdseed of the ordinary parrot. And still smaller and even more beautiful are the tiny Nasiternas (*Micropsitta*) from New Guinea and the Solomon Islands, some not so large as a canary and yet perfect short-tailed, miniature parrots. I have never seen any out of their native habitat, but undoubtedly they will eventually come into collections. We know nothing of their habits.

Though the parrots seem particularly adaptable to captivity, certain relatives of theirs, such as the king-fishers and the bee-eaters do not do well and are rarely exhibited, while other relatives, the hornbills and owls, again are hardy birds frequently seen. The hornbills, confined to the Old World, are notable for their enormous and grotesque bills. They become tame and do well in captive quarters. We often roll food up in balls which we toss into the air for our hornbills. Some of the Indian species exhibit a curious custom; during the egg-laying and incubating season the male seals the female in the cavity of a tree, with mud. Here she remains until the young birds are almost fully fledged, the male assiduously supplying her with food. I recently saw such nesting by two captive Jackson's hornbills in Frankfurt, Germany.

The heavy forests of the remote Solomon Islands are frequented by a fine large hornbill which I have never seen in captivity. The natives call it *"kuri-kuri"* from the sound which it makes as it flies out of a tree. I once shot one as a specimen, and then the pounds of good-looking flesh on the bird seemed to me, tired of tinned New Caledonia meats, too good to waste; so I gave it to the wife of my planter host, insisting that it would make

PLATE 89

King vultures from South America. One of them is the sole survivor
of the famous Bostock menagerie

good Hamburg steak. It did when mixed with onions, and from then on we varied our tinned diet with hornbill. Later, when I returned to the States, I read a natural history of this bird and learned that because of its filthy feeding habits even the Malayans disdain to eat it. I still hope that my friends in the Islands, who to this day are perhaps having an occasional feast of kuri-kuri, never come across the same natural history that I did.

Hornbills are generally shy in the wild state, but become very tame in captivity, so much so that they will come to the bars of their cage and respond to friendly greetings. They have a curious habit of hopping about sideways both on the perch and on the ground.

The fantastic American toucans have bills developed proportionately even more than the hornbills, and in addition are birds of brilliant plumage, rivaling the parrots and macaws in this respect. In flight one gets the impression of a long beak, with an engine behind to propel it. They also become tame quickly.

The proverbially grave and sedate owls take kindly to captivity, where they sit in the gloomiest part of their cage, perfectly motionless throughout the day, staring at an intruder with a wild dazed look, sometimes hissing and snapping their beaks. Yet they are attractive to visitors. Twelve species are represented in our collection, among them the rare morepork owl from New Zealand, which derives its name from its peculiar cry.

There is at times a periodic scarcity of food in the sub-Arctic regions which drives south hordes of snowy owls, and in these years it has been necessary for zoological gardens actually to publish notices in the papers that they do not wish to purchase any more of these usually rare birds. Despite their size and strength and the fact that they feed well, they do not thrive in captivity.

Our prize owl specimen is the albino of the great horned owl, the second one known. The collector took it from its nest with an ordinary colored brother in one of the southernmost States, and from the letter offering it to the Park for sale I had some doubt as to whether it was merely a young one in the down or an albino. It proved to be the latter, and so far as I know, the second specimen on record.

Despite the fact that the barn owl, or monkey-faced owl, is one of the commonest of the family, and frequents barns and old buildings, it seems to be, judging from Zoo correspondence, unknown to the great majority of people. The letter which commences with "I have just caught a large bird never seen here before" usually goes on to describe a barn owl.

In the same general group of birds come the woodpeckers and flickers. Our experience with woodpeckers has been such that we no longer attempt to exhibit them, but a lovely Gila woodpecker from Tucson, Arizona, has now been living here for three years as a contented cage bird.

The passerine birds are legion, and include most of the smaller species exhibited, the majority of which prove joyous captives, living, I believe, longer in captivity than they would if left at liberty. Five or six years is an average life in the wild state for the small perching birds, while our longevity records shows that they average much more than this in captivity.

We do not keep native local birds; they can be seen at home in the Park. But we do try to maintain a representative collection of the foreign birds which would not otherwise be seen by the bird-lover. So in the small bird room at the bird house there are flocks of bulbuls, Japanese hill-tits, weaver birds, and various finches, interspersed with an occasional unusual or striking form such as a bird of Paradise—really an ornate relative of the crow with an unusually raucous call. There is our Australian crow, a great favorite, who greets visitors in the morning with "Hello!" and toward the middle of the afternoon changes it to "All out!" He has friends who come to see him from far and wide, and they give him pennies which he plays with for a time and then secretes in one corner of his cage, where they eventually become the property of the keeper. He has contributed as much as twenty-one cents to his keeper in a single day. Could this be kept up regularly, rivalry for the chance of tending him would develop. He has lived here more than thirteen years, welcoming and dismissing visitors in the same way, and garnering pennies when afforded the opportunity.

The weavers, plain-colored birds at times and vividly colored at others, and the finches make up most of the collection of small birds. The orioles, cardinals, and others having a place here are too numerous to discuss in a work of this sort. However, any account of birds in the National Zoological Park would be incomplete without the tale of our Javanese mynah. The mynahs occur throughout the East Indies in numerous species, and also in various parts of the world, such as Fiji, Hawaii, and even British Columbia, where they have been introduced for supposedly beneficial purposes, but have usually developed into pests.

The crested mynah from Eastern Asia, which is now a common inhabitant in parts of British Columbia, has been represented by only one specimen, which came here as a gift from the writing traveler, Miss Genevieve Wimsatt. When it arrived at the Zoo it would call a 'ricksha in Chinese and whistle a bar or two of song in the same language, but the report that it read for the keepers their Chinese laundry slips is gross exaggeration. All of these birds can be taught to talk, and their voices are much more humanlike than those of any of the parrots. Two placed in adjoining cages will learn phrases from each other and greatly increase their vocabulary.

Our most noted bird was brought to us from Java by Dr. H. C. Kellers of the Navy, who was then surgeon to an astronomical expedition. When the bird was secured it could speak a sentence or two in Javanese. The sailors aboard the transport increased its vocabulary somewhat, and then some unknown person at the Zoo put on the final touch. The Smithsonian Institution held a conference to which the President and his Cabinet came, with the Board of Regents and other most consequential people, to listen to speeches and to visit small booths, each containing an exhibit from one of the branches of the Institution. The Zoo booth contained a rare small mammal or two, a pen of turtles, a tank of frogs, and the Javanese mynah as one of the bird exhibits. When the speeches were over, the party broke up to look at the collections, and as no less a person than the Director of the Budget, General H. M. Lord himself, entered the Zoo booth, the mynah asked him with perfect clarity, "How about the appropriation?"

There was just the proper amount of irritation in his voice, and the General turned and asked, "Who educated that bird?"

The bird reiterated, "How about the appropriation?"

The General, visibly nonplussed, and perhaps dismayed also at the sight of newspaper reporters snapping lead pencils in their hurry to take notes, turned to a friend and remarked, "That is impertinent," to which the mynah rejoined, "So's your old man."

We of the Zoo were, of course, deeply humiliated at this unseemly conduct on the part of one of our charges, but the story became one of the General's favorites.

An animal dealer heard the bird one day, and turned to me to say, "That is a two-hundred-dollar bird." The month before we had received an appropriation of $30,000, and even as he mentioned his paltry idea of the value of the bird we could hear the activities of workmen on the outside of the bird house, preparing ground to install outdoor cages, amply provided for by the new appropriation.

CHAPTER XXI

THE COLD-BLOODED TRIBE

THE zoological park which includes a reptile house invariably finds this the most crowded and popular of its buildings, so much so that in certain foreign zoos where admission is charged the visitor must pay an extra fee to visit the reptile house. This popularity may be traceable in part to a genuine interest in these lower vertebrates and to an admiration for their beauty, but in the main we must account for it as a fascination caused by repugnance. The great majority of reptiles are perfectly harmless animals, but the few that have the power of dealing sinister and horrible death have given a malign reputation to all. To some of the most innocent and harmless forms, solicitous nature has given a horrible appearance as a means, and sometimes an only means, of defense.

Though the National Zoological Park has hitherto lacked adequate quarters to exhibit reptiles, it has shown some two hundred species at various times during its history, and under present plans will construct a suitable house for reptiles by 1930.

The tuatara, or Sphenodon, which is now known only from New Zealand, was at two different periods the real star of our reptile collection. This, one of the strangest of reptiles, is the single living representative of a group the rest of which became extinct during the Triassic period of geologic history, long before the first mammals or birds appeared on earth, even antedating the great dinosaurs. Since this period race after race of living

[261]

creatures has flourished and then vanished, but the tuatara lived on in isolated New Zealand until the coming of white settlers. They introduced pigs, who found this large, chunky, lizardlike animal good to eat, so that today it can no longer be found alive on the larger islands, but only on two or three small rocky islets off the coast of the north island, where a few remain, thanks to the rigid protection afforded by the Government. Through the courtesy of the New Zealand Government the National Zoological Park received a specimen a few years ago.

Aside from the antiquity of its family the animal is not particularly interesting. It looks and acts like a large stout lizard. One of our specimens was about two feet in length, dark olive-green in color, with a row of short, yellowish, horn-sheathed spines along the vertebrae. In their native habitat they dig burrows. They forage mostly in the dark, feeding upon insects, worms, small fishes, and crustaceans. One of their peculiarities is that the eggs do not hatch for thirteen months, although the embryo reaches half its full size in less than half that time. Neither of our specimens lived more than a year, but one has lived in the London Zoo for fourteen years, hiding during the day in sphagnum moss provided for the purpose, and coming out at night to feed on earthworms.

Lizards in general require sunshine and will not do well without it. Where natural or even artificial sunlight can be given, there is no reason why they should not live their full span of life in the zoo, for when kept in good condition they are ready feeders, especially if provided with natural food.

Among those exhibited in American zoos are the Gila monster and the Mexican beaded lizard. One of the former lived in our Park for nineteen years and four months. We feed them chiefly raw eggs, which they eat with avidity, especially during the warm seasons of the year. They are handsome animals, large in size and easily cared for, and one may point to the case containing the two species and assure the visitor that it contains a collection of all of the poisonous lizards known.

The Gila monster has developed poison glands. When it bites it holds on and chews, and the poison runs into the wound. The toxicity of this venom has furnished a topic for perennial dispute, but there is little doubt that under certain conditions the bite can be very serious.

The several species of little horned "toads" of the Southwest, of all the lizards, appear most often on exhibition. People bring them North as curiosities or pets and deposit them sometimes by the dozen in the Zoo. Though they appear hardy and phlegmatic, they prove almost impossible to keep for any length of time. If they live through the winter they almost invariably die in the spring. To acclimatize them to captivity, a diet of live ants in quantities greater than is practicable to provide for them would be necessary.

Recently a wide revival of interest in the horned toad has resulted from a newspaper story about a living specimen reported to have been sealed for thirty-five years in the cornerstone of a Texas courthouse. Absurd as the story was, thousands believed it and came to zoos in great numbers to look at the animal which could endure for so long without food, air, water, and sunshine. Just how this lizard got into the cornerstone we probably shall never know, but it is certain that it had not been there long. Considering the difficulty that we have had in keeping this little animal alive for more than a year, it occurred to us after the story came out that perhaps a solution of our problem would be to seal one up in a cement block and simply exhibit the block.

It has been known for years that the horned toad has the odd defensive habit of shooting blood from its eyes. This is not at all a common occurrence, and of many hundreds that I have caught I have seen only two who made use of the capacity. One of these shot blood in sharp spurts a distance of several feet.

Various types of small lizards from the Southwest, such as the collared lizard (*Crotaphytus collaris*), the alligator lizard (*Dracaena guianensis*), and *Gerrhonotus* species, make attractive exhibits, but do not live long in captivity.

The larger forms exhibited include the monitors, which do rather better than most in captivity, displaying a fondness for old raw eggs, and the tegu from South America (*Tupinambis teguixin*), large and conspicuously marked, which does well. This species occasionally does damage to the natives in South America by catching and eating small chickens from the barnyard. In a yard in Brazil I once saw one grab a tiny chick. The mother hen, by the way, atavistically indulged in a ruse common to wild birds of her family, namely, of pretending herself to be wounded, flopping along the ground as though she had a broken wing, in a vain attempt to attract the lizard's attention. I have never seen this repeated.

Especially familar to all circus and carnival visitors is the American or false chameleon from the Southeastern States, which is exposed for sale collared and chained to large green boards. When treated sensibly it will live for a long time, and makes an attractive and pretty pet. The circus man tells us to feed it sugar water, which it never touches, but during the warmer weather it will eat flies and other small insects with avidity. One which I kept for some time would lie stretched out on my forefinger and when I would "point" at a fly, he would suddenly dart forward and grab the fly without losing his hold of the finger.

These, of course, are not true chameleons, but they have remarkable powers of changing color, ranging from dark brown to pale greenish yellow, according to their condition, disposition, and temperature. Only in very warm weather do they display activity. In the West Indies other species of the genus are the dominant lizards, and can be seen by the dozens on bright days disporting

PLATE 90

The tegu, a lizard from South America which sometimes
preys on small chicks

PLATE 91

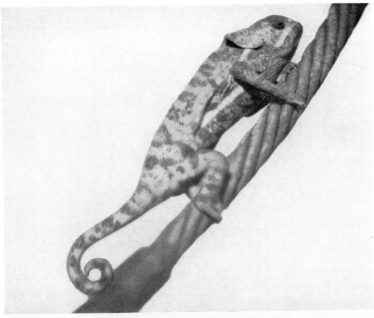

Upper: African chameleon, the true chameleon
Lower: Soft-shelled tortoise from Tanganyika

on trees and fences, and from time to time inflating their throats.

The true chameleons are sluggish, delicate animals, which seldom do well in captivity or live for more than a few months. Few animals arouse more popular interest than these, due to their curious habit of changing color in response to emotional excitation, to their weird ability of moving their large conical eyes independently of each other, to their large and curious feet, to their watch-springlike prehensile tails, and above all, to the enormously developed tongues, which they can shoot out to an incredible distance, accurately pegging a fly.

One of the older naturalists, writing of a pet chameleon, states that only once did he ever see it miss a fly, and then the fly was on the other side of the glass. In the zoo at Gizeh, Egypt, it was a common practice to tip the caretaker of the small-reptile house a penny or so, in return for which he would put a fly or two in the chameleon cage.

We brought some fifty of these (*Chamaeleon dilepis*) home from Tanganyika, but none of them lived longer than six months, despite everything we could do.

Australia harbors a number of large lizards, the water dragon (*Physignathus lesueurii*), the blue-tongued lizard (*Tiliqua scincoides*), the stump-tailed lizard (*Trachysaurus rugosus*), and Cunningham's or Australian skink (*Egernia cunninghami*), some of which have done very well here. All of these feed on bits of meat or raw egg.

The vegetarian lizards lend themselves better to life in captivity, chief among these being the Neo-tropical iguana, which grows to a large size, and with its relatives, the Mexican comb lizard (*Ctenosaura teres*), the rhinoceros iguana (*Cyclura stejnegeri*) from Mona Island, and others, feeds on bananas, other fruits, and lettuce. Though vegetarian, some of them are not too strict to take an occasional ration of raw meat.

The common tuberculated iguana (*Iguana iguana*) is a favorite food in many parts of tropical America, and its eggs, strung together, are seen for sale in the markets. The Colombian Indians will seize an iguana, slit it open with a knife, remove the eggs, and then let the mutilated animal go, with the idea that it will heal itself, or more often with no idea at all, one of the vilest examples of cruelty to animals that I have encountered.

The basilisk lizard (*Basiliscus vittatus*), with the curious topknot on its head, has twice appeared in our collection. This forms one of the commoner lizards in Central America, and is known to the English-speaking natives of Panama as the Jesus lizard, from its curious habit of skipping across the surface of water.

We have a cage of four large African rock pythons (*Python sebae*), the best eaters I know of among snakes. When mealtime comes (and with this particular group appetites are developed at least every two weeks), we supply a crate of thirty dead pigeons. If live specimens were placed in the reptiles' quarters, fights would result when two snakes seized the same pigeon. Sometimes, when such fights do occur, the snake that reaches the other one first will keep on swallowing, and swallow not only the pigeon but its cage mate. So we hand the pigeons one by one to the snakes with a pair of long wooden forceps. These particular pythons take them right off the forceps and commence swallowing. Sometimes when one pigeon has nearly disappeared down the gullet, another one is pushed up against it, and so on with four or five in succession, till the snake is gorged.

The pythons and boas are the commonest of the large snakes and the best suited for life in captivity. The well-known South American boa constrictor itself comes regularly into the market. It is usually a small snake compared with the pythons, though the name is commonly applied to any large tropical snake. Two that I had as pets became very tame. They were about four feet long, and lived in a glass hood in my laboratory.

It is obviously difficult to estimate the length of a

living snake, always in coils and twisted, and invariably the size is exaggerated, especially by people who have been "pursued" by them and by dealers who have them for sale. Receiving a dealer's price list offering boa constrictors up to twelve feet in length at $2.00 a foot, I hurried to New York and asked to see them. A large packing case full of snakes was brought out and we took out the largest, stretched it on a table, the dealer pulling at one end and I at the other, while a friend took the measurement. It was eight and a half feet, which meant a saving of exactly seven dollars for the United States Government.

The condition as well as the disposition of these big snakes varies with the temperature, and at Pará, Brazil, where a collection is kept in the open, covered with wire mesh, they will throw themselves at the visitor, hissing and striking.

Ten years is the longest that a boa constrictor has lived in our Park. A Cuban tree boa (*Epicrates angulifer*) has been here nearly twelve years and an Indian python (*Python molurus*) over eleven, but our record is held by a specimen of the great water boa, or anaconda, which was presented to the Park by the Governor of the State of Pará, Brazil, and lived for more than twenty-eight years in a gloomy cage.

Eight years has been our record for longevity in rattlesnakes, and this was made by only one of 110 specimens of a single species, the Florida diamond, largest of its genus. One may venture a guess that this comparatively short span of life in captivity results from lack of the sunshine which the snake requires. The rattlers make peaceful reptiles in a cage and, though they rattle fiercely, very seldom strike at the keeper.

While on a camping trip in northern Texas one early autumn, I caught twenty-two rattlers, of which only two showed any particular fight. One of them behaved so well that to this day I regret having killed and pickled

him, even though in the cause of science. I was fishing
for frogs with bits of bright-red paper torn from the cover
of my notebook as bait, when a cowboy friend shouted
that there was a rattler beneath me. I looked down and
saw one crawling between my legs. I struck it a number
of times with a fishing rod, and then wrapped it in a
handkerchief and put it in the shade until I finished
obtaining a mess of frog legs for supper. Later, as I was
carrying the handkerchief package in one hand and the
rod in the other toward the chuck wagon, the same cowboy
yelled that the snake was coming out. I looked down
again. It was not dead, and its head and twelve inches
of body were swinging alongside my leg as I carried it.
In either instance it could have bitten and did not.

The copperhead, equally poisonous, does as well as
the rattler in captivity, especially when fed on frogs, if
kept in a moderately moist cage. It is, despite its awful
reputation, a beautiful snake, and easy to obtain, especially
in the southeastern part of the United States. One of our
specimens actually came from within the city limits of
Boston, caught there on Great Blue Hill by Mr. Arthur
Loveridge.

Despite the fact that during early boyhood snakes
were my commonest pets, I have had but one bad experience with them, and that was with the copperhead.
While wandering along Christian Creek in Virginia looking
for snakes to occupy a new snake cage—formerly a honey
box with a glass front which we had purchased from
the local grocery—my roommate and I turned a log.
A small copperhead on the other side was turned over
and lay there, belly up. I thought it a milk snake and
picked it up, to discover that I had mistaken the identity.
My roommate, who had never seen one alive before, was
thrilled. Holding the snake's head between thumb and
finger, I opened its mouth with a pair of forceps, and
lectured learnedly on the fangs and poison sac. At the
end of the lecture the demonstration occurred. The

PLATE 92

Land iguana, a lizard two and a half feet long, collected in the Galápagos and presented to the Zoo by Gifford Pinchot

PLATE 93

American rattlesnake. A peaceful Zoo animal

snake, by a quick effort, wriggled loose and sunk his fangs into my left forefinger. In those days there were no serums. We wouldn't have had any with us even if there had been. So we tied the finger at the base, and then proceeded, with a knife whose dullness I remember vividly to this day, to make a cut and let out the blood. There followed a three-mile walk back to Staunton, where we stopped at the doctor's before returning to the dormitory. The only thing the doctor did was to suggest with several strong words my absolute lack of brains, and to pull the band off the finger. The book in which I had read about letting out blood had said nothing about letting any back, so for four months I had a numb finger. Being ordered to bed for a day or two gave me ample time to read some more about copperheads, and the statement "This snake is very dangerous, causing serious illness and frequent death by its bite" is all I can remember of what I read at the time.

The only other American representative of this group of poison snakes is the water moccasin, usually vicious, but attractive and hardy in captivity.

Belonging to the same family as the above three snakes are those of the genus *Bothrops*, which includes a famous bushmaster and a fer-de-lance. Dr. Vital Brazil, the celebrated student of snakes and their venom, sent us a collection of six species in this genus, in the care of Dr. Waldo Schmitt of the National Museum. Schmitt, taking wonderful care of them, landed in New York on a cold day, and got the snakes all alive to Washington by putting them in his Pullman berth adjacent to a couple of hot-water bottles. The snakes, by the way, were in boxes.

We have had few cobras, only those we brought home from Tanganyika, the Egyptian species (*Naja haie*), and the black-necked spitting cobra (*Naja nigricollis*). The latter can shoot its poison to a distance of five or six feet, and the first month that it was here filled one of the eyes of the head keeper with its venom. He washed it immediately with a strong boracic acid solution, and the result was only an inflamed condition that lasted a week. There are records of more serious damage having been done. This snake prefers small rabbits to any other food, and will eat a half dozen of them at a meal.

On the same expedition we secured a collection of boomslangs (*Dispholidus typus*). They lived but a short time because we could not get enough lizards, their usual food, to satisfy them. At first, when excited they would inflate their throats to a length of perhaps six inches, which gave them a grotesque appearance, as though they had suddenly swallowed a large frankfurter sausage, but they soon became tame and refused to make this display.

Of the nonpoisonous American snakes that we have had in the collection, the common black snake (*Coluber constrictor*), the chicken snake (*Elaphe quadrivittata*), and the water snake (*Natrix sipedon*) have made the best records. The last is very easy to keep, as it will feed readily on fish cut in small strips and thrown into the tank of water in the cage.

Heterodon contortrix, the spreading adder or blowing viper, one of our most feared reptiles, not only lives well in captivity but makes an admirable pet, becoming gentle. One soon notices one of its curious habits—that of "playing 'possum." A freshly-caught adder will roll over on its back and lie motionless, simulating death even to the extent of hanging its tongue, half distended, from its mouth. When the annoyer leaves, it will wriggle right side up and crawl off, but if caught again will repeat the performance. After a short time in captivity the snake becomes so accustomed to its caretakers that it will no longer go through this interesting ceremony.

Various types of Crocodilia are known in zoos. They are usually sluggish animals, restricting their activity to lying about.

THE COLD-BLOODED TRIBE

We have had 358 of the common American alligators in the Zoo since its inception. The longest that one has lived has been nineteen years. Most of our accessions were small ones, brought North as pets and soon discarded. They spend most of their time lying about or floating in the water, but on Mondays and Thursdays, when they are fed, there is a great commotion in the cage. Fish are handed to them on the end of long sticks, and eagerly torn off and devoured. Formerly we kept them in an open lake during the summer, where, invigorated by the long hot season with lots of sunshine, they became very active, and there was always an exciting time in the early fall when they had to be caught and put back in the heated house for the winter. In the new reptile house which we are to build the coming year, we plan an open lake for these animals in the summer time, but expect to have a chute through which to drive them back when the weather begins to get cold.

Mr. Blackburne contributes the following reminiscences:

The Park has always been well supplied with alligators. Many tourists to Florida have brought back with them as souvenirs small ones ranging in length from eight to ten and twelve inches. Their owners kept them in bathtubs, wash tubs in the cellar, and all sorts of places. In most cases the alligators refused to eat, and were finally presented to the Park. The largest specimens exhibited here, from six feet nine inches to nine feet long, were all little alligators when received.

One day in summer two of the larger alligators had a severe battle. One was gripped by the foreleg above the foot, and as they thrashed about in the water the foot was severed and hung by the skin. We caught and removed the wounded alligator, lashed him to a board nine feet long and one foot wide, and cut the skin holding the dangling foot, entirely separating it from the body. We got together needle, thread, splints, cotton, plaster, and bandages. Then we sewed the foot back in place, wrapped it in cotton, arranged splints, and made a plaster cast. The alligator was returned to his quarters and ten weeks later the cast was removed. The foot proved to be as good as before the accident, except for some stiffness and a small seam, which showed where it had been sewed together.

Because of lack of housing facilities we have never made any particular attempt to secure crocodiles, but have had two at different times. Once, at Miami, Florida, a dealer in curios called my attention to a baby alligator in his possession which had a nose altogether too long for such an animal. It was in reality a young American crocodile, quite a different thing, which I purchased and brought home in a pasteboard box.

In the swamp of San Antonio, in Bolivia, when traveling in a carreton drawn by oxen, which carries one over dry land, through mud and water, and even through deep water, I once saw a spectacled cayman, about three feet long, swim beneath the cart. I caught it with the aid of the handle of a butterfly net, and brought it home.

The various turtles, tortoises, and terrapins make ideal exhibition animals, provided they are given reasonably good quarters. The purely aquatic species are best shown in aquaria. Others require access both to water and to dry areas in their inclosure. Among the most interesting are the giant tortoises of the Galápagos Islands (*Testudo* species), of which we have six, two of them having been here for more than thirty years. These spend the summer in an open paddock, and the winter in a gloomy, though well heated, shed. Throughout the year they feed heartily on green vegetables. Almost as large is the calcarated tortoise of Abyssinia, which lives with the other giants and on the same diet.

Of land turtles, the species common to the Eastern States, the box turtle, is one of the most difficult to keep

PLATE 94

Giant Albemarle Island tortoise

PLATE 95

Tortoises from the Galápagos Islands. Recent additions from the Gifford Pinchot expedition, with old Zoo residents of thirty years

in a house. It requires a chance to hibernate, and when given such facilities will thrive for many years.

The box turtles of Africa (*Cinixys belliana*) are curious in that they have the hinge on the upper shell posterior to the middle instead of only on the plastron, as in the other box turtles.

The gopher tortoise from Florida (*Gopherus polyphemus*) takes to captivity readily, as do Agassiz' or the desert tortoise (*Gopherus agassizii*) from the Mohave Desert, the African leopard tortoise (*Testudo pardalis*), and various East Indian and South American species.

The most curious of all of the land tortoises is the soft-shelled or Loveridge's tortoise from Tanganyika Territory (*Testudo tornieri*). We secured numbers of these at Dodoma, an arid region not unlike southern Arizona, the country dotted here and there by rocky kopjes. These turtles, flat and with a flexible shell, were fond of nesting in crevices in these rocks. When we arrived we found that the natives were ignorant of their existence, but directions that we gave for finding them resulted in a great series. On our return we distributed these to various parts of the United States. They did only moderately well in captivity, due to very heavy infestation of internal parasitic worms.

Of the purely aquatic species, the snapping turtle (*Chelydra serpentina*) is the commonest. When given a tank of water to live in and meat or fish to eat, this lives in captivity indefinitely. Other varieties, the Florida snapping turtle (*Chelydra osceola*) and Rossignon's snapping turtle (*Chelydra rossignonii*) from Honduras, do equally well.

The matamata (*Chelys fimbriata*), the most extraordinarily put together and decorated of all the turtles, is very delicate, though the New York and Philadelphia zoos have maintained them for many years. They will lie for hours motionless, and then come to the surface and elevate their long, pointed nostrils for a breath.

The Maw's turtle (*Dermatemys mawii*), representing a peculiar type found only in the rivers of Tehuantepec, attains a large size, but is seldom seen in captivity. At Santa Lucrezia, in Mexico, I once employed an Indian to secure five of these for me at a price arranged beforehand. He caught them and arrived at my lodgings with 150 pounds of turtle in a sack on his back. It was a long, steep climb from the river to my house, and when he got there he commenced the customary attempt to treble to the foreigner the price agreed upon originally. For the only time in my life in a bargaining encounter with a native I had things entirely my way. I knew that he would not carry them away when I told him to, so I finally secured them at the original price, plus a mere fifty-percent gratuity as a token of my high esteem.

The giant turtle of the Amazon (*Podocnemis expansa*), well-known through the account by Bates, is a very large species. It feeds in nature on water weed, and does not last long under captive conditions. We once rescued some from the meat market at Manáos, where they are commonly sold, and brought them to Washington, but they lived scarcely a year.

While seining for fishes in the small tributaries of the Rio Beni, we secured a number of interesting turtles, among them *Platemys planiceps*, a species with a shell about six inches long, heavily ridged on top, and at the same time of very flat form. Visitors have remarked that it appeared to be upside down.

Another rather hideous turtle is *Phrynops geoffroyana*, with a flat head and a long flat neck which it has to twist into an S-shape and fold around the side of its body to get under the shell. This long-necked feature is common to several South American turtles, but more especially to *Chelodina longicollis*, the common Australian species, specimens of which I have had in captivity a year at my home, and at the Zoo for more than seven

PLATE 96

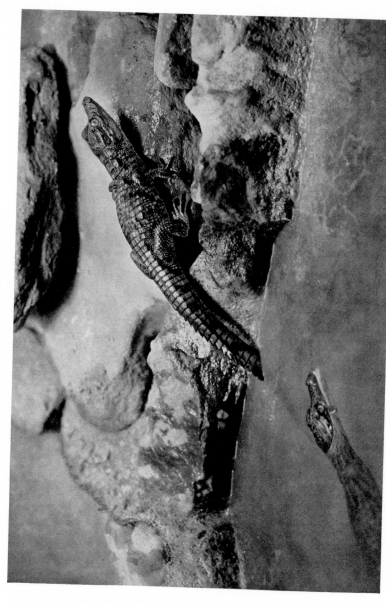

West African broad-nosed crocodile babies. They attain a length of four feet
Photo by Underwood & Underwood

PLATE 97

Mountain chicken of the Island of Dominica. Famous for its delicacy of flavor

Photo by Underwood & Underwood

years. They have become exceedingly tame, and will eat from the fingers.

It may indicate a peculiar taste to like turtles, but many people are fond of them, especially in Europe, where dealers handle species from all parts of the world. Always on the lookout for rare and interesting members of this family, I asked the proprietor of a small pet shop in Rotterdam if he had any turtles. He had. There were some cement tanks in the floor, the water in them heavily covered with water weed and slime. He bared his arm to his elbow and, groping about, produced several of the interesting little Reeves turtle (*Geoclemmys reevesii*) from China, some of the common spotted European pond turtle (*Emys orbicularis*), and a leprous terrapin (*Clemmys leprosa*) from Tunis. Six specimens from three continents were put into a little box for me, and the price for the lot was eighty cents.

In the zoo at Basel I heard that the local pet shop had just secured a very large shipment of interesting turtles. With the address written on the back of an envelope, and stopping from time to time to show it to people on the street who would point the general direction, I hurried to the shop. I got there just a moment or two before closing time. It proved to be a typical pet store, with aquaria and birds in the window. Answering my inquiry as to whether he had any nice turtles, the proprietor replied that he had just received the finest shipment he had ever had. I was all excited, thinking that here at last was a chance to pick up some of the wonderful East Indian forms which I had never seen alive. Advancing toward the boxes containing the collection, I asked where they were from. He replied, "Every one direct from Texas."

Some of Mr. Blackburne's reminiscences of snakes in the National Zoological Park should be preserved. He writes:

At one time we had in the collection a large boa constrictor, eighteen feet long and rather well filled out. It was a good feeder, and we noticed nothing strange in its appearance. One morning I was surprised to see the case in which this snake lived full of little snakes. Sixty boa constrictors had during the night been added to the collection. Each snake was born in a separate transparent sac, and when I discovered them each snake had broken its sac and worked itself part way through. Their heads were pointed upwards, and their forked tongues wiggled back and forth. When they had freed themselves entirely they scattered in every direction, but eventually they bunched up and lay in one corner of the case. They measured about fifteen inches and appeared to be in good condition.

The mother snake paid no attention to her young ones, and it became our task to find food for them. We started by feeding them mice, which were about the right size for them. They all had good appetites and at times several would go after the same mouse or small rat, and then there would be as many as six tied up in a ball. As they grew larger we gave them chicken heads to eat, as well as pigeons cut up into small pieces, with a few feathers left on each piece. These they ate without hesitation. Later they managed to eat the body of a whole pigeon, if the wings were cut off close to the body. Finally we came to realize that we had more snakes than we had room for, so they were disposed of to other zoos in lots of ten. We retained a dozen.

Water snakes, copperheads, and rattlesnakes have been born in the collection. Pine snakes and pythons have laid eggs but no young were hatched.

Two of the keepers have suffered bites from venomous snakes, one by a Florida moccasin and one by a diamond rattlesnake. In the latter case the keeper lost a finger, but his life was saved.

CHAPTER XXII

THE MESS

THERE is really no need for visitors to feed the animals in the Zoo. They are well provided for by a staff of cooks and caterers, and approximately $30,000 a year is spent in purchasing the food served to them. One man specializes in baking special breads. Electric grinding machines are used, and there is an efficiently conducted butcher shop at one end of the cook house. The animals are, in short, fed amply and carefully.

But there are other reasons why zoological parks prohibit indiscriminate feeding of their tenants. Certain animals may perhaps eat unusual things without harm to themselves, but unless the public is very discriminating, much damage can be done, and years of experience show that the public is not very discriminating. In the menagerie tent of one of our larger circuses there will be as many as thirty elephants in a line, and 40,000 visitors make a good day's audience. That allows a thousand visitors to one elephant. In the Zoo we sometimes have 80,000 visitors in a day, which is too great odds against our two elephants. Then, small boys, when permitted to throw peanuts, are sometimes fond of putting a little English on a peanut and hitting a monkey in the eye. Consequently there is strict prohibition in parks against throwing anything whatever into the cages.

All zoos have their sad history of damage to animals occasioned by ignorant or vicious visitors. In our own Park a visitor tossed some laurel leaves into an inclosure where there had lived for some years six Angora goats, and all of them died that evening. A beautiful Diana monkey, for many years the only one of its kind in America, and known and admired by a large public, was presented with some laurel leaves by another visitor. Monkeys are very fond of leaves, and will eat practically any kind. The Diana went into convulsions and died in a short time. Since then we have been unable to obtain another, and the public is denied the privilege of seeing such a splendid animal. A magnificent Andean condor was found dead one morning. A post-mortem showed a ball of lead foil in his stomach. Some one had tossed this into the cage. Eight magpies died in one morning through being fed too many salted peanuts. An otter, an old resident in the Park, also died from eating peanuts, as did a cassowary. For some reason a cassowary, who swallows his food whole, is unable to handle a peanut.

So a visitor very casually may create havoc through an attempt to attract an animal's attention by feeding. When several animals are together, feeding is done carefully so that each gets his proper share. One peanut tossed into the cage when the keeper is not looking may result in a quarrel and a fatal fight among the inmates of the cage, and the more or less innocent donor will have done great damage to the collection.

Certain animals, especially the bears and some of the very hardy monkeys like the rhesus, can stand a great deal. So while the public should trust the Zoo personnel to feed and care for the animals, one feels like making a compromise and paraphrasing the Italian fruit-store proprietor's request, "If you mus' pincha da fruit—pincha da coconut," to "If you must feed the animals—feed the bears."

The question most commonly asked in connection with the feeding of the animals may be answered by the statement that the majority of them have one meal a day. Some—elephants, tapirs, hippos, bears, certain fruit-eating birds, monkeys, seals, and sea lions—have two meals.

PLATE 98

Condor from the Andes, generally considered the largest bird that flies
From a painting by Benson B. Moore

Long years of experience have shown that the big cats do best if given one fast day a week, so Sundays they do not get fed—a terrible thing, by the way, when Christmas falls on Sunday.

The sea lion is one of the most expensive of all our animals to keep, as an adult will eat about twenty pounds of fish a day, an elephant seal a hundred. This food must be perfectly fresh, as tainted fish would almost certainly kill the animal. Of the birds, the pelican costs most to keep, as he devours two pounds of the same fine quality of fish each day.

For the two meals of the elephant the staples are seventy-five pounds of hay a day, eight to ten loaves of bread, and a bucket of crushed oats. Twice a week a bucket of bran mash containing a tablespoonful of salt is substituted for the oats. Occasionally apples, green grass, and leaves are added.

The hippo has three bushels of chopped-up hay for his evening meal, and during the day a heaping bucketful of crushed oats, dampened bran, carrots, apples, sweet potatoes, and bread, all chopped and mixed together.

The bears receive a special bread made of two parts of wheat flour to one part of bran, with salt. This is mixed with yeast cakes and left over night, baked in sixteen-pound loaves, and aged one day before feeding. Formerly molasses was used, but this made it too soggy. The bear, according to its size, eats from eight to twenty pounds of this bread daily, and in addition vegetables, fish, and an occasional ration of horse meat. The polar bear gets much more meat and fish, preferring the ribs and breast cuts from a horse, so that he can eat a soft bone.

The cats, of course, eat meat. We feed them horse meat, though some zoos use beef. The larger lions and tigers eat from ten to sixteen pounds a day, and on Mondays and Thursdays a pound or so of liver is added. Leopards eat four or five pounds, and the smaller cats, like servals and caracals, one and a half to two pounds a day. Sometimes dead pigeons and chickens are fed them. It is curious that duck meat is not popular with the cat family. Younger cats receive cod-liver oil with their meat.

Ruminants in general eat hay and grain in quantities according to the size and condition of the animal. We have found crushed oats preferable for most of them, though the goat family seems to like whole oats best.

The monkeys receive a varied diet. They are fed twice daily, and each meal differs from the last. In general they prefer raw to cooked food.

MONKEY MENU

HORS D'OEUVRE
Green grass Fresh leaves Cod-liver oil

CEREAL
Boiled rice

ENTRÉES
Meal worms
Eggs—raw and boiled

ROAST
Horse meat, small portions

VEGETABLES
Sweet potatoes, baked, boiled, and raw
Carrots Onions, boiled and raw Sugar beets
Irish potatoes, boiled and baked
Cabbage, boiled and raw

BREAD
Bran White Raisin

SALAD
Lettuce Kale

DESSERT
Rice custard Baked custard
Oranges Apples Bananas
Other fruits in season

BEVERAGE
Milk

Nuts Raisins Whole wheat Sunflower seeds

PLATE 99

The herd of Angora goats which died from eating laurel

PLATE 100

Two bottle-fed babies: Sarah, the olive baboon, and a duiker

THE MESS

In the zoo at Mexico City monkeys also receive *cafe con leche* (coffee with milk) at four in the afternoon, like any human. A diet as above, eked out by contributions from the public of peanuts, chewing gum, safety-razor blades, matches, and an occasional hat, handkerchief, or glove grabbed by the monkey keeps him in good condition as well as spirits.

All supplies for the National Zoo are purchased through competitive bids. The lowest price for first-class produce is accepted. Seconds are permitted in many cases; that is, potatoes may be smaller than usual, a fish may have nicks in it, but everything must be absolutely fresh.

The following is an average year's purchase (1928):

Horse meat	130,331	pounds
Fish	40,895	"
Bread	37,379	"
Yeast	241	"
Bananas	13,800	"
Apples	8,753	"
Sweet potatoes	41,335	"
White potatoes	11,046	"
Carrots	13,145	"
Kale	3,473	"
Onions	3,635	"
Cabbage	3,840	"
Beets	2,065	"
Eggs	585	dozen
Oranges	72	"
Lettuce	105	heads
Spinach	20	pounds
Strawberries	2	boxes
Dates	1	pound
Honey	225	pounds
Figs	1	pound
Grapes	1	basket
Sugar	700	pounds
Milk	83	cases
Table salt	1,200	pounds
Rock salt	3,000	"
Flour, wheat	184	barrels
Flour, graham	2	"

Rice...................................	2,100	pounds
Dried shrimp............................	100	"
Rabbits.................................	17	"
Pigeons.................................	398	"
Hay, timothy and grass mixed............	354,091	"
Hay, clover.............................	10,340	"
Bran....................................	32,000	"
Wheat straw.............................	25,800	"
Feeding wheat...........................	5,600	"
Yellow cracked corn.....................	29,500	"
Yellow shelled corn.....................	30,500	"
Whole oats..............................	55,000	"
Crushed oats............................	130,280	"
Yellow cornmeal.........................	400	"
Laying mash.............................	500	"
Chick mash..............................	625	"
Chick feed..............................	195	"
Oyster shells...........................	400	"
Alfalfa meal............................	1,100	"
Meat meal...............................	400	"
Canary seed.............................	1,500	"
Millet..................................	700	"
Rape....................................	200	"
Sunflower seed..........................	5,850	"
Hemp seed...............................	400	"
Scratch (mixed seeds)...................	2,200	"
Mockingbird food........................	540	"

In addition to the above, last year there were produced in the Zoo the following:

200 white mice	256 dozen eggs
300 white rats	1,900 pounds kale
33 young chickens	1,200 " lettuce
130 pigeons	2,000 " rape
30 hens and ducks	4,000 " beets
113 rabbits	

More than 25 tons of grass; also brush and bamboo for sloths, beavers, and other animals.

We raise things only when it has been shown by experience to be cheaper to do so than to buy in the open market.

Probably the most varied diet of all is found among the birds. Here the meat and fish eaters and the seed eaters are fed once a day, but the others twice. The menu consists of mockingbird food (a commercial preparation of which boiled and ground meat forms a considerable part), meal worms, hard-boiled eggs, cooked rice, vegetables, and fruit. Even Hamburg steak is not unknown in the menu, for meat balls, composed sometimes of meat and vegetables, are made daily, to be tossed into the air and grabbed and eaten by such birds as the East Indian and African hornbills. Of seeds, sunflower, canary, hemp, millet, and rape are most generally used.

To keep the quarters of the animals in good condition requires, during the year:

Sawdust	2,100	bushels
Brooms	22	dozen
Mops	20	"
Scrub cloths	15	"
Scrub brushes	8	"
Soap	750	pounds
Insect powder	40	

The work of a keeper is largely routine, relieved, of course, by unusual events that occur almost every day. He shows up in the morning long before the public is admitted, and by the time the doors of the buildings are thrown open to visitors the buildings have been swept and scrubbed. Freshening up the cages occupies most of the morning.

Then each keeper goes to the cook house, draws rations for the animals under his care, and prepares the meals. Feeding is done usually after lunch, and the rest of the day is spent again in cleaning. Continual scrubbing is the price of an attractive zoo. The work is hard.

A keeper must be quiet in his manner, patient with his animals, and must know enough about them to care properly for them as well as to answer the questions hurled at him by visitors. These are numerous and of infinite variety. I trust that some of them have been answered in the preceding pages.

APPENDIX I

LIST OF ANIMALS EXHIBITED IN THE NATIONAL ZOOLOGICAL PARK SINCE 1890

WITH THE NUMBER OF SPECIMENS AND THE LONGEVITY RECORD OF EACH SPECIES

NUMBER OF SPECIMENS	MAMMALS	LONGEVITY RECORD	
		YEARS	MONTHS
	MONOTREMATA		
4	Echidna aculeata (Spiny anteater)		5
	MARSUPIALIA		
11	Trichosurus fuliginosus (Dusky phalanger)	3	7
8	vulpecula (Australian opossum)	8	4
9	Petaurus breviceps (Flying phalanger)	*8	4
2	sciureus (Flying phalanger)	4	11
4	Phascolomys mitchelli (Common wombat)	*6	5
1	Macropus bicolor (Black-tailed wallaby)	5	10
17	billardieri (Rufous-bellied wallaby)	8	8
4	dorsalis (Black-striped wallaby)	3	9
16	giganteus (Gray kangaroo)	10	9
1	grayi (Wallaby)		
2	melanops (Black-faced kangaroo)	6	
2	parma (Parma wallaby)	5	
20	robustus (Wallaroo)	13	
2	ruficollis (Red-necked wallaby)	1	
5	ruficollis bennetti (Bennett's red-necked wallaby)	6	
43	rufus (Red kangaroo)	9	4
2	ualabatus (Swamp wallaby)	2	6

* Specimen which made longevity record still living in Zoo Feb. 1, 1929.

[284]

MAMMALS

NUMBER OF SPECIMENS	MAMMALS	LONGEVITY RECORD	
		YEARS	MONTHS
	MARSUPIALIA—*Continued*		
21	Petrogale penicillata (Brush-tailed rock wallaby)	8	6
3	xanthopus (Yellow-footed rock wallaby)	1	2
4	Onychogale frenata (Bridled wallaby)	2	
13	Aepyprymnus rufescens (Rufous rat kangaroo)	3	5
2	Perameles sp. (Rat bandicoot)	1	8
1	nasuta (Long-nosed bandicoot)		4
5	Thylacynus cynocephalus (Tasmanian wolf)	7	1
6	Sarcophilus harrisii (Tasmanian devil)	5	7
4	Dasyurus sp. (Native cat)	*3	2
147	Didelphis virginiana (Opossum)	*4	5
2	sp. (Manicou)	1	
1	Metachirops opossum fuscogriseus (Allen's opossum)	1	4
1	Marmosa murina (Murine opossum)		9
	INSECTIVORA		
26	Erinaceus europaeus (European hedgehog)	3	4
1	Atelerix hindei sotikae (White-bellied hedgehog)		7
2	Elephantulus ocularis (Loveridge's elephant shrew)		2
2	Solenodon paradoxus		6
2	Centetes ecaudatus (Tenrec)	1	4
	CHIROPTERA		
2	Pteropus giganteus (Indian fruit bat)	2	10

WILD ANIMALS

NUMBER OF SPECIMENS	MAMMALS	LONGEVITY RECORD	
		YEARS	MONTHS
	CARNIVORA		
11	Thalarctos maritimus (Polar bear)	*27	5
56	Euarctos americanus (American black bear)	*15	11
1	americanus amblyceps (Arizona bear)		4 days
16	americanus cinnamomum (Cinnamon bear)	17	3
2	americanus perniger (Black bear)	17	5
1	Ursus apache (Apache grizzly)	10	8
22	arctos (European brown bear)	*10	5
1	dalli (Yakutat bear)	28	7
1	emmonsii (Glacier bear)	*11	1
2	floridanus (Florida bear)	5	5
7	gyas (Alaska Peninsula brown bear)	*21	
6	gyas × dalli (Hybrid Alaskan bear). Born in Park, eaten by mother	18	9
10	horribilis (Grizzly bear)	4	
2	japonicus (Japanese bear)	*21	4
3	kidderi (Kidder's bear)	2	5
8	kidderi × arctos (Hybrid brown bear)	23	8
3	middendorffi (Kodiak bear)	14	8
2	Selenarctos thibetanus (Himalayan bear)	5	4
7	Helarctos malayanus (Sun bear)	21	6
3	Melursus ursinus (Sloth bear)	3	8
6	Ailurus fulgens (Panda)	11	1
9	Potos flavus (Kinkajou)	*8	11
1	flavus aztecus (Mexican kinkajou)		11

APPENDIX I

NUMBER OF SPECIMENS	MAMMALS	LONGEVITY RECORD	
		YEARS	MONTHS
	CARNIVORA—*Continued*		
14	Bassariscus astutus (Cacomistle or American civet cat)	11	11
21	Nasua narica (Gray coati-mundi)	8	10
8	rufa (Red coati-mundi)	5	5
2	Procyon cancrivorus (Crab-eating racoon)	4	8
201	lotor (Racoon)	5	5
2	lotor elucus (Florida racoon)	*5	8
35	Taxidea americana (American badger)	15	5
1	Meles anakuma (Japanese badger)		
2	meles (European badger)	6	12 days
7	Mephitis elongata (Florida skunk)		6
45	nigra (Skunk)		8
1	Spilogale ambarvalis (Florida spotted skunk)	7	11
1	ringens (Spotted skunk)		1½
5	Gulo luscus (Wolverine)		4
2	Grison vittata (Grison)	1	5
3	Tayra barbara (Tayra)	1	8
21	Martes americana (Marten)	14	11
7	pennanti (Fisher)	4	2
20	Mustela furo (Common ferret)	9	
6	nigripes (Black-footed ferret)	6	
1	noveboracensis (Weasel)	5	1
48	vison (Mink)	3	2
17	Lutra canadensis (American otter)	13	8

NUMBER OF SPECIMENS	MAMMALS	LONGEVITY RECORD	
		YEARS	MONTHS
	CARNIVORA—*Continued*		
9	Lutra canadensis vaga (Florida otter)	13	11
1	Mellivora capensis (Ratel)	*2	4
6	Carcinocyon thous (Rough fox)	7	1
61	Canis dingo (Dingo)	14	9
64	familiaris (Eskimo dog)	9	9
14	familiaris (Russian wolf-hound)	4	8
33	familiaris (Various breeds)	5	5
2	floridanus (Southern wolf)	7	1
9	frustror (Woodhouse's coyote)	11	4
58	latrans (Coyote or prairie wolf)	15	10
5	latrans rufus (Coyote)	*3	10
1	mesomelas (Black-backed jackal)	*4	5
8	mesomelas mcmillani (East African black-backed jackal)	1	7
1	nebracensis (Plains coyote)		10
96	nubilus (Gray wolf)	16	6
1	ochropus (California coyote)	*5	7
1	rufus (Texas red wolf)	*7	7
1	Cerdocyon magellanicus (Magellan fox)		9
2	Vulpes chama (Silver-back fox)		*8
73	fulva (Red fox)	10	2
2	macrotis (Long-eared swift fox)		2
28	velox (Swift or kit fox)	10	4
2	vulpes (European fox)	*5	6

APPENDIX I

NUMBER OF SPECIMENS	MAMMALS	LONGEVITY RECORD	
		YEARS	MONTHS
	CARNIVORA—Continued		
78	Alopex lagopus (Arctic fox)		10
37	Urocyon cinereoargenteus (Gray fox)	7	7
2	Octocyon megalotis (Long-eared fox)	2	2
3	Hyaena brunnea (Brown hyena)	*2	10
5	striata (Striped hyena)	10	10
8	Crocuta crocuta (Spotted hyena)	6	4
5	crocuta germinans (East African spotted hyena)	*2	4
1	Proteles cristatus (Aard-wolf)	*6	9
1	Icticyon venaticus (Bush dog)	*4	8
2	Fennecus zerda (Fennec)		*8
2	Viverra civetta (African civet)	6	8
1	zibetha (Indian civet)	*2	4
10	Genetta dongolana neumanni (Neumann's genet)	*2	4
2	genetta (Common genet)	11	4
1	suahelica (East African genet)	1	1
1	Paradoxurus fasciatus (Banded palm civet)	4	1
3	hermaphroditus (Palm civet)	7	8
2	Arctictis binturong (Binturong or bear-cat)		6
1	Herpestes flaviventris (Ochraceous mongoose)		6
1	gracilis lademanni (Black mongoose)		6
1	griseus (Indian mongoose)		5
1	ichneumon (Egyptian mongoose)	*3	7
1	paludinosus rubescens (Water mongoose)		3

[289]

NUMBER OF SPECIMENS	MAMMALS	LONGEVITY RECORD	
		YEARS	MONTHS
	CARNIVORA—*Continued*		
1	Helogale parvula (Wahlberg's mongoose)	2	11
2	undulata (Lesser mongoose)		5
2	Mungos mungo (Mongoose)	4	8
4	mungo colonus (Banded mongoose)		9
3	Acinonyx jubatus (Cheetah)	13	7
11	Felis azteca (Mexican puma)	*11	8
2	capensis hindei (East African serval)	*2	4
1	caracal nubica (Abyssinian lynx)	*3	4
1	chrysothrix (Gray tiger-cat)		2
5	eyra (Eyra cat)	1	2
1	glaucula (Margay)		1
42	hippolestes (Mountain lion)	8	6
51	leo (Lion)	15	9
2	marmorata (Marbled cat)		7
3	nebulosa (Clouded leopard)	*6	2
15	ocreata (Egyptian cat)		1
10	onca (Jaguar)	13	9
30	pardalis (Ocelot)	6	2
1	pardalis brasiliensis (Brazilian ocelot)	*6	4
13	pardus (Leopard)	15	4
8	pardus suahelicus (East African leopard)	*2	4
5	serval (Serval)	7	4
4	tigrina (Margay cat)	1	8

APPENDIX I

NUMBER OF SPECIMENS	MAMMALS	LONGEVITY RECORD	
		YEARS	MONTHS
	CARNIVORA—*Continued*		
11	Felis tigris (Bengal tiger)	*14	10
9	tigris longipilis (Siberian tiger)	*12	8
2	uncia (Snow leopard)	6	5
2	viverrina (Fishing cat)	3	3
9	yagouaroundi (Yaguarundi cat)	5	3
1	Ailurin planiceps (Fire cat)		4
1	Lynx baileyi (Bailey's lynx)	*1	3
7	canadensis (Canada lynx)	11	4
6	caracal (Caracal)	5	4
1	caracal nubicus (East African caracal)		7
2	fasciatus (Banded lynx)		5
19	rufus (Bay lynx)	15	10
1	rufus californicus (California lynx)	13	11
1	rufus eremicus (Desert lynx)		4
12	rufus floridanus (Florida lynx)	13	
21	rufus texensis (Spotted lynx)	10	
4	uinta (Northern wild cat)	15	4
	PINNIPEDIA		
4	Eumetopias jubata (Stellar's sea lion)	17	3
28	Zalophus californianus (California sea lion)	14	2
3	Phoca richardii (Leopard seal)	*1	7
3	richardii geronimensis (San Geronimo harbor seal)	4	10

NUMBER OF SPECIMENS	MAMMALS	LONGEVITY RECORD	
		YEARS	MONTHS
	PINNIPEDIA—*Continued*		
63	Phoca vitulina (Harbor seal)	12	2
2	Mirounga angustirostris (Elephant seal)		4
2	Monachus tropicalis (West Indian seal)		2
6	Callorhinus alascanus (Northern fur seal)	3	8
	PRIMATES		
6	Lemur catta (Ring-tailed lemur)	3	11
2	fulvus (Fulvous lemur)	1	3
7	macaco (Black lemur)	3	10
4	mongoz (Mongoose lemur)	*3	7
1	rufifrons (Red-fronted lemur)	*3	9
5	variegatus (Black and white lemur)		
10	varius (Ruffed lemur)		3
1	Galago garnetti (Zanzibar lemur)	4	4
4	senaariensis (Senaar lemur)	*2	11
2	senegalensis (Galago)		11
1	Perodicticus potto (Potto)	1	4
1	Callicebus gigot (Gray titi monkey)	*2	1 day
2	Oedipomidas geoffroyi		9
2	oedipus (Pinche marmoset)	1	7
1	Midas nigricollis (Black and red tamarin)		2
5	ursulus (Negro tamarin)		4
22	Callithrix jacchus (Silky marmoset)	1	8

NUMBER OF SPECIMENS	MAMMALS	LONGEVITY RECORD	
		YEARS	MONTHS
	PRIMATES—*Continued*		
2	Alouatta palliata (Mantled howler)		2
5	seniculus (Red howler)		2
1	Aotus azarae (Azara's douroucouli)	1	1
1	infulatus (Feline douroucouli)		5
7	trivirgatus (Three-banded douroucouli)	6	2
3	Cebus albifrons (White-fronted cebus). Returned to owner		
23	apella (Weeping capuchin)	5	9
1	azarae (Azara's capuchin)	2	6
48	capucinus (White-throated capuchin)	8	6
1	capucinus x fatuellus (Hybrid capuchin)		2
31	fatuellus (Brown capuchin)	5	3
2	margaritae (Margarita capuchin)	4	3
3	unicolor (Pale capuchin)	2	8
1	Pithecia pithecia (Humboldt's saki)		1
1	Cacajao melanocephalus (Black-headed ouakari)		9
1	rubicundus (Red ouakari monkey)		5
17	Saimiri örstedii (Panama titi monkey)		1
15	sciureus (Titi monkey)	1	9
39	Ateles ater (Black spider monkey)	2	5
1	geoffroyi (Gray spider monkey)	4	1
2	grisescens (Coaita)	2	4
3	hybridus (Hybrid spider monkey)		1
	neglectus (Mexican spider monkey)	2	10

NUMBER OF SPECIMENS	MAMMALS	LONGEVITY RECORD	
		YEARS	MONTHS
	PRIMATES—*Continued*		
2	Ateles paniscus (Red-faced spider monkey)........		10
5	Lagothrix humboldti (Humboldt's woolly monkey)...	1	9
1	infumata (Brown woolly monkey)..............	1	4
2	ubericola (Black-headed woolly monkey).......		4
5	Cercopithecus albigularis (Sykes or blue monkey)...	*2	4
1	brazzae (De Brazza's guenon).................	*4	4
15	callitrichus (Green monkey)...................	5	8
1	cephus (Moustache monkey)...................		1
1	cynosurus (Malbrouck monkey)...............		8
4	diana (Diana monkey)........................	5	9
4	griseoviridis (Grivet monkey).................	6	6
12	mona (Mona monkey)........................	16	
1	petaurista (Lesser white-nosed guenon)........	*4	2
14	Pygerythra (Vervet monkey)...................	6	11
26	Pygerythra johnstoni (Johnston's vervet)........	*2	4
1	roloway (Roloway monkey)...................	13	
2	sp. (Mozambique monkey)....................		
9	Erythrocebus patas (Patas monkey).............	4	*9
1	Cercocebus aterrimus (Black mangabey).........	5	9
14	fuliginosus (Sooty mangabey)................	8	2
2	hagenbecki (Hagenbeck's mangabey)..........	8	5
2	torquatus (White-collared mangabey).........	6	6
1	Macacus andamanensis (Burmese macaque)......	*9	8

APPENDIX I

NUMBER OF SPECIMENS	MAMMALS	LONGEVITY RECORD	
		YEARS	MONTHS
	PRIMATES—*Continued*		
1	Macacus arctoides (Red-faced macaque)		*8
1	cyclopis (?) (Formosan rock macaque)		8
8	fuscatus (Japanese monkey)	2	6
52	irus (Common macaque)	15	8
9	mordax (Javan macaque)	17	3
13	nemestrina (Pig-tailed monkey)	*8	4
170	rhesus (Rhesus monkey)	9	
2	silenus (Wanderoo)	21	9
4	sinicus (Bonnet macaque)	3	5
4	speciosus (Brown macaque)	13	4
3	syrichta (Philippine macaque)	10	1
3	(undetermined)	4	4½
17	Pygathrix cephalopterus (Cingalee purple-faced langur)		10
2	entellus (Hanuman or sacred langur)		2
1	sp. (Langur)		1
3	Simia sylvanus (Barbary macaque)	*8	6
4	Theropithecus obscurus (Gelada baboon)	3	1
3	Cynopithecus maurus (Moor macaque)	15	4
11	niger (Black baboon)	4	8
7	Papio anubis (Anubis baboon)	2	3
19	cynocephalus (Common baboon)	*6	11
2	doguera (Doguera baboon)	2	8
15	hamadryas (Arabian baboon)	7	10

NUMBER OF SPECIMENS	MAMMALS	LONGEVITY RECORD	
		YEARS	MONTHS
	PRIMATES—*Continued*		
1	Papio ibeanus (East African baboon)	7	2
2	leucophaeus (Drill baboon)	*12	7
5	maimon (Mandrill)	6	5
11	neumanni (Olive baboon)	*2	4
11	papio (Sphinx or Guinea baboon)	3	6
8	porcarius (Chacma baboon)	*17	6
1	rhodesiae (Rhodesian baboon)	1	8
2	sphinx (Mandrill)	*17	10
1	Hylobates agilis (Agile gibbon)		5½
2	lar (White-handed gibbon)		*8
3	leuciscus (Silver gibbon)		5
1	sp. (Gibbon)		1
3	Pongo pygmaeus (Orang-utan)	1	10
2	Pan satyrus (Chimpanzee)	*2	4
1	Gorilla gorilla (Gorilla)	*13	*2
	RODENTIA		
10	Glaucomys volans (Flying squirrel)		9
4	Paraxerus ochraceus (Olive squirrel)		7
2	Ratufa indica (Malabar squirrel)	3	5
1	Sciurus aberti (Abert's squirrel)		6
1	adolphei dorsalis (Squirrel)	1	9
6	aureogaster (Red-bellied squirrel)	5	9

MAMMALS

RODENTIA—*Continued*

Number of Specimens		Longevity Record Years	Longevity Record Months
3	Sciurus boothiae (Honduras squirrel)	3	6
205	carolinensis {Black / Gray / Albino} squirrel. Liberated in Park		
2	hudsonius (Red squirrel)		
2	hudsonius fremonti (Fremont's red squirrel)	1	4
9	ludovicianus (Western fox squirrel). Liberated in Park		
23	niger (Fox squirrel). Liberated in Park		
1	prevosti (Prevost's squirrel)	1	1
7	vulgaris (European red squirrel)		1½
4	Eutamias neglectus (Chipmunk)		
36	speciosus (Mountain chipmunk). Liberated in Park	3	
3	Tamias striatus (Chipmunk)		
2	Ammospermophilus harrisii (Arizona antelope squirrel)	1	10
3	leucurus (Antelope squirrel)	1	3
16	Citellus beecheyi (Beechey's ground squirrel)	1	1
20	brevicaudus (Yellow-headed ground squirrel)		
1	franklinii (Franklin's spermophile)	1	
1	mexicanus (Mexican ground squirrel)		
6	mollis (Spermophile)		5
1	parryi kodiacensis (Kodiak spermophile)	1	
1	spilosoma (Spotted spermophile)		5
5	tereticaudus (Round-tailed spermophile)		7

NUMBER OF SPECIMENS	MAMMALS	LONGEVITY RECORD	
		YEARS	MONTHS
	RODENTIA—*Continued*		
27	Citellus tridecimlineatus (13-lined spermophile)	2	
182	Cynomys ludovicianus (Prairie dog)		10
1	Marmota flaviventris obscura (Dusky marmot)	7	
3	marmota (European marmot)	3	3
53	monax (Woodchuck)	9	11
81	Castor canadensis (American beaver)	11	
4	Aplodontia rufa (Mountain beaver)	2	9
11	Mus musculus (Albino mouse)		
1	Lophiomys ibeanus		9
1	Cricetulus songarus (Hamster)		½
1	Onychomys leucogaster fuscogriseus (Gray grasshopper mouse)		9
16	leucogaster melanophrys (Grasshopper mouse)	5	
4	torridus (Grasshopper mouse)		8
2	Peromyscus boylii rowleyi (Rowley's deer mouse)		1
2	californicus (Parasitic mouse)		5
2	eremicus (Desert mouse)		5
2	leucocephalus (White-headed beach mouse)	3	
2	leucopus aridulus (Mountain white-footed mouse)	3	4
2	leucopus noveboracensis (Northern white-footed mouse)		4
2	maniculatus osgoodi (Nebraska white-footed mouse)	2	9
2	Sigmodon hispidus arizonae (Cotton rat)		20 days
2	Neotoma albigula (Woodrat)		6
6	cinerea (Mountain pack rat)	1	

APPENDIX I

MAMMALS

RODENTIA—Continued

NUMBER OF SPECIMENS	MAMMALS	LONGEVITY RECORD	
		YEARS	MONTHS
9	Microtus pennsylvanicus (Meadow mouse)		2
15	Ondatra zibethica (Muskrat)	2	6
4	Geomys bursarius (Pocket gopher)		
1	Graphiurus sp. (East African dormouse)		
3	Dipodomys merriami (Merriam's kangaroo rat)	1	4
4	ordii (Ord's kangaroo rat)		6
4	spectabilis (Kangaroo rat)		8
4	Perognathus baileyi (Bailey's pocket mouse)		
4	flavescens perniger (Dusky pocket mouse)	1	7
2	flavus (Baird's pocket mouse)	1	9
1	Zapus hudsonius americanus (Jumping mouse)		6
52	Myocastor coypus (Coypu)	5	7
38	Capromys pilorides (Hutia-conga)	9	5
1	Hystrix africaeaustralis (African porcupine)	*8	4
12	cristata (European porcupine)	13	2
9	galeata (East African porcupine)	*2	4
2	leucura (Indian porcupine)	6	
33	Erethizon dorsatum (Canada porcupine)	3	5
11	epixanthum (Western porcupine)	2	8
2	Acanthion brachyurum (Malay porcupine)	*8	3
3	Coendou prehensilis (Tree porcupine)	2	2
11	Lagostomus trichodactylus (Viscacha)	4	10
10	Dasyprocta acouchy (Olive agouti)	8	1

NUMBER OF SPECIMENS	MAMMALS	LONGEVITY RECORD	
		YEARS	MONTHS
	RODENTIA—*Continued*		
7	Dasyprocta aguti (Common agouti)	13	4
6	azarae (Azara's agouti)	9	2
5	cristata (Crested agouti)	21	10
1	fuliginosa (Sooty agouti)	*6	10
1	lucifer cayennae (Yellow-rumped agouti)	5	6
3	mexicana (Mexican agouti)	13	1
3	prymnolopha (Hairy-rumped agouti)	6	3
2	punctata (Speckled agouti)	*8	10
2	punctata isthmica (Panama agouti)	4	8
15	rubrata (Trinidad agouti)	*8	5
7	Cuniculus paca (Paca)	12	9
5	paca virgatus (Central American paca)	*8	10
	Cavia aperia (Guinea pig). Numerous.		
7	tschudii pallidior (Peruvian guinea pig)	6	4
8	Dolichotis patagonica (Patagonian cavy)	6	10
11	Hydrochoerus hydrochoerus (Capybara)	7	2
	LAGOMORPHA		
12	Lepus americanus (Varying hare). Liberated in Park.		
1	americanus bairdii (Snowshoe rabbit)	3	7
2	campestris (White-tailed "jack rabbit")		
1	Sylvilagus floridanus mallurus (Cotton-tail rabbit)		
90	Oryctolagus cuniculus (Rabbit)		

NUMBER OF SPECIMENS	MAMMALS	LONGEVITY RECORD	
		YEARS	MONTHS
	HYRACOIDEA		
5	Procavia brucei prittwitzii (East African hyrax)	*2	4
4	capensis (Cape hyrax)	3	
	PROBOSCIDEA		
2	Loxodonta africana oxyotis (African elephant)	*15	6
4	Elephas maximus (Indian elephant)	25	11
1	sumatranus (Sumatran elephant)	*10	2
	PERISSODACTYLA		
1	Dicerorhinus sumatrensis (Sumatran rhinoceros)	2	4
1	Diceros bicornis (Black rhinoceros)	1	7
3	Acrocodia indica (Malay tapir)	7	4
16	Tapirus terrestris (Brazilian tapir)	20	8
2	Elasmognathus bairdi (Baird's tapir)	*4	8
3	Equus grevyi (Grevy's zebra)	15	8
6	grevyi x asinus (Zebra-ass hybrid)	*17	8
2	grevyi x caballus (Zebra-horse hybrid)	*13	9
3	przewalskii (Wild horse)	6	8
1	quagga granti (Grant's zebra)	15	2
3	quagga chapmani (Chapman's zebra)	*1	9
2	zebra (Mountain zebra)	*1	11

NUMBER OF SPECIMENS	MAMMALS	LONGEVITY RECORD	
		YEARS	MONTHS
	ARTIODACTYLA		
44	Pecari angulatus (Collared peccary)	11	5
2	Tayassu labiatus (White-lipped peccary)	3	4
5	Sus scrofa (Wild boar)	15	3
13	Phacochoerus aethiopicus (Wart hog)	13	6
4	Potamochoerus koiropotamus (East African bush pig)	*2	4
8	Hippopotamus amphibius (Hippopotamus)	*17	9
1	Choeropsis liberiensis (Pygmy hippopotamus)	*1	7
62	Lama glama (Llama)	17	11
16	huanacus (Guanaco)	13	8
4	pacos (Alpaca)	14	4
2	Vicugna vicugna (Vicuña)	11	10
10	Camelus bactrianus (Bactrian camel)	14	3
9	dromedarius (Dromedary)	*15	5
1	Muntiacus muntjac (Barking deer or muntjac)	3	5
2	Rusa philippinus (Philippine deer)	15	7
7	unicolor (Sambar deer)	16	
46	Rucervus duvaucelii (Barasingha deer)	12	3
1	eldii (Burmese deer)	*9	4
32	Axis axis (Axis deer)	9	11
78	Sika nippon (Japanese deer)	*20	7
140	Cervus canadensis (American elk)	18	9
93	elaphus (Red deer)	*13	8
9	hanglu (Kashmir deer)	*12	8

APPENDIX I

NUMBER OF SPECIMENS	MAMMALS	LONGEVITY RECORD YEARS	MONTHS
	ARTIODACTYLA—*Continued*		
8	Cervus xanthopygus (Bedford deer)	*12	2
44	Dama dama (Fallow deer)	*11	8
33	Hyelaphus porcinus (Hog deer)	13	
10	Alces americanus (Moose)	2	4
1	Rangifer caribou (Woodland caribou)	2	4
20	tarandus (Reindeer)	*5	1
4	terrae-novae (Newfoundland caribou)	9	11
10	Capreolus capreolus (Roe deer)	1	7
1	Odocoileus chiriquensis (Panama deer)	3	8
9	sp. (Cuban deer)	10	7
1	sp. (Guatemala deer)	*3	3
19	columbianus (Columbian black-tailed deer)	11	3
2	costaricensis (Costa Rica deer)		*7
55	hemionus (Mule deer)	13	11
1	sitkensis (Sitka deer)		10
111	virginianus (Virginia deer)	13	9
1	Mazama sartorii (Brocket)	2	6
2	simplicicornis (Brazilian brocket)	2	1
36	Antilocapra americana (Prong-horned antelope)	5	3
2	Bubalis cokei (Coke's hartebeest)	4	6
2	tora (Tora antelope)	1	
1	Onotragus leche (Lechwe)	*8	4
6	Damaliscus albifrons (Blesbok)	7	10

[303]

NUMBER OF SPECIMENS	MAMMALS	LONGEVITY RECORD	
		YEARS	MONTHS
	ARTIODACTYLA—*Continued*		
1	Damaliscus pygargus (Bontebok)	2	1
3	Connochaetes gnu (White-tailed gnu)	13	5
1	taurinus (Brindled gnu)	*6	8
3	taurinus albojubatus (White-bearded gnu)	*2	4
4	Cephalophus grimmi (Duiker antelope)		3
4	Aepyceros melampus suara (East African impalla)	*2	4
1	Madoqua kirki nyikae (Dikdik)		10 days
1	Redunca sp. (Reed buck)	*2	4
1	Kobus defassa (Defassa water-buck)	9	5
2	ellipsiprymnus (Common water-buck)	1	6
28	Antilope cervicapra (Indian antelope or black buck)	12	11
5	Antidorcas euchore (Springbuck)	2	
5	Gazella arabica (Arabian gazelle)	3	2
5	dorcas (Dorcas gazelle)	1	
1	granti (Grant's gazelle)	2	
1	ruffrons (Red-fronted or Korin gazelle)		4
2	Egocerus niger (Sable antelope)	5	3
6	Taurotragus oryx livingstonii (Livingstone's eland)	10	2
3	oryx pattersonianus (East African eland)	2	9
1	Tragelaphus angasi (Inyala)	*1	5
6	gratus (Congo harnessed antelope)	11	6
1	sylvaticus (Cape bushbuck)		7
1	Oryx beisa (Oryx)		4 days

NUMBER OF SPECIMENS	MAMMALS	LONGEVITY RECORD	
		YEARS	MONTHS
	ARTIODACTYLA—*Continued*		
2	Oryx gazella (Gemsbok)	2	9
1	leucoryx (Leucoryx)	4	5
17	Boselaphus tragocamelus (Nilgai)	*11	
1	Strepsiceros strepsiceros bea (East African greater koodoo)		6
7	Rupicapra rupicapra (Chamois)	5	11
12	Oreamnos americanus (Mountain goat)	*6	
1	Capra falconeri (Markhor)	1	2
1	falconeri x hircus (Hybrid goat)		2
4	ibex (Alpine ibex)	4	11
23	Hemitragus jemlahicus (Tahr)	*16	9
63	Ammotragus lervia (Barbary sheep)	14	10
22	Ovis aries tragelaphus (Barbados sheep)	13	5
32	canadensis (Rocky Mountain sheep)	7	8
2	canadensis gaillardi (Arizona mountain sheep)	9	11
4	europaeus (Mouflon)	*5	
1	mexicana (Mexican mountain sheep)	1	
2	nahoor (Burrhel sheep)	1	9
2	nelsoni (Nelson's sheep)	1	11
2	Giraffa camelopardalis (Giraffe)	1	3
2	Anoa depressicornis (Anoa)	12	7
7	Bubalus bubalis (Indian buffalo)	*10	3
1	Synceros caffer (South African buffalo)	*1	7
1	neumanni (East African buffalo)	3	4

MAMMALS

NUMBER OF SPECIMENS		LONGEVITY RECORD	
		YEARS	MONTHS
	ARTIODACTYLA—Continued		
25	Poephagus grunniens (Yak)............................	18	3
81	Bison bison (American bison).........................	*22	6
22	Bos indicus (Zebu)...................................	20	6
2	Ovibos moschatus wardi (Greenland musk ox)...........	*6	3
	XENARTHRA		
7	Bradypus griseus (3-toed sloth)......................	1	3
4	Choloepus didactylus (2-toed sloth)..................	1	4
2	Myrmecophaga jubata (Great anteater).................	6	8
40	Dasypus novemcinctus (Armadillo)....................	6	6
12	Euphractus villosus (Hairy armadillo)...............	9	7
	SIRENIA		
1	Trichechus latirostris (Florida manatee)............		1

APPENDIX I

NUMBER OF SPECIMENS	BIRDS	LONGEVITY RECORD	
		YEARS	MONTHS
	RATITAE		
9	Struthio camelus (Nubian ostrich)	*7	4
2	molybdophanes (Somaliland ostrich)	*24	3
14	australis (South African ostrich)	8	9
9	Rhea americana (Common rhea)	13	7
1	pennata (Darwin's rhea)	1	8
4	Dromiceius novae-hollandiae (Emu)	*25	11
2	Casuarius casuarius casuarius (Helmeted cassowary)	8	7
3	casuarius johnsoni (Cassowary)	6	7
1	uniappendiculatus (Single-wattled cassowary)	*3	6
1	philipi (Sclater's cassowary)	*9	3
2	Apteryx mantelli (North Island kiwi)	2	3
4	Rhynchotus rufescens (Rufous tinamou)	3	11
1	Calopezus elegans (Crested tinamou)		1
	SPHENISCIFORMES		
4	Catarrhactes pachyrhynchus (Rock-hopper penguin)	1	5
6	Spheniscus humboldti (Humboldt's penguin)		2
	COLYMBIFORMES		
11	Gavia immer (Loon)		2
1	Colymbus auritus (Horned grebe)		1½
2	Podilymbus podiceps (Pied-billed grebe)	2	
2	Puffinus griseus (Sooty shearwater)		1

NUMBER OF SPECIMENS	BIRDS	LONGEVITY RECORD	
		YEARS	MONTHS
	ᶜCICONIIFORMES		
4	Pelecanus onocrotalus (European white pelican)	*25	4
3	roseus (Rose-colored pelican)	*14	6
15	occidentalis (Brown pelican)	*29	5
5	californicus (California brown pelican)	*4	6
39	erythrorhynchos (American white pelican)	*31	4
2	conspicillatus (Australian pelican)	*14	11
8	Sula bassana (Common gannet)	4	5
2	brewsteri (Brewster's booby)		11
1	Phalacrocorax auritus auritus (Double-crested cormorant)		1
55	auritus floridanus (Florida cormorant)	13	
1	vigua mexicanus (Mexican cormorant)		
4	penicillatus (Brandt's cormorant)	*2	7
33	Anhinga anhinga (Snake bird)	16	5
2	Pyrrherodia purpurea (Purple heron)		5
1	manillensis (Philippine heron)		6
1	Ardea goliath (Goliath heron)	*9	7
1	cocoi (Great black-crowned heron)	6	11
37	herodias (Great blue heron)	10	11
8	occidentalis (Great white heron)	6	
3	herodias x occidentalis (Hybrid heron)	*1	7
1	melanocephala (East African heron)	*2	4
14	Casmerodius egretta (American egret)	8	7
9	Egretta candidissima (Snowy heron)	16	10

NUMBER OF SPECIMENS	BIRDS	LONGEVITY RECORD	
		YEARS	MONTHS
	CICONIIFORMES—*Continued*		
16	Florida caerulea (Little blue heron)	4	7
5	Dichromanassa rufescens (Reddish egret)	9	11
15	Hydranassa tricolor ruficollis (Louisiana heron)	2	11
1	Nycticorax nycticorax (European night heron)		10 days
300	nycticorax naevius (Black-crowned night heron)	*16	7
6	Butorides virescens (Green heron)	3	11
1	Ixobrychus exilis (Least bittern)	*2	6
19	Botaurus lentiginosus (American bittern)	1	
5	Cochlearius cochlearius (Boatbill heron)	13	3
2	Balaeniceps rex (Shoebill)	1	2
34	Mycteria americana (Wood ibis)	6	8
1	Ibis ibis (African wood ibis)		1
1	Dissoura episcopus (White-necked stork)		*7
2	Euxenura maguari (Maguari stork)	2	11
16	Ciconia ciconia (European white stork)	15	7
2	nigra (Black stork)	26	
2	Xenorhynchus asiaticus (Indian jabiru)	1	10
6	Leptoptilus dubius (Marabou stork)	15	4
1	javanicus (Lesser adjutant)	2	
12	Threskiornis aethiopicus (Sacred ibis)	*25	5
3	melanocephalus (Black-headed ibis)	*6	6
4	molucca strictipennis (Australian white ibis)	7	
2	Carphibis spinicollis (Straw-necked ibis)	6	4

BIRDS

NUMBER OF SPECIMENS	BIRDS	LONGEVITY RECORD	
		YEARS	MONTHS
	CICONIIFORMES—*Continued*		
3	Plegadis autumnalis (Glossy ibis)	1	10
3	guarauna (White-faced glossy ibis)	3	4
57	Guara alba (White ibis)	18	6
10	rubra (Scarlet ibis)	*7	7
25	Ajaia ajaja (Roseate spoonbill)	10	5
19	Phoenicopterus ruber (American flamingo)	1	1
27	roseus (European flamingo)	12	11
	ANSERIFORMES		
1	Anhima cornuta (Horned screamer)	2	7
14	Chauna chavaria (Crested screamer)	2	2
4	torquata (Black-necked screamer)	4	2
8	Cygnus buccinator (Trumpeter swan)	13	
23	columbianus (Whistling swan)	15	2
57	olor (Mute swan)	16	9
4	melancoryphus (Black-necked swan)	1	
15	Chenopis atrata (Black swan)	*13	10
2	Anseranas semipalmata (Pied goose)	7	3
9	Plectropterus gambensis (Spur-winged goose)	10	
14	Cairina moschata (Muscovy duck)	11	10
2	Sarkidiornis sylvicola (Carunculated duck)	1	1
88	Aix sponsa (Wood duck)	14	1
63	Dendronessa galericulata (Mandarin duck)	16	3

APPENDIX I

NUMBER OF SPECIMENS	BIRDS	LONGEVITY RECORD	
		YEARS	MONTHS
	ANSERIFORMES—Continued		
4	Ceropsis novae-hollandiae (Cape Barren goose)	4	1
1	Coscoroba coscoroba (Coscoroba swan)	2	8
16	Chen caerulescens (Blue goose)	*9	7
9	hyperboreus hyperboreus (Lesser snow goose)	15	11
9	hyperboreus nivalis (Greater snow goose)	9	2
28	Anser anser domesticus (Domestic goose)	3	
12	albifrons albifrons (White-fronted goose)	*20	10
2	albifrons gambeli (American white-fronted goose)	*9	10
2	fabalis (Bean goose)	*6	10
2	brachyrhynchus (Pink-footed goose)	*4	10
4	Eulabeia indica (Bar-headed goose)	8	
18	Cygnopsis cygnoides (Chinese goose)	5	3
3	Philacte canagica (Emperor goose)	2	5
69	Branta canadensis canadensis (Canada goose)	15	2
17	canadensis hutchinsi (Hutchins's goose)	20	
18	canadensis occidentalis (White-cheeked goose)	*5	4
2	canadensis minima (Cackling goose)	*13	10
12	leucopsis (Barnacle goose)	*9	
8	bernicla (Brant)	3	
32	bernicla glaucogastra (Brant)	*8	9
2	Nesochen sandvicensis (Hawaiian goose)	*7	2
9	Chloëphaga leucoptera (Upland goose)	5	9
2	Chenonetta jubata (Maned goose)	7	4

NUMBER OF SPECIMENS	BIRDS	LONGEVITY RECORD	
		YEARS	MONTHS
	ANSERIFORMES—Continued		
5	Dendrocygna viduata (White-faced tree-duck)	7	3
2	bicolor (Fulvous tree-duck)		10
8	arcuata (Wandering tree-duck)	13	7
8	autumnalis (Black-bellied tree-duck)	11	6
1	discolor (Gray-breasted tree-duck)	6	
4	eytoni (Eyton's tree-duck)	8	2
8	Alopochen aegyptiacus (Egyptian goose)	*7	3
3	Casarca ferruginea (Ruddy sheldrake)	5	5
2	variegata (Paradise duck)		10
30	Anas domestica (Pekin duck)	6	6
236	platyrhynchos (Mallard duck)	*12	2
70	rubripes (Black duck)	*10	
4	superciliosa (Australian black duck)	*8	2
2	Eunetta falcata (Falcated teal)	*6	7
2	falcata x Chaulelasmus streperus (Falcated teal-gadwall, hybrid)		9
22	Chaulelasmus streperus (Gadwall)	6	5
13	Mareca penelope (Widgeon)	*9	10
17	americana (Baldpate)	7	9
4	sibilatrix (Chiloé widgeon)	1	
7	Nettion formosum (Baikal teal)	*8	11
3	crecca (European teal)	*9	10
44	carolinense (Green-winged teal)	9	6
42	Dafila acuta (Pintail duck)	*11	10

NUMBER OF SPECIMENS	BIRDS	LONGEVITY RECORD	
		YEARS	MONTHS
	ANSERIFORMES—*Continued*		
2	Dafila bahamensis (Bahama pintail)	*4	2
2	erythrorhyncha (African pintail)	*2	4
13	Querquedula querquedula (Garganey)	*9	10
27	discors (Blue-winged teal)	*6	10
3	cyanoptera (Cinnamon teal)	6	5
12	Spatula clypeata (Shoveller)	6	6
3	Netta rufina (Red-crested pochard)	1	5
8	Metopiana peposaca (Rosy-billed pochard)	1	
4	Marila ferina (European pochard)	*6	10
47	americana (Redhead)	*8	
1	nyroca (White-eyed duck)	3	5
22	valisneria (Canvas-back duck)	*12	6
16	marila (Scaup or blue-billed duck)	*6	11
11	affinis (Lesser scaup duck)	8	8
4	fuligula (Tufted duck)	*6	10
2	collaris (Ring-necked duck)	*10	10
2	Erismatura jamaicensis (Ruddy duck)		4 days
2	Mergus americanus (Merganser)		5
2	serrator (Red-breasted merganser)		5
	FALCONIFORMES		
3	Vultur gryphus (South American condor)	14	5
7	Sarcorhamphus papa (King vulture)	*28	2

NUMBER OF SPECIMENS	BIRDS	LONGEVITY RECORD	
		YEARS	MONTHS
	FALCONIFORMES—*Continued*		
3	Coragyps urubu (Black vulture)	21	1
17	Cathartes aura septentrionalis (Turkey vulture)	20	9
6	Gymnogyps californianus (California condor)	*27	7
2	Sagittarius serpentarius (Secretary vulture)	*12	10
2	Aegypius monachus (Cinereous vulture)	*17	8
2	Gyps fulvus (Griffon vulture)	*20	4
1	Torgos tracheliotus (African black vulture)	*6	9
1	Trigonoceps occipitalis (White-headed vulture)	*2	4
1	Neophron percnopterus (Egyptian vulture)	7	3
1	Necrosyrtes pileatus (Pileated vulture)	2	4
1	Ibycter ater (Yellow-throated caracara)	13	4
3	Circus hudsonius (Marsh hawk)		½
1	Micrastur melanoleucus (Collared harrier-hawk)		7
1	Melierax poliopterus (East African chanting goshawk)	*2	4
6	Accipiter velox (Sharp-shinned hawk)	1	3
7	cooperi (Cooper's hawk)		5
2	Geranoaetus melanoleucus (Chilean eagle)	3	3
1	Buteo rufo-fuscus augur (Augur buzzard)		11
7	swainsoni (Swainson's hawk)		2
71	borealis borealis (Red-tailed hawk)	*11	2
2	borealis jamaicensis (Jamaican red-tail)		5
16	lineatus (Red-shouldered hawk)	*1	11
6	platypterus (Broad-winged hawk)		9

[314]

APPENDIX I

NUMBER OF SPECIMENS	BIRDS	LONGEVITY RECORD	
		YEARS	MONTHS
	FALCONIFORMES—*Continued*		
1	Thrasaëtus harpyia (Harpy eagle)	17	11
2	Gypaëtus barbatus (Lammergeyer)	7	1
4	Uroaëtus audax (Wedge-tailed eagle)	*12	9
41	Aquila chrysaëtos (Golden eagle)	11	8
2	rapax (Tawny eagle)	*2	4
1	Archibuteo lagopus sancti-johannis (Rough-legged hawk)		10
1	ferrugineus (Ferruginous rough-leg)		1
1	Spizaëtus bellicosus (Warlike crested eagle)	1	
1	coronatus (Crowned hawk-eagle)	17	9
2	Terathopius ecaudatus (Bateleur eagle)	3	5
82	Haliaeetus leucocephalus leucocephalus (Bald eagle)	*30	5
3	leucocephalus alascanus (Alaskan bald eagle)	28	8
2	Cuncuma leucogaster (White-bellied sea eagle)	7	5
1	Milvus migrans parasitus (African black kite)		7
1	Elanus caeruleus (Black-shouldered kite)	*2	4
1	Ictinia mississippiensis (Mississippi kite)		3
4	Poliohierax semitorquatus (Pygmy falcon)	*3	8
2	Falco peregrinus anatum (Duck hawk)	1	
1	biarmicus (South African lanner)	1	
2	columbarius (Pigeon hawk)		
32	sparverius (Sparrow hawk)	6	10
2	Pandion haliaetus haliaetus (Osprey)	*1	6
5	haliaetus carolinensis (Fish hawk)		4

NUMBER OF SPECIMENS	BIRDS	LONGEVITY RECORD	
		YEARS	MONTHS
	FALCONIFORMES—*Continued*		
4	Polyborus cheriway (Audubon's caracara)	*21	3
	GALLIFORMES		
2	Catheturus lathami (Brush turkey)	5	5
1	Crax sp. (Curassow)	2	6
1	alector (Crested curassow)		9
1	fasciolata (Barred curassow)	3	
9	globicera (Mexican curassow)	7	
2	chapmani (Chapman's curassow)	4	2
3	panamensis (Panama curassow)	2	
2	carunculata (Red-billed curassow)	2	11
3	globulosa (Spix's wattled curassow)		*8
14	daubentoni (Daubenton's curassow)	7	10
7	Mitua mitu (Razor-billed curassow)	*6	2
1	tomentosa (Lesser razor-billed curassow)	12	2
2	Penelope purpurascens (Purplish guan)	5	3
3	cristata (Rufous-bellied guan)	2	10
1	jacquacu (Crested guan)	*6	*9
2	sp. (Guan)		1
2	Ortalis ruficauda (Guan)	2	2
1	albiventris (Guan)	3	11
8	vetula vetula (Chachalaca)	4	11
10	vetula mccalli (Chachalaca)	7	

NUMBER OF SPECIMENS	BIRDS	LONGEVITY RECORD	
		YEARS	MONTHS
	GALLIFORMES—*Continued*		
2	Ortalis garrula (Chestnut-winged guan)	*2	8
3	sp. (Guan)		10
1	Lyrurus tetrix (Black cock)		3
9	Tympanuchus americanus (Prairie hen). Liberated.		
4	Pedioecetes phasianellus (Sharp-tailed grouse)	3	3
1	Alectoris graeca saxatilis (Rock red-legged partridge)	1	2
2	chukar (Chukar partridge)	1	11
1	Francolinus sephaena (Crested francolin)		7
1	natalensis (Natal francolin)		5
13	Perdix perdix (Common partridge)	2	*7
2	Rollulus roulroul (Wood partridge)		
26	Coturnix coturnix (Migratory quail)	10	4
1	Gennaeus edwardsi (Edwards's pheasant)	*2	8
7	nycthemerus (Silver pheasant)	9	5
6	Phasianus colchicus (English pheasant)	2	4
2	mongolicus (Mongolian pheasant)		6
20	torquatus (Ring-necked pheasant)	*6	3
1	reevesi (Bar-tail or Reeves pheasant)	4	1
15	Chrysolophus pictus (Golden pheasant)	3	2
2	amherstiae (Lady Amherst's pheasant)	*5	10
30	Gallus bankiva (Jungle fowl)	5	*7
2	varius (Javan jungle fowl)		
1	x Numida (Chicken-guinea hybrid)	1	4

NUMBER OF SPECIMENS	BIRDS	LONGEVITY RECORD	
		YEARS	MONTHS
	GALLIFORMES—*Continued*		
1	Polyplectron bicalcaratum (Peacock pheasant)	10	4
2	Argusianus argus (Argus pheasant)		*8
329	Pavo cristatus (Pea fowl). Liberated		6
2	Numida meleagris (Guinea fowl)	1	4
36	mitrata reichenowi (Reichenow's helmeted guinea fowl)	*2	4
1	Guttera granti (Grant's crested guinea fowl)	*2	8
5	Acryllium vulturinum (Vulturine guinea fowl)	*4	8
114	Meleagris gallopavo silvestris (Wild turkey)	6	7
2	Agriocharis ocellata (Ocellated turkey)		9
55	Callipepla squamata squamata (Blue or scaled quail)	6	1
8	squamata castanogastris (Chestnut-bellied scaled quail)		½
1	× Colinus (Hybrid quail)		
16	Oreortyx pictus (Mountain partridge)	5	9
48	Lophortyx californica (California partridge)	7	10
7	californica vallicola (Valley quail)	*9	7
32	gambeli (Gambel's quail)	6	1
4	Eupsychortyx cristatus (Curaçao crested quail)	3	4
70	Colinus virginianus (Bob-white)	8	7
28	Cyrtonyx montezumae (Massena quail)	5	1
	GRUIFORMES		
2	Otis tarda (Great bustard)	2	11
2	Grus grus (European crane)	4	4

BIRDS

NUMBER OF SPECIMENS	BIRDS	LONGEVITY RECORD YEARS	LONGEVITY RECORD MONTHS
	GRUIFORMES—*Continued*		
4	Grus lilfordi (Lilford's crane)	*12	10
24	mexicanus (Sand-hill crane)	23	10
8	canadensis (Little brown crane)	*8	8
3	americanus (Whooping crane)	12	8
5	leucogeranus (Indian white crane)	*22	7
2	antigone (Sarus crane)	2	10
4	sharpei (Sarus crane)	1	9
1	leucauchen (White-naped crane)	*12	11
3	Mathewsena rubicunda (Australian crane)	*24	5
22	Anthropoides virgo (Demoiselle crane)	17	11
2	Balearica pavonina (Crowned crane)	14	7
6	regulorum gibbericeps (East African crowned crane)	*2	4
4	Rhynochetos jubatus (Kagu)	*6	7
2	Eurypyga helias (Sun bittern)		9
3	Psophia leucoptera (White-backed trumpeter)	3	8
4	Cariama cristata (Cariama)	13	4
2	Chunga burmeisteri (Burmeister's cariama)	2	10
1	Rallus elegans (King rail)	1	
1	virginianus (Virginia rail)		1
2	Hypotaenidia philippensis (Lesser rail)	*3	4
8	Ocydromus australis (Weka or flightless rail)	*10	11
1	earli (Earl's weka)	6	9
2	brachypterus (Short-winged weka)	*10	11

NUMBER OF SPECIMENS	BIRDS	LONGEVITY RECORD	
		YEARS	MONTHS
	GRUIFORMES—*Continued*		
1	Porzana carolina (Ortolan or Carolina rail)	3	8
1	Coturnicops noveboracensis (Yellow rail)		46 days
1	Limnocorax flavirostra (Black crake)	*2	4
2	Microtribonyx ventralis (Black-tailed moor hen)	*6	5
4	Gallinula chloropus brachyptera (African moor hen)	*2	4
4	galeata (Florida gallinule)		7
1	Ionornis martinicus (Purple gallinule)	1	9
2	Porphyrio caeruleus (Purple water hen)	8	2
7	calvus (East Indian gallinule)	8	3
3	melanotus (Black-backed porphyrio)	11	4
2	melanotus stanleyi (Pukeko)	*5	
1	Fulica australis (Marsh hen)		2
55	americana (American coot)	*11	9
	CHARADRIIFORMES		
2	Oedicnemus bistriatus vocifer (South American stone plover)	*3	11
3	Burhinus magnirostris (Australian thick-knee)	9	9
6	Vanellus vanellus (Lapwing)	*6	9
1	Sarcogrammus indicus (Yellow-wattled lapwing)	*7	8
1	Charadrius pecuarius pecuarius (Kittlitz's sand plover)		6
1	Philohela minor (Woodcock)		2 days
8	Philomachus pugnax (Ruff)	6	11
1	Larus franklini (Franklin's gull)		1 day

APPENDIX I

NUMBER OF SPECIMENS	BIRDS	LONGEVITY RECORD YEARS	LONGEVITY RECORD MONTHS
	CHARADRIIFORMES—*Continued*		
13	Larus atricilla (Laughing gull)	*19	7
41	novaehollandiae (Silver gull)	*6	6
8	marinus (Great black-backed gull)	17	5
6	occidentalis (Western gull)	*2	7
17	argentatus smithsonianus (Herring gull)	13	7
2	Gabianus pacificus (Pacific gull)	*8	2
4	Sterna dougalli (Roseate tern)		4
2	Noddi inca (Inca tern)	*3	7
2	Rhynchops nigra (Black skimmer)		3
3	Lunda cirrhata (Tufted puffin)		2
1	Dendrophassa pompadora (Pompadour green pigeon)		5
2	Lamprotreron superba (Fruit pigeon)	4	1
2	Globicera pacifica (Pacific pigeon)	*1	11
5	Muscadivores aenea (Green imperial pigeon)	*2	10
6	Columba leuconota (Snow pigeon)	4	8
4	livia (Fan-tail pigeon)	4	6
1	guinea (Speckled pigeon)	*2	4
9	phaeonota (Cape speckled pigeon)	1	11
4	palumbus (Wood pigeon)	*9	6
4	Patagioenas leucocephala (White-crowned pigeon)	4	4
7	Chloroenas fasciata (Band-tailed pigeon)	4	11
12	flavirostris (Red-billed pigeon)	10	11
	Zenaidura macroura (Mourning dove)	9	8

[321]

NUMBER OF SPECIMENS	BIRDS	LONGEVITY RECORD	
		YEARS	MONTHS
	CHARADRIIFORMES—*Continued*		
1	Zenaidura graysoni (Mexican dove)	*3	6
2	Melopelia asiatica (White-winged dove)	3	4
37	Streptopelia risoria (Ringed turtledove)	16	1
12	decipiens perspicillata (Masai mourning dove)	*2	4
40	capicola tropica (East African ring-necked dove)	*2	4
10	Spilopelia tigrina (Necklaced dove)	6	
26	Turtur chalcospilos (Emerald-spotted dove)	*2	4
2	Geopelia humeralis (Bar-shouldered dove)	*9	9
4	tranquilla (Peaceful dove)	7	5
24	striata (Zebra dove)	*12	8
2	cuneata (Diamond dove)		6
1	Scardafella inca (Inca dove)	*12	
6	Chaemepelia passerina aflavida (Cuban ground dove)	*8	3
18	Oena capensis (Cape dove)	5	6
6	Chalcophaps chrysochlora (New Guinea green dove)	2	10
5	indica (Green-winged dove)	6	5
10	Phaps chalcoptera (Bronze-winged pigeon)	*7	4
5	Lophophaps plumifera (Plumed pigeon)		6
33	Ocyphaps lophotes (Crested pigeon)	6	3
7	Leptotila fulviventris brachyptera (White-fronted dove)	*4	11
1	Oreopeleia montana (Ruddy quail-dove)	1	7
18	Gallicolumba luzonica (Bleeding-heart dove)	4	2
12	rubescens (Marquesan dove)	3	3

NUMBER OF SPECIMENS	BIRDS	LONGEVITY RECORD	
		YEARS	MONTHS
	CHARADRIIFORMES—*Continued*		
15	Leucosarcia picata (Wonga-wonga pigeon)	8	3
2	Starnoenas cyanocephala (Blue-headed quail-dove)	3	8
6	Caloenas nicobarica (Nicobar pigeon)	2	6
4	Goura coronata (Crowned pigeon)		1
5	victoria (Victoria crowned pigeon)	*6	3
	PSITTACIFORMES		
7	Nestor notabilis (Kea)	*11	6
2	Eos variegata (Violet-necked lory)		*2
2	Domicella garrula (Chattering lory)	6	4
1	Lorius pectoralis (Red-sided eclectus)		5
4	Trichoglossus forsteni (Forsten's paroquet)		*8
12	Psitteuteles chlorolepidotus (Scaly-breasted lorikeet)	1	8
2	Glossopsitta concinna (Musk lorikeet)	1	10
2	Callocephalon galeatum (Gang-gang cockatoo)	8	6
23	Kakatoe galerita (Sulphur-crested cockatoo)	*38	10
14	leadbeateri (Leadbeater's cockatoo)	18	5
6	alba (White cockatoo)	*20	11
1	moluccensis (Great red-crested cockatoo)		*11
8	gymnopis (Bare-eyed cockatoo)	*16	4
1	haematuropygia (Philippine cockatoo)		
30	roseicapilla (Roseate cockatoo)	*26	
2	Prosciger aterrimus (Great black cockatoo)	*2	3

BIRDS

PSITTACIFORMES—*Continued*

NUMBER OF SPECIMENS	BIRDS	LONGEVITY RECORD	
		YEARS	MONTHS
9	Leptolophus hollandicus (Cockateel)	5	4
8	Anodorhynchus hyacinthinus (Hyacinthine macaw)	*1	5
18	Ara ararauna (Yellow and blue macaw)	10	2
21	macao (Red and blue and yellow macaw)	19	11
4	chloroptera (Red and blue macaw)	20	11
1	militaris (Great green macaw)		11
2	militaris mexicana (Mexican green macaw)	*8	
1	ambigua (Great green macaw)	12	6
2	severa (Brazilian green macaw)	*5	7
1	maracana (Illiger's macaw)		*11
1	auricollis (Cassin's macaw)	3	9
1	Diopsittaca hahni (Hahn's macaw)	3	10
2	Rhynchopsitta pachyrhyncha (Thick-billed parrot)	3	5
5	Aratinga holochlora (Green paroquet)	11	10
1	chloroptera (Haitian paroquet)	2	1
1	leucophthalmus callogenys (White-eyed paroquet)	3	1
6	Nandayus nanday (Nanday paroquet)	*10	10
4	Eupsittula weddelli (Weddell's paroquet)	*6	10
4	aurea (Golden-crowned paroquet)	*6	10
1	pertinax xanthogenia (Yellow-headed paroquet)	1	4
12	canicularis (Petz's paroquet)	*5	8
3	Conuropsis carolinensis (Carolina paroquet)	15	7
2	Pyrrhura picta (Blue-winged conure)		*8

NUMBER OF SPECIMENS	BIRDS	LONGEVITY RECORD	
		YEARS	MONTHS
	PSITTACIFORMES—Continued		
14	Myopsittacus monachus (Quaker paroquet)	5	7
62	Psittacula passerina (Blue-winged parrotlet)	*6	5
4	vivida (Blue-backed parrotlet)	1	4
27	Brotogeris jugularis (Tovi paroquet)	7	6
8	chrysosema (Golden paroquet)	*6	10
4	sanctithomae (Tui paroquet)	2	9
8	Tirica chiriri (Orange-winged paroquet)	5	5
2	virescens (Yellow-winged paroquet)	3	2
2	Amazona farinosa (Mealy parrot)	*5	4
1	farinosa inornata (Plain-colored parrot)	*8	11
15	amazonica (Orange-winged parrot)	*6	8
6	aestiva (Blue-fronted parrot)	18	4
2	barbadensis (Yellow-shouldered Amazon)	15	1
19	ochrocephala (Yellow-headed Amazon)	6	7
2	ochrocephala panamensis (Yellow-fronted Amazon)	*12	5
15	auropalliata (Yellow-naped parrot)	*10	8
30	oratrix (Double yellow-headed parrot)	2	4
1	rhodocorytha (Red-fronted parrot)	*8	11
9	viridigenalis (Red-crowned parrot)	2	5
2	autumnalis (Yellow-cheeked parrot)	*8	8
6	festiva (Festive Amazon)	10	11
1	vittata (Porto Rican parrot)	9	5
2	albifrons (White-fronted parrot)	2	9

NUMBER OF SPECIMENS	BIRDS	LONGEVITY RECORD	
		YEARS	MONTHS
	PSITTACIFORMES—*Continued*		
2	Amazona albifrons nana (Lesser white-fronted parrot)	*5	8
6	ventralis (Santo Domingo parrot)	*6	8
27	leucocephala (White-fronted Amazon)	6	4
1	leucocephala palmarum (Isle of Pines parrot)		9
1	Graydidascalus brachyurus (Short-tailed parrot)	1	9
4	Pionus menstruus (Blue-headed parrot)	*6	4
1	maximiliani (Maximilian's parrot)	*6	4
4	fuscus (Dusky parrot)	*6	4
1	Deroptyus accipitrinus (Hawk-head parrot)		*11
2	Pionites melanocephala (Black-headed caique)	1	7
8	xanthomeria (Flower-headed caique)	*6	10
1	Poicephalus gulielmi (West African scaled parrot)		5
1	flavifrons (Yellow-fronted paroquet)		1
2	rufiventris (Orange-breasted paroquet)		½
2	meyeri matschiei (East African brown parrot)	*2	4
13	Psittacus erithacus (African gray parrot)	5	4
2	Coracopsis vasa (Greater vasa parrot)	*7	1
2	nigra (Lesser vasa parrot)	*22	8
1	Tanygnathus lucionensis (Philippine green parrot)		8
2	Conurus nepalensis (Nepalese paroquet)	*8	6
6	torquatus (Ring-necked paroquet)	*8	11
1	cyanocephalus (Blossom-headed paroquet)	*1	9
3	columboides (Pigeon paroquet)		4

NUMBER OF SPECIMENS	BIRDS	LONGEVITY RECORD	
		YEARS	MONTHS
	PSITTACIFORMES—*Continued*		
9	Conurus fasciatus (Banded paroquet)	10	9
1	longicaudus (Long-tailed paroquet)		*8
2	Polytelis swainsoni (Lory)		3
4	anthopeplus (Black-tailed paroquet)	*8	
3	Aprosmictus scapularis (King paroquet)	*2	1
1	erythropterus (Crimson-winged paroquet)	*5	7
2	Pyrrhulopsis splendens (Red shining paroquet)		2
11	Agapornis madagascariensis (Gray-headed lovebird)	*3	1
10	pullaria (Red-faced lovebird)	*3	8
7	fischeri (Fischer's lovebird)	*2	4
12	lilianae (Nyassa lovebird)		*9
8	personata (Yellow-collared lovebird)	*2	4
2	Loriculus galgulus (Blue-crowned hanging paroquet)		*8
9	Platycercus elegans (Pennant's paroquet)	6	
2	palliceps (Lory)	3	4
9	eximius (Rosella paroquet)	5	3
8	Psephotus haematorrhous (Red-vented blue-bonnet paroquet)	8	6
1	chrysopterygius (Golden-shouldered paroquet)		2
113	Melopsittacus undulatus (Australian grass paroquet)	*7	8
	CUCULIFORMES		
1	Turacus corythaix (White-crested touracou)	1	6
2	donaldsoni (Donaldson's touracou)		

NUMBER OF SPECIMENS	BIRDS	LONGEVITY RECORD	
		YEARS	MONTHS
	CUCULIFORMES—*Continued*		
15	Geococcyx californianus (Road-runner)	5	3
	CORACIIFORMES		
64	Tyto alba pratincola (Barn owl)	4	9
12	alba affinis (African barn owl)	*2	4
5	Asio flammeus (Short-eared owl)		5
2	Bubo bubo (Eagle owl)	*6	3
108	virginianus (Great horned owl)	8	8
1	virginianus pallescens (Western horned owl)	3	3
2	virginianus subarcticus (Arctic horned owl)	4	
1	africanus (Spotted eagle owl)	1	5
20	Nyctea nyctea (Snowy owl)	6	4
2	Pulsatrix perspicillata (Spectacled owl)	3	1
2	Otus leucotis granti (Southern white-eared Scops owl)		11
1	choliba (Choliba screech owl)	1	6
43	asio (Screech owl)	*4	4
68	Strix varia (Barred owl)	8	5
1	varia alleni (Florida barred owl)	*3	11
1	Spiloglaux novaesealandiae (Morepork owl)	4	2
1	Podargus strigoides (Frogmouth)		3
1	Antrostomus carolinensis (Chuck-will's-widow)		½
12	Dacelo gigas (Kookaboora)	12	7
2	Momotus subrufescens (Reddish motmot)	2	1

NUMBER OF SPECIMENS	BIRDS	LONGEVITY RECORD	
		YEARS	MONTHS
	CORACIIFORMES—*Continued*		
1	Coracias caudatus (Lilac-breasted roller)		6
1	Phoeniculus purpureus (Cape kakelaar)		2
1	Bucorvus cafer (Ground hornbill)		2
1	Buceros rhinoceros (Rhinoceros hornbill)	1	1
4	Dichoceros bicornis (Concave-casqued hornbill)	3	10
3	Lophoceros erythrorhynchus (Red-beaked hornbill)	*2	4
2	leucomelas (Yellow-billed hornbill)	3	7
1	Trachyphonus emini (Emin Pasha's barbet)	*2	4
1	Ramphastos swainsoni (Swainson's toucan)	6	4
9	piscivorus piscivorus (Keel-billed toucan)	*1	8
1	piscivorus brevicarinatus (Short-keeled toucan)	2	3
1	monilis (Red-billed toucan)		1
1	ariel (Ariel toucan)		5
1	Aulacorhynchus sulcatus (Groove-billed toucanet)	2	2
3	Centurus uropygialis uropygialis (Gila woodpecker)	*3	
1	Colaptes auratus (Golden-winged woodpecker)		3 days
	PASSERIFORMES		
1	Rupicola rupicola (Cock of the rock)	7	1
3	Casmarhinchos nudicollis (Bell bird)	*1	10
2	Pitangus sulphuratus (Kiskadee flycatcher)	3	2
2	derbianus (Derby flycatcher)		11
1	Corvus corax (Raven)	*24	6

[329]

BIRDS

PASSERIFORMES—Continued

NUMBER OF SPECIMENS	BIRDS	LONGEVITY RECORD	
		YEARS	MONTHS
24	Corvus corax sinuatus (American raven)	5	4
2	coronoides (Australian crow)	*13	2
18	albus (White-breasted crow)	*2	4
2	ossifragus (Fish crow)	1	11
20	brachyrhynchos (Common crow)	*6	9
6	monedula (Jackdaw)	1	8
4	Corvultur albicollis (White-necked raven)	*2	4
21	Nucifraga columbiana (Clark's nutcracker)	5	4
1	Pica pica (European magpie)	11	6
44	hudsonia (American magpie)		7
2	Urocissa occipitalis (Red-billed magpie)	5	6
1	Garrulus leucotis (Burmese jay)	1	10
10	Perisoreus canadensis capitalis (Rocky Mountain jay)	1	7
18	Cyanocitta cristata (Blue jay)	*9	2
2	stelleri annectens (Black-headed jay)	2	1
7	Aphelocoma californica (California jay)	1	7
2	Cyanocorax chrysops (Urraca jay)		*9
17	Xanthoura luxuosa (Green jay)	*10	10
7	Cissilopha yucatanica (Yucatan jay)	*8	10
3	Struthidea cinerea (Australian gray jumper)		11
2	Pyrrhocorax pyrrhocorax (Chough)		1
2	Ptilonorhynchus violaceus (Satin bower bird)	3	6
1	Chlamydera maculata (Spotted bower bird)	3	1

NUMBER OF SPECIMENS	BIRDS	LONGEVITY RECORD	
		YEARS	MONTHS
	PASSERIFORMES—Continued		
1	Ailuroedus crassirostris (Australian green catbird)		5
2	Paradisaea raggiana (Count Raggi's bird of paradise)	1	3
2	rubra (Red bird of paradise)		*9
62	Leiothrix luteus (Red-billed hill-tit)	*8	11
3	Otocompsa haemorrhous bengalensis (Black-headed bulbul)	*2	8
2	leucogenys (Silver-eared hill-tit)	*2	8
3	leucotis (White-earned bulbul)	*8	9
3	jocosa (Red-eared bulbul)	*4	8
2	Garrulax leucolophus (Himalayan white-crested laughing thrush)	7	9
1	albigularis (White-throated laughing thrush)	4	9
4	pectoralis (Black-gorgeted laughing thrush)	*9	6
10	Mimus polyglottos (Mocking bird)	*2	9
2	polyglottos leucopterus (Western mocking bird)		
2	Dumetella carolinensis (Catbird)	7	2
5	Toxostoma rufum (Brown thrasher)	5	9
11	Planesticus merula (European blackbird)	6	8
1	migratorius (Robin)	1	6
3	Turdus philomelos (European song thrush)	2	½
1	viscivorus (Mistle thrush)		6
1	Hylocichla guttata pallasi (Hermit thrush)	2	9
1	Luscinia megarhyncha (Nightingale)		1
3	Erithacus rubecula (European robin)	1	6
3	Sylvia atricapilla (Blackcap)	2	6

NUMBER OF SPECIMENS	BIRDS	LONGEVITY RECORD	
		YEARS	MONTHS
	PASSERIFORMES—*Continued*		
2	Bombycilla cedrorum (Cedar waxwing)	1	10
10	Gymnorhina tibicen (Piping crow)	10	
2	Cracticus torquatus (Gray butcher bird)	5	9
10	Sturnus vulgaris (Starling)	*9	1
2	Spodiopsar malabaricus (Malabar mynah)	5	6
1	Acridotheres tristis (Common mynah)		2
1	Aethiopsar cristatellus (Crested mynah)	*3	3
3	Gracula sp. (Mynah)	2	5
	javanensis (Mynah)	*2	10
5	Lamprocorax metallicus (Shining starling)	*6	6
1	Lamprotornis caudatus (Glossy starling)	5	3
9	Lamprocolius pestis (Southern glossy starling)	*2	4
1	Cosmopsar unicolor (Olive long-tailed glossy starling)		6
1	Galeopsar salvadorii (Crested starling)		*8
1	Heteropsar albicapillus (White-capped starling)		*8
1	Buphagus erythrorhynchus (Red-bellied oxpecker)		6
2	Cyanerpes cyaneus (Blue honey creeper)	*4	6
27	Telespyza cantans (Laysan finch)		7
1	Seiurus aurocapillus (Ovenbird)		1
2	Vidua macroura (Pin-tailed whydah)		10
2	Tetraenura regia (Shaft-tailed whydah)	*8	6
31	Steganura paradisea (Whydah weaver)	7	4
3	Diatropura progne (Giant whydah)	*4	4

NUMBER OF SPECIMENS	BIRDS	LONGEVITY RECORD	
		YEARS	MONTHS
	PASSERIFORMES—Continued		
4	(Whydah)............................	2	4
12	Pyromelana flammiceps sylvatica (Red-crowned bishop bird)......	*2	4
4	franciscana (Orange weaver)............	8	4
4	afra (Napoleon weaver)...............	5	
60	Quelea quelea (Red-billed weaver)............	*2	4
12	sanguinirostris intermedia (Southern masked weaver finch)......	*2	4
10	Amauresthes fringilloides (Magpie finch)............	2	6
3	Lagonosticta senegala (Fire finch)............	2	1
64	Amadina fasciata (Cut-throat finch)............	7	7
2	erythrocephala (Red-headed finch)............	*5	7
13	Steganopleura guttata (Diamond finch)............	*5	4
10	Pytilia kirki (East African fire-throated finch)......	*2	8
33	Taeniopygia castanotis (Zebra finch)............	5	
57	Amandava amandava (Strawberry finch)............	5	10
39	melpoda (Waxbill)...............	5	
89	Munia oryzivora (Java sparrow)............	12	1
7	malacca (Tricolor finch)............	6	
35	maja (White-headed nun)............	*8	10
66	atricapilla (Black-headed finch or "nun")......	7	2
15	castaneithorax (Chestnut-breasted finch)......	*5	7
126	punctulata (Spice finch)............	*10	9
5	nisoria (Bar-breasted finch)............	5	
4	Bathilda ruficauda (Rufous-tailed finch)............	4	6

[333]

NUMBER OF SPECIMENS	BIRDS	LONGEVITY RECORD	
		YEARS	MONTHS
	PASSERIFORMES—*Continued*		
8	Poephila acuticauda (Parson finch)	10	8
11	personata (Masked grass finch)	*7	3
19	gouldiae (Lady Gould's finch)	4	7
28	mirabilis (Red-faced Gouldian finch)	4	7
5	Estrilda astrilda (St. Helena waxbill)	*5	6
2	cinerea (Waxbill finch)	*5	4
1	rhodopyga (Rosy-rumped waxbill)	3	7
11	Uraeginthus bengalus (Crimson-eared waxbill)	*2	7
6	bengalus cyanocephalus (Blue-headed blue waxbill)	*2	4
25	Sporopipes frontalis emini (Emin's scaly-headed finch)	*2	4
2	Textor albirostris (Buffalo weaver)	*2	6
25	niger nyassae (Black-winged coral-billed weaver)	5	10
30	Hyphanturgus nigriceps (Black-headed weaver)	1	2
12	Foudia madagascariensis (Madagascar weaver)		
8	Cacicus cela (Yellow-backed cacique)		
1	Dolichonyx oryzivorus (Bobolink)		
1	Molothrus ater (Cowbird)	8	5
1	Agelaius phoeniceus (Red-winged blackbird)		3
2	phoeniceus richmondi (Vera Cruz redwing)	5	8
2	icterocephalus (Yellow-headed marsh bird)	*4	5
2	Sturnella magna (Common meadow lark)	1	4
1	Gymnomystax melanicterus (Bare-jawed troupial)	*3	2
2	Icterus galbula (Baltimore oriole)		4

NUMBER OF SPECIMENS	BIRDS	LONGEVITY RECORD	
		YEARS	MONTHS
	PASSERIFORMES—*Continued*		
1	Icterus chrysocephalus (Golden-hooded oriole)		6
1	wagleri (Black-headed oriole)		7
5	cucullatus (Hooded oriole)	*4	8
1	mesomelas (Yellow-tailed oriole)	*4	7
8	gularis (Vera Cruz troupial)		8
1	Quiscalus quiscula (Purple grackle)	1	9
1	Tanagra affinis (Lesson's euphonia)		2
4	Thraupis episcopus (Bishop tanager)	*4	9
6	cana (Silver-blue tanager)	*8	6
2	cyanoptera (Blue-winged tanager)	4	5
2	Ramphocelus dimidiatus (Crimson tanager)	5	
4	Chloris chloris (Green finch)	*9	7
2	Eophona melanura (Black-tailed hawfinch)	2	9
2	migratoria sowerbyi (Chinese grosbeak)		
5	Hedymeles ludoviciana (Rose-breasted grosbeak)	10	6
4	Guiraca caerulea (Blue grosbeak)	*4	4
1	Oryzoborus angolensis (Curio)		3
1	Sporophila hypoleuca (White-bellied seed eater)	7	
2	gutturalis (Yellow-bellied seed eater)		6
12	Richmondena cardinalis (Cardinal)	13	
2	cardinalis yucatanicus (Yucatan cardinal)	1	2
4	Fringilla coelebs (European chaffinch)	3	
6	montifringilla (Bramble finch)	*9	1

NUMBER OF SPECIMENS	BIRDS	LONGEVITY RECORD	
		YEARS	MONTHS
	PASSERIFORMES—*Continued*		
16	Carduelis carduelis (European goldfinch)	9	
19	Spinus spinus (Siskin)	11	
1	Astragalinus psaltria mexicanus (Mexican goldfinch)	4	
7	Linota cannabina (Linnet)	1	
20	Passer griseus suahelicus (Coastal pale-bellied sparrow)	*2	4
140	Serinus canarius (Common canary)	*10	3
18	icterus (Green singing finch)	6	10
10	Poliospiza leucopygia (Gray singing finch)	*4	9
31	Sicalis flaveola (Saffron finch)	8	11
5	Carpodacus purpureus (Purple finch)	1	4
2	purpureus californicus (California linnet)	1	
6	mexicanus frontalis (House finch)	*9	4
2	mexicanus ruberrimus (San Lucas house finch)	*5	11
38	Pyrrhula europaea (Bullfinch)	4	
21	Emberiza citrinella (Yellowhammer)	*4	9
5	Junco hyemalis (Slate-colored junco)	5	7
2	Spizella monticola (Tree sparrow)	2	6
4	Zonotrichia albicollis (White-throated sparrow)	*9	
5	Melospiza melodia (Song sparrow)	3	
8	melodia cooperi (San Diego song sparrow)	*9	2
4	Passerella iliaca (Fox sparrow)	3	1
3	Passerina cyanea (Indigo bunting)	1	6
28	ciris (Painted bunting)	7	10

APPENDIX I

NUMBER OF SPECIMENS	BIRDS	LONGEVITY RECORD	
		YEARS	MONTHS
	PASSERIFORMES—*Continued*		
3	Passerina leclancheri (Leclancher's nonpareil).............		1
1	Pipilo erythrophthalmus (Towhee).........................		6
1	maculatus (Towhee).............................	1	6
5	crissalis (California towhee).....................	3	4
1	Phrygilus gayi (Gay's finch).............................	1	6
41	Paroaria cucullata (Brazilian cardinal)..................	10	8

REPTILES

LACERTILIA

NUMBER OF SPECIMENS	Species	LONGEVITY RECORD	
		YEARS	MONTHS
4	Chamaeleon vulgaris (Chameleon)		4
7	dilepis (Common African chameleon)		6
5	Tiliqua scincoides (Blue-tongued lizard)	2	2
7	Trachysaurus rugosus (Stump-tailed lizard)		9
4	Egernia cunninghami (Australian skink)		4
1	Latastia longicaudata revoili (Long-tailed lizard)	*2	
2	Lacerta viridis (Green lizard)	6	
5	Cnemidophorus gularis (Whip-tailed lizard)		4
1	Dracaena guianensis (Alligator lizard)		11
5	Tupinambis teguixin (Tegu)	1	6
3	Varanus gouldii (Gould's monitor)	6	1
4	niloticus (Egyptian monitor)	*2	4
1	salvator (Monitor lizard)	2	8
34	Heloderma suspectum (Gila monster)	19	4
3	horridum (Beaded lizard)	*3	3
9	Ophisaurus ventralis (Glass-snake)	1	5
1	Gerrhonotus scincicauda (Skink-tailed lizard)		
6	Zonurus giganteus (Giant zonure)		
159	Phrynosoma cornutum (Horned lizard)	1	10
5	platyrhinos (Great Basin horned lizard)		8
9	Sceloporus undulatus (Common or fence lizard)		6
13	Callisaurus ventralis (Spotted-tailed dragon)	4	1
5	Crotaphytus collaris baileyi (Bailey's lizard)	2	6

NUMBER OF SPECIMENS	REPTILES	LONGEVITY RECORD	
		YEARS	MONTHS
	LACERTILIA—*Continued*		
1	Crotaphytus wislizenii (Wislizenius's lizard)	1	6
4	Sauromalus ater (Chuckwalla)	1	6
5	Dipsosaurus dorsalis (Desert iguana)		8
62	Ctenosaura teres (Mexican comb lizard)	1	2
2	sp. (Nicaragua comb lizard)		2
4	Cyclura baeolopha (Ground iguana)		11
1	stejnegeri (Mona Island iguana)	2	4
2	rileyi (Bahama rock iguana)		1
19	sp. (Iguana)	*2	3
2	carinata (Clouded iguana)	1	4
1	Iguana rhinolopha (Mexican tree iguana)		2
6	sp.	2	5
11	iguana (Tuberculated iguana)	3	2
1	Amblyrhynchus cristatus (Marine iguana)		3
2	Basiliscus vittatus (Banded basilisk)	3	10
7	Anolis carolinensis (American or false chameleon)		3
2	Uromastix spinipes (Spiny-tailed lizard)		
4	Physignathus lesueurii (Water dragon)		3
	SERPENTES		
110	Crotalus adamanteus (Diamond rattlesnake)	8	2
12	atrox (Western rattlesnake)	*3	4
2	cerastes (Horned rattlesnake)		3

NUMBER OF SPECIMENS	REPTILES	LONGEVITY RECORD	
		YEARS	MONTHS
	SERPENTES—*Continued*		
26	Crotalus confluentus (Prairie rattlesnake)	1	9
4	confluentus lucifer (California rattlesnake)	1	6
2	exsul (Red rattlesnake)		
90	horridus (Banded rattlesnake)	3	4
1	tigris (Tiger rattlesnake)		
2	terrificus (Dog-faced rattlesnake)		
4	sp. (Rattlesnake)	3	8
5	Sistrurus catenatus (Massasauga)	1	6
18	miliarius (Ground rattlesnake)	4	6
1	Bothrops neuwiedii (White-tail jararaca)		
2	atrox (Caiçaca)		
1	cotiara		
1	jararacussu (Jararacussú)		
13	alternata (Cross viper)	*3	10
13	lanceolatus (Fer-de-lance)	3	7
96	Agkistrodon mokasen (Copperhead)	5	1 day
66	piscivorus (Water moccasin)		
2	Micrurus sp. (Coral snake)		
5	fulvius (Harlequin snake)	*2	5
7	Naja haie (Egyptian cobra)	*2	4
5	nigricollis (Black-necked spiting cobra)		6
25	Dispholidus typus (Boomslang)		
2	Philodryas schotti		

NUMBER OF SPECIMENS	REPTILES	LONGEVITY RECORD	
		YEARS	MONTHS
	SERPENTES—*Continued*		
1	Petalognathus nebulatus (Slug-eating snake)		8
1	Farancia abacura (Red-bellied snake)		1
1	Abastor erythrogrammus (Rainbow snake)		5
1	Sonora occipitalis (Mohave snake)		6
7	Liopeltis vernalis (Grass snake)		6
5	Opheodrys aestivus (Green snake)	2	5
23	Masticophis flagellum (Coach-whip snake)	2	
1	flagellum frenatum (Western whip snake)	4	
7	Coluber constrictor (Black snake)	*5	4
2	Cemophora coccinea (Scarlet snake)	1	6
1	Rhinocheilus lecontei (Le Conte's snake)		3
48	Lampropeltis getulus (King snake)	9	4
2	getulus boylii (Boyle's king snake)	1	
1	elapsoides (Scarlet king snake)		
4	calligaster (Yellow-bellied king snake)	4	6
5	triangulum triangulum (Milk snake)	1	5
49	Heterodon contortrix (Spreading adder)	6	
1	Xenodon guentheri		
2	merremii		
1	Liophis almadensis		
131	Pituophis melanoleucus (Pine snake)	3	6
1	catenifer (Western bull snake)		
2	catenifer annectans (California bull snake)		

REPTILES

SERPENTES—*Continued*

NUMBER OF SPECIMENS	REPTILES	LONGEVITY RECORD	
		YEARS	MONTHS
74	Pituophis sayi (Bull snake)	4	8
2	Gonyosoma oxycephalum (Philippine green snake)		1
13	Elaphe obsoleta (Pilot black snake)	4	6
1	obsoleta confinis (Southern pilot black snake)		10
9	quadrivittata (Chicken snake)	7	
3	vulpina (Fox snake)	1	6
6	guttata (Corn snake)	3	
45	Drymarchon corais couperi (Gopher snake)	5	2
1	Spilotes pullatus		
1	Drymobius bifossatus		
1	margaritiferus (Beaded snake)		1
3	Helicops angulatus (Water coral snake)		10
40	Natrix sipedon (Water snake)	7	
2	taxispilota (Water pilot)		2
1	septemvittata (Queen snake)	1	11
40	Thamnophis sirtalis (Garter snake)	6	
2	proxima (Texas water snake)	6	
1	Boa hortulana (Tree boa)		6
1	cookii (Cook's tree boa)		1
100	Constrictor constrictor (Boa constrictor)	10	
1	imperator (Emperor boa)	2	5
4	Eunectes murinus (Anaconda)	28	
8	Epicrates angulifer (Cuban tree boa)	11	9

NUMBER OF SPECIMENS	REPTILES	LONGEVITY RECORD	
		YEARS	MONTHS
	SERPENTES—*Continued*		
34	Epicrates inornatus (Yellow tree boa)	*2	5
3	cenchris (Velvet snake)	5	5
4	Python reticulatus (Regal python)	1	8
9	molurus (Indian python)	11	1
6	spilotes (Diamond python)	*2	9
19	sebae (African python)	*2	4
4	sp.	2	4
	RHYNCHOCEPHALIA		
2	Sphenodon punctatus (Tuatara)	1	
	TESTUDINATA		
1	Amyda ferox (Leather-back terrapin)	*1	8
4	Platemys planiceps (Ridge-back turtle)	5	
3	Phrynops geoffroyana (South American long-necked turtle)	5	
4	Chelodina longicollis (Long-necked turtle)	*7	10
3	Chelys fimbriata (Matamata turtle)	1	6
3	Podocnemis expansa (Amazon turtle)		3
1	Pelomedusa galeata (Common African water tortoise)	*2	4
1	Pelusios nigricans (Black water tortoise)	*2	4
1	Caretta caretta (Loggerhead turtle)		2
17	Testudo sp.	*3	5
1	angulata (Angulated tortoise)	*3	5

[343]

NUMBER OF SPECIMENS	REPTILES	LONGEVITY RECORD	
		YEARS	MONTHS
	TESTUDINATA—*Continued*		
1	Testudo calcarata (Abyssinian tortoise)	*3	4
10	denticulata (South American tortoise)	4	4
3	ephippium (Duncan Island tortoise)	*30	1
5	hermanni (African tortoise)	*4	4
2	horsfieldii	*1	4
37	tornieri (Soft-shelled land tortoise). Numerous.	*2	4
1	pardalis (Leopard tortoise)	*2	4
2	porteri (Indefatigable Island tortoise)	*7	8
	vicina (Albemarle Island tortoise)	*30	4
8	Gopherus polyphemus (Gopher tortoise)	*4	7
3	agassizii (Desert tortoise)	*2	3
1	berlandieri (Mexican gopher tortoise)	1	3
1	Homopus areolatus (Tortoise)	*3	5
5	Cinixys belliana (Bell's hinged tortoise)	*2	4
1	Nicoria punctularia (South American terrapin)	*6	8
2	Terrapene carolina (Box turtle)	2	
5	Emys orbicularis (European pond turtle)	*4	
2	blandingii (Blanding's terrapin)	*1	10
2	Clemmys insculpta (Wood turtle)	5	10
1	leprosa (Leprous terrapin)	*3	5
1	Geoclemmys reevesii (Reeves turtle)	*4	
1	Geoemyda spengleri (Loochoo terrapin)	*3	5
3	Pseudemys ornata (Central American cooter)	*5	8

APPENDIX I

NUMBER OF SPECIMENS	REPTILES	LONGEVITY RECORD	
		YEARS	MONTHS
	TESTUDINATA—*Continued*		
2	Pseudemys scripta (Cooter).....................	7	1
1	Deirochelys reticularia (Chicken turtle)...........	*4	6
6	Chrysemys belli (Western painted turtle)...........	*3	6
6	picta (Painted turtle)...........................	*4	5
1	Sternotherus odoratus (Musk turtle)..............	*5	6
6	Kinosternon scorpioides (South American mud turtle)..	*6	8
1	sonoriense (Mexican musk turtle)................	*5	3
2	subrubrum (Pennsylvania musk turtle)............	*5	9
5	Dermatemys mawii (Maw's turtle).................		9
1	Chelydra osceola (Florida snapping turtle).........	*4	6
11	serpentina (Snapping turtle)....................	*4	5
1	rossignonii (Rossignon's snapping turtle)..........	6	2
	CROCODILIA		
1	Caiman sclerops (Spectacled cayman).............		10
358	Alligator mississippiensis (Alligator)...............	19	
1	Crocodylus cataphractus (Long-nosed crocodile)....		*7
1	acutus (American crocodile).....................		9

[345]

AMPHIBIANS

NUMBER OF SPECIMENS		LONGEVITY RECORD	
		YEARS	MONTHS
	CAUDATA		
4	Megalobatrachus maximus (Giant salamander)...............	*3	4
	ANURA		
78	Xenopus mülleri (East African smooth-clawed frog).........	*2	4

APPENDIX II
LIST OF ANIMALS BORN IN THE NATIONAL ZOOLOGICAL PARK

MARSUPIALIA

3   Trichosurus fuliginosus (Dusky phalanger).
3   vulpecula (Australian opposum).
3   Macropus bicolor (Black-tailed wallaby).
10   billardieri (Rufous-bellied wallaby).
7   giganteus (Gray kangaroo).
13   robustus (Wallaroo)[1].
25   rufus (Red kangaroo)[2].
17   Petrogale penicillata (Brush-tailed rock wallaby).
10   Aepyprymnus rufescens (Rufous rat kangaroo).
16   Didelphis virginiana (Opossum).

CARNIVORA

4   Thalarctos maritimus (Polar bear).
5   Euarctos americanus (American black bear).
20   Ursus arctos (European brown bear).
6   gyas x dalli (Hybrid Alaskan bear).
3   horribilis (Grizzly bear).
8   kidderi x arctos (Hybrid brown bear).
3   Nasua narica (Gray coati-mundi).
1   rufa (Red coati-mundi).
34   Procyon lotor (Racoon).
18   Mephitis nigra (Skunk).
2   Mustela vison (Mink).
2   Lutra canadensis (American otter).
2   canadensis vaga (Florida otter).
56   Canis dingo (Dingo).
42   familiaris (Eskimo dog).
11   familiaris (Russian wolf-hound).
4   familiaris (Various breeds).
4   frustror (Woodhouse's coyote).

[1] Bred Oct. 27, 1916; motion in pouch first seen Dec. 13; head of young first seen March 27, 1917.

[2] Bred Oct. 19, 1916; motion in pouch first seen Dec. 8; head of young first seen March 19, 1917.

[347]

24 Canis latrans (Coyote or prairie wolf).
66   nubilus (Gray wolf).
5   rufus (Texan wolf).
7 Vulpes fulva (Red fox).
4   velox (Swift or kit fox).
64 Alopex lagopus (Arctic fox).
2 Genetta dongolana neumanni (Neumann's genet).
20 Felis hippolestes (Mountain lion). Period of gestation, 13 weeks.
19   leo (Lion). Period of gestation, 16 weeks.
4   pardus suahelicus (East African leopard). Period of gestation, 13 weeks.
4   tigris (Bengal tiger). Period of gestation, 16 weeks.
6   tigris longipilis (Siberian tiger).
6 Lynx rufus texensis (Spotted lynx).

PRIMATES

1 Cebus capucinus (White-throated capuchin).
1   capucinus x fatuellus (Hybrid capuchin).
8 Cercopithecus mona (Mona monkey). Period of gestation, 7 months.
3 Macacus fuscatus (Japanese monkey).
3   irus (Common macaque).
3   mordax (Javan macaque).
4   nemestrina (Pig-tailed monkey).
23   rhesus (Rhesus monkey). Period of gestation, 7 months.

RODENTIA

30 Cynomys ludovicianus (Prairie dog).
13 Castor canadensis (American beaver).
5 Onychomys leucogaster melanophrys (Grasshopper mouse).
39 Myocastor coypus (Coypu).
30 Capromys pilorides (Hutia-conga).
6 Hystrix cristata (European porcupine).
5 Erethizon dorsatum (Canada porcupine).
4 Lagostomus trichodactylus (Viscacha).
6 Dasyprocta acouchy (Olive agouti).
1   aguti (Common agouti).
3   cristata (Crested agouti).
13   rubrata (Trinidad agouti).
1   sp. (Agouti).
3 Cuniculus paca (Paca).
Cavia aperia (Guinea pig). Numerous.
4   tschudii pallidior (Peruvian guinea pig).

APPENDIX II

1   Dolichotis patagonica (**Patagonian cavy**).   Period of gestation, 58 days.

113   Oryctolagus cuniculus (Rabbit) (in 1928).

9   Tapirus terrestris (Brazilian tapir). Period of gestation, 13 months.

2   Equus grevyi × asinus (Zebra-ass hybrid).

21   Pecari angulatus (Collared peccary).

5   Phacochoerus aethiopicus (Wart hog).

5   Hippopotamus amphibius (Hippopotamus).   Period of gestation, 237 days.

49   Lama glama (Llama).   Period of gestation, 11 months.

11   huanacus (Guanaco).

1   pacos (Alpaca).

2   Camelus bactrianus (Bactrian camel).

1   dromedarius (Dromedary).   Period of gestation, 409 days.

2   Rusa unicolor (Sambar deer).

43   Rucervus duvaucelii (Barasingha deer).

20   Axis axis (Axis deer).

75   Sika nippon (Japanese deer).

110   Cervus canadensis (American elk).

86   elaphus (Red deer).

5   hanglu (Kashmir deer).

4   xanthopygus (Bedford deer).

37   Dama dama (Fallow deer).

31   Hyelaphus porcinus (Hog deer).

2   Rangifer tarandus (Reindeer).

11   Odocoileus columbianus (Columbian black-tailed deer).

26   hemionus (Mule deer).

78   virginianus (Virginia deer).

1   sp. (Cuban deer).

6   Antilocapra americana (Prong-horned antelope).

21   Antilope cervicapra (Indian antelope).

1   Gazella arabica (Arabian gazelle).

2   Taurotragus oryx livingstonii (Livingstone's eland).

4   Tragelaphus gratus (Congo harnessed antelope).

10   Boselaphus tragocamelus (Nilgai).

2   Rupicapra rupicapra (Chamois).

2   Oreamnos americanus (Mountain goat).

WILD ANIMALS

 1 Capra falconeri *x* hircus (Hybrid goat).
 2   ibex (Alpine ibex).
18 Hemitragus jemlahicus (Tahr).
56 Ammotragus lervia (Barbary sheep).
12 Ovis aries tragelaphus (Barbados sheep).
20   canadensis (Rocky Mountain sheep).
 9   europaeus (Mouflon).
 4 Bubalus bubalus (Indian buffalo).
21 Poephagus grunniens (Yak).
57 Bison bison (American bison).
11 Bos indicus (Zebu).

XENARTHRA

 4 Euphractus villosus (Hairy armadillo).

BIRDS

CICONIIFORMES

 3 Pelecanus erythrorhynchos (American white pelican).
35 Phalacrocorax auritus floridanus (Florida cormorant).
 3 Ardea herodias *x* occidentalis (Hybrid heron).
 2 Casmerodius egretta (American egret).
277 Nycticorax nycticorax naevius (Black-crowned night heron).
 8 Threskiornis aethiopicus (Sacred ibis).
18 Guara alba (White ibis).

ANSERIFORMES

31 Cygnus olor (Mute swan).
27 Aix sponsa (Wood duck).
 6 Chen caerulescens (Blue goose).
 5   hyperboreus nivalis (Greater snow goose).
34 Branta canadensis canadensis (Canada goose).
 4   canadensis occidentalis (White-cheeked goose).
 7 Anas domestica (Pekin duck).
67   platyrhynchos (Mallard duck).
31   rubripes (Black duck).
 2 Eunetta falcata *x* Chaulelasmus streperus (Falcated teal-gadwall, hybrid).
 3 Dafila acuta (Pintail duck).
 2 Metopiana peposaca (Rosy-billed pochard).

GALLIFORMES

 4 Gennaeus nycthemerus (Silver pheasant).
10 Phasianus torquatus (Ring-necked pheasant).

APPENDIX II

5   Chrysolophus pictus (Golden pheasant).
11 Gallus bankiva (Jungle fowl).
282 Pavo cristatus (Pea fowl).
44 Meleagris gallopavo silvestris (Wild turkey).
19 Colinus virginianus (Bob-white).

GRUIFORMES

4   Grus mexicanus (Sand-hill crane).
1   Anthropoides virgo (Demoiselle crane).
13 Fulica americana (American coot).

CHARADRIIFORMES

16 Larus novaehollandiae (Silver gull).
3   argentatus smithsonianus (Herring gull).
2   Columba palumbus (Wood pigeon).
7   Streptopelia risoria (Ringed turtledove).

PSITTACIFORMES

5   Melopsittacus undulatus (Warbling grass paroquet).

PASSERIFORMES

4   Munia oryzivora (Java sparrow).
2   Serinus canarius (Common canary).
2   Sicalis flavecla (Saffron finch).

REPTILES

SERPENTES

23 Crotalus adamanteus (Diamond rattlesnake).
6   confluentus (Prairie rattlesnake).
27 Agkistrodon mokasen (Copperhead).
19   piscivorus (Water moccasin).
26 Pituophis sayi (Bull snake).
60 Constrictor constrictor (Boa constrictor).
30 Epicrates inornatus (Yellow tree boa).

INDEX

INDEX

INDEX

INDEX

INDEX

INDEX

INDEX

INDEX

INDEX

INDEX